Penguin Referer

Additives: A Guide

Erik Millstone was born and brought [...] Austrian parents. He gained a physics degree from the University of Kent and then earned three postgraduate degrees in philosophy. Since 1973 he has held a teaching post at the University of Sussex concerned with the social impact of science and technology. For many years he has been studying the causes and consequences of technical change in the British food industry; this book and his *Food Additives* (Penguin 1986) are products of that work.

John Abraham has a B.Sc. in Mathematics and an M.Sc. in Science Policy Studies from the University of Sussex. His M.Sc. thesis focussed on mechanisms for the control of food additives. He has worked as a research officer at the Sussex Science Policy Research Unit, and more recently has pursued further research on the safety of additives.

ERIK MILLSTONE
WITH JOHN ABRAHAM

ADDITIVES: A GUIDE
FOR EVERYONE

PENGUIN BOOKS

Penguin Books Ltd, 27 Wrights Lane, London W8 5TZ (Publishing and Editorial)
and Harmondsworth, Middlesex, England (Distribution and Warehouse)
Viking Penguin Inc., 40 West 23rd Street, New York, New York 10010, USA
Penguin Books Australia Ltd, Ringwood, Victoria, Australia
Penguin Books Canada Ltd, 2801 John Street, Markham, Ontario, Canada L3R 1B4
Penguin Books (NZ) Ltd, 182–190 Wairau Road, Auckland 10, New Zealand

First published 1988

Made and printed in Great Britain by
Richard Clay Ltd, Bungay, Suffolk
Filmset in 8/9½pt Monophoto Times

This book is dedicated to
Ida Millstone and Jannet King

CONTENTS

ACKNOWLEDGEMENTS

The authors gratefully acknowledge that some of the main sources used in compiling this book were:

OFFICIAL REPORTS

The reports of the Joint Expert Committee on Food Additives (JECFA) of the World Health Organization and the United Nations Food and Agriculture Organization, and especially *FAO/WHO Food Additives Data System*, UNFAO, Rome, 1984

The reports of the Scientific Committee for Food (SCF) of the European Economic Community

The reports of the British Food Standards Committee (FSC), the Food Additives and Contaminants Committee (FACC), the Food Advisory Committee (FAC) and the Committee on the Toxicity of Chemicals in Food (COT)

BOOKS

Conning, D. M. & Lansdown, A. B. G., *Toxic Hazards in Food*, Croom Helm, London, 1983

Doyal, L. et al., *Cancer in Britain: The Politics of Prevention*, Pluto Press, London, 1983

Fisher, J., *Additives: What Are They?*, Safeway Nutrition Advisory Service, Aylesford, Kent, 1986

Furia, T. (ed.), *CRC Handbook of Food Additives*, vol. 1, CRC Press, Boca Raton, Florida, 1983

Gibson, G. G. & Walker, R. (eds), *Food Toxicology: Real or Imaginary Problems?*, Taylor & Francis, London, 1985

Hanssen, M., *E for Additives*, Thorsons, Wellingborough, 1984

Hightower, J., *Eat Your Heart Out*, Vintage Books, New York, 1975

Hunter, B. T., *Consumer Beware!*, Simon & Schuster, New York, 1971

Hunter, B. T., *Fact Book on Food Additives and Your Health*, Keats, Connecticut, 1972

Hunter, B. T., *Additives Book*, Keats, Connecticut, 1980

Jacobson, M., *Eater's Digest: The Consumer's Factbook of Food Additives*, Anchor Books, New York, 1976 and 1985

Jacobson, M., *How Sodium Nitrite Can Affect Your Health*, Centre for Science in the Public Interest, Washington, DC, 1980

Jukes, D. J., *Food Legislation in the UK: A Concise Guide*, Butterworths, London, 1984

Lawrence, F. (ed.), *Additives: Your Complete Survival Guide*, Century, London, 1986

Lipske, M. et al., *Chemical Additives in Booze*, Centre for Science in the Public Interest, Washington, DC, 1982

Marine, G. & van Allen, J., *Food Pollution*, Holt Rinehart, New York, 1972

Miller, M., *Danger! Additives at Work*, London Food Commission, 1985

Millstone, E., *Food Additives*, Penguin, Harmondsworth, 1986

National Research Council, *Diet, Nutrition, and Cancer*, National Academy Press, Washington DC, 1982

Polunin, M., *The Right Way To Eat*, Dent, London, 1984

Roe, F. J. C. (ed.), *Metabolic Aspects of Food Safety*, Blackwell, Oxford, 1970

Steele, F. & Bourne, A., *The Man/Food Equation*, Academic Press, London, 1975

Taylor R. J., *Food Additives*, J. Wiley & Sons, Chichester, 1980

Verrett, J. & Carper, J., *Eating May Be Hazardous to Your Health*, Anchor Books, New York, 1975

Vettorazzi, G. (ed.), *Handbook of International Food Regulatory Toxicology*, vol. 2, MTP Press, Lancaster, 1981

Winter, R., *A Consumer's Dictionary of Food Additives*, Crown, New York, 1978

We are also very grateful to David Crouch and to Jannet King for their invaluable assistance in preparing the manuscript.

INTRODUCTION

The British public's thirst for information about food additives has made itself forcefully conspicuous only since 1984. One of the initial events which stimulated this thirst was the decision, taken in the mid-1970s by the Council of Ministers of the EEC, to require that the labels on (at least many) food products should identify (at least some of) the food additives which have been deliberately introduced into those products. It was in 1978 that the EEC issued its Labelling Directive, but it was a full six years before the rules even started to be implemented in Britain. The initial response of the British government was to introduce what is called, rather obscurely, a derogation. Individual member states can choose to derogate from all sorts of EEC rules, and to derogate means that you decide that the rules don't apply within your national borders. The British food industry were not keen on the full vigour of the Labelling Directive and persuaded the government to derogate, and they compromised by agreeing to list the general categories of the additives being used, but not their identities. You may remember labels which used to say just: 'permitted preservative' or 'permitted colours' without actually identifying the particular chemicals which were being used.

This compromise broke down because of increasing evidence that some additives provoke problems of acute discomfort in a significant minority of the population. For example, children and adults can suffer, among other things, from hyperactivity, headaches, skin inflammations and asthma. Matters came to a head in 1981 with the publication of a report from the EEC Scientific Committee for Food. The penultimate paragraph of their report was headed: *Label? or Ban?*

The industry did not have to read between the lines for the message was spelt out: they either had to own up and identify precisely which chemicals they were using, or else all those substances suspected of provoking acute intolerance would be banned. From the industry's point of view this was a very serious threat because many of the most controversial compounds are among the most useful and commercially valuable chemicals. These include many colours, antioxidants and flavour enhancers. Preferring what to them seemed the lesser of two evils, industry shifted its ground and argued that there was no need to ban them, just list them on the label, and leave it to the consumers to eat and to avoid what they chose. This resulted in the introduction into Britain of the 'E'-number system; 'E' because it is a standard EEC European identification code.

When 'E' numbers started to appear on the labels of British food products, many people made the understandable mistake of supposing that these chemicals had only recently been introduced into our food supply, when in reality they had been there on average for about forty years, and in some cases for a hundred years, although none had ever previously been specified on the label. As soon as the 'E'-numbering system had been well established, many consumers made the equally understandable mistake of assuming that all additives have these 'E' numbers, and that labelling regulations required a complete list of all additives. In reality, less than 10 per cent of all additives are ever listed on labels, and some foods don't have to be labelled at all. There are about 4,000 additives in use in the UK, but only about 350 of them are ever specified on labels. At least 3,500 flavourings are used, and this entire class of chemicals is exempted from these labelling regulations. At most, a product may list 'flavourings' on the label, but it is never stated whether one chemical or fifty are being used, much less gives their names. It remains the case, however, that most categories of additive, such as colours, preservatives and antioxidants, have to be labelled on most foods and drinks. This dictionary provides a comprehensive list of the additives which are listed on food and drink products in Britain and the EEC, but it also includes many of those currently used in the USA and other countries.

Some of the chemicals listed in this dictionary do not have 'E' numbers: there are two reasons for this. In some cases, the government of one or more EEC member countries, or the Scientific Committee for Food, may have doubts about the safety of the compound, but in other cases this committee has not yet had time to consider the substance and has not yet submitted any recommendation to the Council of Ministers whose responsibility it is to assign the 'E' numbers.

Many chemicals are introduced into our food supply, but only some of them count as additives and appear on the labels. Of course, all foods are nothing but chemicals, but food chemicals are intrinsic constituents of the fruits, vegetables and meats. Farmers introduce many extrinsic chemicals to our food supply in the form of fertilizers, pesticides, antibiotics and hormones, but these don't count as additives because they should be used in ways which ensure that no significant residues remain in the food by the time it is sold or eaten. Food additives, in the slightly narrow sense in which we, along with industry and government, use the expression, refer to chemicals deliberately added during industrial food processing, and which are added because of the effects they have on the consumer.

Food additives are used by the food industry to perform a wide range of different technical functions, but all the uses have one thing in common: they occur if, and only if, the manufacturers or retailers believe that using chemicals makes their products easier to sell. For a detailed explanation of how additives are used, see chaper 2 of *Food Additives* by Erik Millstone (Penguin Books, 1986). Food additives appear on the label only because governments regulate their use. All the additives listed in this dictionary have been explicitly approved for use by the British government, and most (but not all) of them have been approved by the governments of other countries. In Britain, it is the Ministry of Agriculture, Fisheries and Food (MAFF) which has the responsibility for regulating, approving and restricting the use of food additives. A detailed account of the regulatory process can be found in chapter 3 of *Food Additives* but, briefly, ministers set regulations on the basis of advice from scientific experts, civil servants and industrial representatives.

The names of the expert committees have changed over the years, but in the entries to this dictionary we shall mention five of them. In 1942, during the Second World War, the government first established the Food Standards Committee (FSC) whose responsibility was to advise the government on a wide range of issues concerning food, diet and health. From 1965 to 1983 it was supplemented by the Food Additives and Contaminants Committee (FACC), but in 1983 these two were merged to form the Food Advisory Committee (FAC). When the FAC decide whether or not to recommend that ministers approve the use of specific additives they are supposed to make a judgement based on two criteria: need and safety. Issues of need are settled by this committee, but on questions of safety advice is taken from other committees. Formerly they turned to a Pharmacology sub-committee, but more recently they have established a Committee on the Toxicity of Chemicals in Food (CoT) which is the responsibility of the Department of Health and Social Security (DHSS). These committees have published a series of reports which are discussed in the entries in this dictionary. An account of the composition and operation of these committees can be found in chapters 3 and 5 of *Food Additives*.

In the USA, responsibility for regulating food additives lies with the Food and Drug Administration (FDA). Their procedures are significantly different from those which operate in the UK and the EEC. The single most important difference is that their activities are subject to the provisions of the Freedom of Information Act, and so are not as secretive as those which occur in Europe, and furthermore their judgements can be, and sometimes are, scrutinized and challenged by Congress and in the civil courts.

While the regulation of food additives has been primarily a national activity, there has been some international co-operation for at least thirty years. With the support of most governments of the industrialized countries, the World Health Organization (WHO) and the United Nations Food and Agriculture Organization (FAO) established the Codex Alimentarius Commission in the early 1960s, and Codex (as it is usually called) then established a Joint Expert Committee on Food Additives (JECFA) in the mid-1960s. Of all the formal and official committees involved in the regulation of food additives, JECFA has been most thorough and most open about their evaluations of chemicals. They have published a long series of reports and it is these which have provided the basis for the production of this dictionary. They have, moreover, given a lead to national governments, so that, for example, the British advisory committees frequently rely upon, refer and defer to, the judgements of JECFA.

Extra problems arise within the European Economic Community (EEC) which wants to reduce barriers to trade, and so to harmonize regulations among all the countries. To help with this, and as a step towards providing uniformity, it has established the Scientific Committee for Food (SCF). Since the establishment of the SCF we find that the British committees (the FACC, FAC and the CoT) have referred and deferred to the SCF; and in turn the SCF refers and defers to JECFA. We have, therefore, a hierarchy of committees from the worldwide body through the European level to the national. This sequence is reflected in the structure of the entries in this dictionary. The usual pattern is to start from JECFA, then deal with such comments as the SCF and the British committees have made, and then discuss the views of other scientific commentators who are not part of the official process.

One of the problems which confronts anyone who tries to learn about food additives is the extent and the depth of the cloak of secrecy which covers these chemicals. In the UK, all the scientific and technical information which is provided by the food and chemical industries to the government is protected by the Official Secrets Act. Some of it may be published if it suits the industry, but if they want it kept secret the government will oblige. The current position is that it is illegal for us to know precisely what information the government has received, or the standards it applies in its judgements. The reports of the FACC and FAC, including reports from the CoT, frequently fail to provide details of the content or sources of the information received.

Our problems are aggravated by the fact that JECFA and the SCF also receive, accept and conceal the details of unpublished reports, and so the entire regulatory system rests on an undisclosed base. Despite this concealment, every effort has been made, in compiling this dictionary, to trace and examine as much of the original information as can be obtained.

Secrecy is defended by industry and government on the grounds that disclosure might adversely affect the commercial interests of companies. Indeed it might, but most readers would be surprised to discover that the MAFF puts the commercial interests of industry above the right of consumers to receive adequate information. The secrecy means that because the firms in the chemical and food industries do not trust each other, a rule is set which means that all consumers are expected to trust the entire industry and government together. In the summer of 1986 the British government issued a set of proposals which would improve the situation, but only very marginally. They proposed to make available some undisclosed portion of some of the new information which they may receive in the future. They do not propose to provide the public with access to any of the information which was submitted in the past.

When it comes to judging the safety of a chemical, we have to turn to the science of toxicology. Experimental toxicologists seek to estimate the likely effects of chemicals on the people exposed to them. Toxicology is a very complex and troublesome science, and of course it has to deal not just with food additives but also, for example, with agricultural chemicals such as pesticides, pharmaceutical products, cosmetics and the whole range of chemicals in our environment. The science of toxicology is made up of three distinct sub-disciplines, and an overall evaluation of a chemical must take into account information from each of these.

The first two parts of toxicology do not study the effects on humans, but study instead the effects which chemicals have in model systems, in the hope that these models might shed some light on the likely effects on humans. The first part involves tests conducted on bacteria or cell cultures in glass dishes and the second part comprises tests on whole live animals.

One of the most important reasons for testing the effects of chemicals on bacteria is because it might provide an indication that the chemical under test could cause genetic mutations to the bacteria, and so possibly to humans. This is important for two reasons, first because we want to avoid chemicals which would cause mutations to humans: we all want healthy and normal children and we don't want to produce deformed or damaged off-spring. Second, a chemical which can cause a mutation, called a mutagen, might well also cause cancer, in other words it might be a carcinogen. If, by causing mutations in the bacteria, a chemical fails these bacterial culture tests, then we have some reason for supposing that it is not safe. If a chemical is not shown to be harmful in these bacterial tests this does not prove that it is safe, because it might well cause all sorts of harm which these tests cannot detect. It might even cause cancer by a non-genotoxic route.

The second, and in effect the most important part of toxicology, concerns the testing of chemicals on whole live animals. A range of different species is used including dogs, cats, monkeys, ferrets, rabbits and of course guinea-pigs, but most commonly mice and rats. A wide range of different tests comprises this over-all group. You can feed chemicals to animals at high or low doses for long or short periods, and even over several generations. You can inject them under their skins or directly into their digestive tracts, or you can mix them into their food. Whatever test is performed, it is important to monitor a wide range of indicators of the animals' health, and to in-vestigate carefully their remains after they die or are killed. Animal tests provide the main source of information for industry and governments, and most official evaluations of food additives are based on the interpretation of the results of tests with animals.

The third part of toxicology is information on the direct effects which chemicals have on humans. In principle, but not yet in practice, this could be the most crucial segment of the science. It consists of two parts, namely epidemiology and clinical reports. The term 'epidemiology' has the same root as the word 'epidemic', and it is the study of patterns of health and illness within and between human populations. Clinical information is provided by doctors and hospitals when they report the effects of chemicals on particular individuals who come to them as patients, or very occasionally as experimental subjects.

If human evidence is available it can be particularly informative because it tells us directly what we want to know, whereas the other parts of toxicology give us information about non-human organisms from which we have to draw inferences as to the likely effects of the chemicals on people. One major problem, however, is that the methods and techniques of epidemiology are currently too insensitive to enable us to detect the effects which additives may be having over the long term. We consume many different chemicals, in numerous complex combinations, and only rarely can we distinguish two population groups, which differ only in that one group avoids a chemical which the other consumes. Consequently the science of epidemiology has very little to contribute to food additive toxicology. Clinical studies have their limitations because the people who are investigated are at best a very small and unrepresentative sample of the population as a whole. As a result, almost all our evaluations of the possible effects of food additives have to depend on inferences drawn from toxicological models. The most fundamental problem with human studies is that we want to know precisely what effects chemicals would have on humans before they come into use, and we don't want to have to wait until after people have been poisoned.

When they evaluate and review the safety of a food additive, international agencies and national governments often review the same information, but they usually make different kinds of judgement. JECFA and the SCF consider specific chemicals in abstraction from their uses, and seek to assess how much, if any, of a chemical can be safely consumed in food and drinks on a regular basis. National agencies consider, in the light of the evaluations provided by JECFA and the SCF, whether to approve the use of specific food additives in specific groups of products.

The main regulatory concept employed by both JECFA and the SCF is the notion of an 'acceptable daily intake' or ADI. Underlying their approach is the assumption that the results of animal tests can provide a reliable guide to the likely effects which chemicals will have on humans. JECFA and the SCF define an ADI as a dose level at which the chemical is safe for humans. It is derived from a dose level at which it can be administered to a group of animals without causing them any observable adverse effects. In the animal tests they seek to identify what is called a 'no effect level' or NEL, and they define the ADI directly in relation to the

NEL. To be precise, the ADI is equal to the NEL divided by a safety factor (SF). (For a more detailed discussion, see chapter 4 of *Food Additives*.) According to the textbook accounts, this safety factor is normally set at 100. This figure is obtained by assuming that humans as a whole may be ten times more sensitive to chemicals than the laboratory animals, and that there may be a ten-fold variation in sensitivity within a population of humans. The safety factor of 100 is then simply the product of the two factors of ten. In practice, we often find that different safety factors are employed by JECFA and the SCF, but these other numbers are no less arbitrary than the figure of 100. The units in which both the NELs and ADIs are specified is milligrams of chemical per kilogram of body weight of the animal or human, and in this dictionary, as in the official publications, it is abbreviated as 'mg/kg bw'. In exceptional cases, instead of setting an ADI, JECFA will approve the use of a chemical up to a particular level of use, in parts per million (ppm) by weight of the food.

In the reports of JECFA and the SCF we find brief summaries of the results of toxicological tests, and wherever possible an NEL is identified, and from it an ADI is set, but it is important to remember that these numbers change through time, and the two committees do not always agree with each other. The British advisory committees do not set ADIs and comment only rarely on those which have been specified by JECFA and the SCF; instead the CoT lists chemicals into five groups, from A to E. These are defined as follows:

Group A   Substances that the available evidence suggests are acceptable for use in food

Group B   Substances that on the available evidence may be regarded meanwhile as provisionally acceptable for use in food, but about which further information is necessary and which must be reviewed within a specified period of time

Group C   Substances for which the available evidence suggests possible toxicity and which ought not to be allowed in food without further evidence establishing their acceptability

Group D   Substances for which the available evidence suggests probable toxicity and which ought not to be allowed in food

Group E   Substances for which the available evidence is inadequate to enable an opinion to be expressed as to their suitability for use in food

For those chemicals which the CoT list in Groups A or B, the FAC will recommend to ministers that they approve the inclusion of those substances in specific groups of products.

We shall also mention the regulatory status of many of these additives in the USA. A particularly important, and uniquely American, regulatory concept is the category of chemicals which are 'generally regarded as safe', commonly abbreviated as GRAS. This concept is used in the USA by the FDA, but also by other bodies including non-governmental industrial organizations, which have produced their own lists of substances they take to be GRAS. The concept itself is not free of controversy, but it remains one indicator of how the safety of chemicals is judged (by at least some scientists) in the USA. When the expression 'GRAS' is used in this dictionary it means that the substance in question is listed as GRAS by the FDA.

If you read a handful of official documents, and listen to the public statements of industry and government, you will have the impression that scientists are able to identify accurately which chemicals are safe and which are toxic. If, however, you read large quantities of documents, and listen to the professional discussions, you will discover that the science of toxicology is actually a shambles, and that its methods and techniques do not give precise or simple answers to the straightforward questions which we ask.

Toxicology is a very uncertain and unreliable science. It is not possible to take at face value all the information which is generated by each of the three parts of toxicology. There are innumerable contradictions both within and between the results of different studies in all parts of toxicology. Consider the example of the artificial sweetener Saccharin. In long-term animal feeding studies Saccharin has been shown to cause cancer in the bladders of male rats, but in other studies using different animals this effect has not been found. When Saccharin has been tested to see if it causes mutations in bacteria some scientists have reported that under some circumstances it does, while other investigators, using different conditions, say that it does not. Since people suffering from diabetes are more likely than most of us to have been using artificial sweeteners, this is a rare example where it has been possible to conduct some epidemiological studies. You can either examine the population of diabetics to see if they are more likely than the average to have suffered from bladder cancer, or you can study bladder cancer sufferers to see if they include an over-representation of diabetics and Saccharin users. Quite a few such studies have been conducted, and some indicate that there may be a connection between Saccharin consumption and human bladder cancer, while others suggest that there is no connection. A senior American scientist has 'guestimated' that: '... over the next 70 years, the expected number of cases of human bladder cancer in the USA resulting from daily exposure of 120mg Saccharin might range from 0.22 to 1,144,000'. The truth is that we just don't know whether or not it is safe.

Another major problem with food additive toxicology is that officials are relying on the results of animal and bacteria tests even though we know that these model organisms cannot detect the chemicals which provoke symptoms of acute intolerance. The problems with toxicology are legion, and this is not the place to discuss them at length (although the reader will find a more detailed account in chapter 4 of *Food Additives*), but suffice it to say that there is no consensus among experts, and the available evidence is not by itself sufficient to enable experts to settle the question of what should be permitted and what banned.

As far as consumers are concerned, the crucial question is: who is getting the benefit of the doubt? If experts, officials and government are giving the benefit of the doubt to consumers then they will assume that a chemical is toxic until it is proved to be safe, but if they are giving the benefit of the doubt to industry then they will assume it to be safe until proved harmful. We believe, and this is argued at length in chapter 5 of *Food Additives*, that the benefit of the doubt has consistently been awarded to industry and not to consumers, where it rightfully belongs. The entries in this dictionary provide further evidence for this contention.

This dictionary has been compiled by reviewing a huge amount of data, much of it overlapping with that which has been reviewed by the official committees, but it differs from their reports in at least three crucial respects. First, we do not pretend that toxicology is certain or reliable; second, we do not pretend that decisions to permit or forbid an additive can be made on purely scientific grounds; and third, we explicitly identify the way in which we are choosing to award the benefit of the doubt.

We have not taken the results of bacterial and animal tests at face value, but have questioned the extent to which they can provide a reliable guide to the effects which chemicals will have on humans. Even if we were able to estimate the extent of any particular hazard, we recognize that any decision on whether a hazard is acceptable or not is a social and political matter and not just a scientific one. The official reports are making social judgements but misrepresenting them as purely scientific ones. In this dictionary we face the fact that these issues are not, and cannot be, settled by science alone. We are, furthermore, explicitly acknowledging that we are giving the benefit of the doubt to consumers because that is where we think it belongs.

We are not arguing that all additives are unsafe, but that given that there is so much doubt, and given that consumers, for the most part, do not need them, far fewer chemicals should be permitted and used, and that it is often in the interest of consumers to choose foods free of unnecessary chemicals. Our assessment is that a few dozen additives are almost certainly safe, a similar number almost certainly pose definite hazards to at least some consumers, and as for the remainder, we just don't know.

ABBREVIATIONS

ADI	acceptable daily intake of a chemical, measured in mg/kg bw
BIBRA	British Industrial Biological Research Association
Codex	Codex Alimentarius Commission
CoT	Committee on the Toxicity (of Chemicals in Food, Consumer Products and the Environment) at the DHSS
DHSS	Department of Health and Social Security
EEC	European Economic Community
FAC	Food Advisory Committee (of MAFF)
FACC	Food Additives and Contaminants Committee (of MAFF)
FAO	Food and Agriculture Organization (of the United Nations)
FDA	(the United States) Food and Drug Administration
FSC	Food Standards Committee (of MAFF)
GRAS	generally regarded as safe
JECFA	Joint Expert Committee on Food Additives
mg/kg bw	milligrams per kilogram of body weight of a laboratory animal or a human consumer
MAFF	Ministry of Agriculture, Fisheries and Food
NEL	no (observable adverse) effect level in laboratory animals, measured in mg/kg bw
ppm	parts per million
SCF	Scientific Committee for Food (of the EEC)
SF	safety factor
WHO	World Health Organization

GLOSSARY

ACCEPTABLE DAILY INTAKE (ADI)   This figure is supposed to specify a maximum average daily level at which people can safely consume an additive for their entire life span. It is expressed in terms of the number of milligrams of the chemical which may safely be consumed by a human, for each kilogram of the consumer's body weight, abbreviated to mg/kg bw. This figure is obtained by first identifying in animal tests a daily dosing level at which no adverse effects are observed, and this is called the 'no effect level' (or NEL). The ADI is directly obtained from the NEL simply by dividing it by what is usually termed a 'safety factor' (or SF).

ACUTE   An adverse effect is acute if it arises shortly after the offending substance has been consumed. This might be a matter of minutes, hours or at the most a few days. Adverse effects which are provoked over the long term by persistent or cumulative consumption are termed 'chronic'.

ALLERGY   People have an allergy, strictly speaking, only if their acute adverse reactions to chemicals have demonstrable abnormal effects on their immune system. There are many kinds of adverse acute reactions and the general term 'intolerance' is used to cover them, but only a portion of these demonstrably involve the immune system, in so far as that is currently understood. Allergic reactions are therefore that sub-set of intolerant reactions which depend upon a mechanism which immunologists are currently capable of identifying.

AMINO ACID   These organic acids are the building blocks which together constitute proteins. There are 20 major amino acids, but the body is capable of synthesizing only 12 of them. The other 8 have to be obtained as nutrients from our diet, and are known as essential amino acids.

ANTI-CAKING AGENT   Chemical food additives are used as anti-caking agents if they prevent granular and powdered products from absorbing moisture and so sticking together or becoming lumpy.

ANTI-FOAMING AGENT   Chemical food additives are used as anti-foaming agents if they can be used to stop ingredients and products from frothing, boiling over, or to help in the formation of a scum.

ANTIOXIDANT   When oils and fats are stored they tend to react with oxygen in the air, and in so doing they turn rancid, damaging their taste and smell. This can make them unpalatable, unsaleable, and in extreme cases unsafe. Chemical food additives are used as antioxidants if they inhibit the oxidation of oils and fats. The main effect of their use is to extend the shelflife of products containing oils and fats.

AZO DYES This term is used to refer to a large group of synthetic colourings which are chemically similar in that they are produced from the reactions between diazonium compounds and phenols. Many of these compounds were first identified in the late nineteenth century, when they were distilled from coal tar, and are part of the group of coal tar dyes.

BASE This is the general term which is used to apply to alkaline chemicals, and they are used as food additives to make products less acidic, or to react with acids to produce gases so that they can act as raising agents.

BLEACHING AGENT Chemical food additives are used as bleaching agents if they interact with flour to whiten it. They achieve this effect by oxidizing the components of the grain which are naturally coloured.

BUFFER Chemical food additives are used as buffers if they serve to keep the acidity of a solution fairly constant.

CARCINOGEN A chemical which causes cancer in animals or humans is called a carcinogen.

CHELATING AGENT Chemical food additives are used as chelating agents if they can trap or collect metallic contaminants which are found in food products. These may have entered the product with the ingredients, or be contamination from the processing machinery. If these metals are not removed they can accelerate the oxidation of oils and fats, and provoke rancidity. As a result chelating agents are often used in combination with antioxidants. Chelating agents are also sometimes called sequestrants.

CHRONIC An adverse effect is chronic if it is provoked over the long term by persistent or cumulative consumption. By contrast, adverse effects which arise within a few minutes, hours, or at the most a few days of consumption are termed 'acute'.

COAL TAR DYE This term is used to refer loosely to a broad group of synthetic organic dyes, which includes but is not exhausted by, the azo dyes. The term originated because many of these compounds were first identified in the late 19th century when they were distilled from coal tar.

EMULSIFIER Chemical food additives are used as emulsifiers to mediate between water-based solutions and oils or fats so that they will mix together, when they would otherwise be immiscible. A successful mixture of water and oils is called an emulsion.

EPIDEMIOLOGY This is the study of patterns of mortality and morbidity in the human population. It is relatively powerful when dealing with problems which are either acute or widespread or both, but it is relatively weak when dealing with problems which are chronic, rare or both.

FIRMING AGENT   Chemical food additives are used as firming agents if they can be applied to fruits and vegetables to inhibit their tendency to turn soft or soggy, especially during processing.

FLAVOUR ENHANCER   Chemical food additives are used as flavour enhancers if they stimulate the taste buds. Flavour enhancers are generally rather tasteless on their own, but they make products in which they are incorporated seem tastier than would otherwise be the case.

FREEZANT   Chemical food additives are used as freezants if they can be applied directly to foods to chill and then freeze them.

GELLING AGENT   Chemical food additives are used as gelling agents if they can thicken food products or to help form a gel.

GLAZING AGENT   Chemical food additives are used as glazing agents if they can be used to create a surface shine, or protective coating.

HAEMOGLOBIN   This is an essential component of blood. It plays a vital role in the transport of oxygen around the body, and its colour varies from red to brown in proportion to the oxygen content.

HUMECTANT   Chemical food additives are used as humectants if they can be used to prevent or inhibit food products from losing water and drying out.

HYDROLYSIS   This term is used to refer to a chemical reaction with water. When organic compounds hydrolyse, the reaction generally causes them to decompose.

HYPERACTIVITY   This term is used to refer to a complex, very unpleasant, and poorly understood syndrome in which the sufferers exhibit frantic restlessness, inattention, an inability to concentrate, frustration and often anger and aggression to themselves and others. There is direct evidence that some food additives can trigger hyperactivity, but there are few recorded hyperactives whose attacks are triggered only by food additives.

INTOLERANCE   A general term which is used to refer to the condition afflicting people who exhibit a wide range of acute adverse effects. These include, but are not exhausted by, allergic effects.

METABOLISM   This term is used to refer to the chemical changes involved in the body as compounds are synthesized and decomposed.

MUTAGEN   A chemical which causes mutations in bacteria, animals or humans is called a mutagen.

MUTATION   A change in the genetic material of an organism which can then be passed on to subsequent generations is called a mutation. Occasionally these might possibly be advantageous in the long evolutionary term, but they are generally assumed to be undesirable.

NO EFFECT LEVEL (NEL)   This is the level of daily consumption, measured in milligrams of chemical per kilogram of the animal's body weight, at which in long-term tests no adverse effects were observed.

PRESERVATIVE   Chemical food additives are used as preservatives if they serve to inhibit the rate at which bacteria can thrive in foods. By restricting the rate of bacterial contamination they can protect consumers from the toxins which the bacteria secrete.

PROTEIN   Proteins are a group of large, complicated and essential molecules which together may constitute at least one half of the dry weight of living cells.

ROPE   This is an undesirable condition which can afflict bread, and is caused by a particular sort of bacterial contamination. The bacteria can survive the baking process and then feed off the bread, causing the dough to degenerate into gelatinous threads resembling rope.

SAFETY FACTOR (SF)   This refers to a numerical factor by which the No Effect Level is divided in order to specify an Acceptable Daily Intake. This is an arbitrary figure, but the textbooks recommend that normally a figure of 100 should be chosen.

SARCOMA   This term is used to refer to a tumour which is found in soft and connective tissues.

SEQUESTRANT   Chemical food additives are used as sequestrants if they can trap or collect metallic contaminants which are found in food products. These may have entered the product with the ingredients, or be contamination from the processing machinery. If these metals are not removed they can accelerate the oxidation of oils and fats, and provoke rancidity. As a result sequestrants are often used in combination with antioxidants. Sequestrant is another term for a chelating agent.

STABILIZER   Chemical food additives are used as stabilizers if they can serve to stop emulsions from once again separating out into aqueous and oil- or fat-based components. They are therefore used in combination with emulsifiers.

SYNERGIST   Chemical food additives are used as synergists if they can enhance the effectiveness of other additives. They are used especially in combination with some antioxidants whose effect can be significantly enhanced by synergists such as Citric Acid.

TERATOGEN A chemical which damages a foetus so that it is born deformed is called a teratogen.

TOXIC A chemical is toxic if it is poisonous.

TOXICOLOGY This is the name of the science which studies the effects of environmental agents on humans, animals and other organisms.

TUMOUR This term is used to refer to a cancerous swelling or growth.

THE COLOURING ADDITIVES
E100–E180

E100: Curcumin
also known as Turmeric

Type An orange-yellow colouring with a distinctive taste and flavour, it is extracted, by the use of solvents, from the Indian herb Turmeric (Haldi), and it has a chemical structure similar to the Anthocyanins (see E163). Turmeric is also a spice which is used to provide the oleoresins which are important constituents of its flavour.

Foods added to Frequently it is used to cover the surface of food products, but it is also sometimes used in salad dressings, sausage casings, curry powder, pastries, confectionery, fish products and soups. Often it is used to restore the colour of food products lost in the course of processing.

Toxicological evaluation and possible health hazards JECFA awarded it a (temporary) ADI in 1969. This ADI, based mainly on the results of tests with dogs and rats, has subsequently been revised upwards from 0.5 to 2.5mg/kg bw, but has always remained temporary, indicating a persistent requirement for further studies and information. One problem which remains unresolved is that Curcumin causes mutations in bacteria or, in other words, it is genotoxic to these organisms. This leaves an unexplained question mark either against the safety of this substance, or against the general validity of the mutagenicity tests. Since 1975, the SCF of the EEC has considered Curcumin sufficiently safe to be gen-

erally acceptable for use in foods without further investigation and without a formal ADI. They confirmed this view in 1983, and have not changed it since.

In Britain, it was listed in Group B by the CoT in 1979, pending the receipt of results of further short-term studies. These were supplied, but not within the two-year limit which the CoT had set. In 1987 the CoT reported that, although no adverse effects had been found in short-term tests on mice and rats, when fed to pigs it increased the weight of their thyroid glands, and at high doses there was evidence of thyroid damage. The CoT did not recommend that its use should be particularly restricted, but reconfirmed its Group B status while calling for the results of long-term studies on rodents, and a more detailed study of the effects it may have on the pigs' thyroids.

Regulatory status It is permitted in many countries, including North America and the EEC, for use in a wide range of products. It is not banned in any country.

E101: Riboflavin
also known as Vitamin B2

Type It is a natural orange-yellow colouring, which can be extracted from natural sources or manufactured synthetically. Since it is a vitamin it is sometimes categorized as a dietetic additive. As far as we know, every plant and animal requires some Vitamin B2 in order to live and grow healthily. It can readily be found in milk, eggs, nuts (especially almonds), yeast and yeast extracts, liver and kidney.

Foods added to It is used in some processed cheeses, and to 'fortify' some processed foods, especially breakfast cereals. It can be found in some baby foods where it is used as a vitamin.

Toxicological evaluation and possible health hazards No adverse effects are known and it is presumed to be safe, despite the fact that like Curcumin (see E100) it is genotoxic to some bacteria. As above, this implies either that there is an unexplained problem with the safety of the substance, or the results of bacterial mutagenicity tests are very hard to interpret. JECFA has established an ADI for this substance at 0.5mg/kg bw for its use as a food additive, and this figure was re-confirmed in 1981. In the course of a laboratory test of a known chemical carcinogen, it was found that the adding of Riboflavin to rats' diet inhibited the genesis of liver tumours. The significance of this fragment of information is hard to assess, but it could mean that it might play a part in protecting humans against some cancer hazards. In 1983 it was approved by the SCF without a formal ADI because they considered it to be un-problematically safe, a view which is also shared by British experts.

Regulatory status It is approved for use in the UK and throughout the EEC. It is also accepted in the USA under the category of chemicals which are GRAS (generally regarded as safe).

E101a: Riboflavin-5'-Phosphate

Type It is a yellow colouring obtained by a chemical treatment of Riboflavin (see E101).

Foods added to Like Riboflavin, it is used in some processed cheeses and to 'fortify' some processed foods, especially breakfast cereals. It can be found in some baby foods where it is used as a vitamin.

Toxicological evaluation and possible health hazards No hazards are known and it is presumed to be safe. When reviewing this substance the SCF observed that since it is a normal metabolite of Vitamin B they would approve its use as a food additive despite the lack of detailed animal toxicological testing.

Regulatory status It has been permitted in the UK since the late 1960s, and in the EEC.

E102: Tartrazine
also known in the USA as FD&C Yellow No. 5

Type It is a bright-yellow coal tar dye. Tartrazine is used unmixed to give a lemon-yellow colour, but is often mixed with Sunset Yellow (see E110) or Amaranth (see E123) to yield a variety of shades from cream to orange. It can also be mixed with Brilliant Blue FCF (see 133) to yield various shades of green. Tartrazine has been in use since the late nineteenth century and remains one of the most widely used coal tar dyes.

Foods added to This is the most widely used and readily recognized synthetic colour. It is used, for example, in many soft drinks, boiled sweets, pastries, jellies, coatings, ice lollies, smoked fish, canned vegetables, dessert mixes, marzipan and brown sauces. It is also widely available from retailers in household dispensers as a food colour. In 1987 MAFF reported that Tartrazine is used in at least 2,295 different products.

Toxicological evaluation and possible health hazards There is an extensive controversy about the safety and/or toxicity of Tartrazine. It was in 1948 that Tartrazine's ability to provoke acute symptoms was first noted and published. Professional allergists have recognized its allergenic potential since 1959. Among those who accept the reality of additive-provoked intolerance, Tartrazine is generally recognized to be responsible for a wide range of allergic and intolerant symptoms including child hyperactivity, asthma, migraine, and skin rashes. Tartrazine is the food colour which is most frequently cited as being responsible for these problems. It would be a mistake, however, to assume that Tartrazine is significantly more likely to be provoking problems than other coal tar dyes. Tartrazine is just particularly widely used and easily recognized and therefore especially easy to study.

It has been established that people who are particularly sensitive to, and intolerant of, aspirin and other similar salicylates are liable to be intolerant of Tartrazine. Since salicylates are naturally present in several fruits and vegetables, a proper test of Tartrazine intolerance should ensure, as far as possible, that other dietary salicylates are also controlled. Tests which are currently being conducted in Britain under the auspices of the DHSS fail to satisfy this condition, and can therefore be expected to underestimate the real incidence of intolerance.

There has been just one suggestion in the technical literature that Tartrazine might cause cancer: an FDA pathologist found some tumours in rats fed with Tartrazine, but the author did not say if this was statistically significant by comparison with a control group.

As recently as 1981, JECFA took the view that Tartrazine was sufficiently safe (to rats at least) for them to award it the comparatively high ADI of 7.5mg/kg bw. The study on which this judgement was based, however, only lasted for 64 weeks rather than the more usual two years. At the same time JECFA indicated several areas of further research on the safety of Tartrazine which they would like to see conducted. These included metabolic studies in more animal species, reproduction studies in several species, and studies of the combined effects of Tartrazine with Sunset Yellow (see E110) and Amaranth (see E123). This implies that the scientists were satisfied that Tartrazine is safe even though a great deal of important information was lacking and does not yet exist.

The SCF has endorsed the JECFA ADI and continues to categorize Tartrazine as unproblematic, even though they recognize that it provokes intolerant reactions. The dose required to provoke adverse reactions in sensitive people can, however, be as little as 1 per cent of the ADI. Scientists who work in, or for, the food or chemical industries often say that hyperactivity and other related intolerance problems occur very infrequently, have hysterical or other psychological causes, and are not really biochemical effects because immunologists can't explain them, and because laboratory animals used in chemical tests do not exhibit these adverse reactions. The fact that rats and mice do not share problems of intolerance does not mean that the phenomena are psychological, and it would be at least as reasonable to conclude that the human reactions are genuine and that animals tests are just unreliable and inadequate. Other scientists say that the incidence of these problems is massively underestimated in industrial and official circles, and that the doctors should be judged against their patients' problems, not vice versa. They emphasize also that whatever may happen in laboratory animals knowledgeable doctors can turn the unpleasant symptoms on or off simply by controlling their patients' diets. The food industry and the government have frequently been asked how many people have to be shown to be suffering before they restrict the use of the chemical agents, but no reply has ever been forthcoming. In 1984 the British Industrial Biological Research Association stated that Tartrazine-sensitive individuals in the UK may number tens of thousands.

In 1979 the CoT listed Tartrazine in Group A, and confirmed this in 1987, indicating their confidence in its safety, despite the evidence concerning acute intolerance. They recognize that this issue remains unresolved, but they choose to give the benefit of the doubt to the chemical rather than to consumers.

Regulatory status The use of Tartrazine has been prohibited in Norway and Finland since 1981. It is permitted in Austria, but its use is highly restricted. It is permitted in Sweden only in spirits, cocktail cherries and imitation caviare. Tartrazine is generally permitted and widely used in the UK, much of the EEC, and also in the USA.

E104: Quinoline Yellow

Type It is a yellow coal tar dye, produced synthetically in two slightly different but closely related forms, but both contain several similar impurities.

Foods added to It is used in some edible ices, soft drinks, fruit syrups and smoked fish products.

Toxicological evaluation and possible health hazards When JECFA first reviewed this substance in the mid-1960s they concluded that they did not have sufficient information about it to reach a judgement. Despite this fact it continued to be used. By the early 1970s, based on the results of tests in dogs and rats, they awarded it a temporary ADI of 0.5mg/kg bw, and this has been reconfirmed several times but remained temporary pending the results of metabolic and chronic toxicity studies. JECFA reviewed it most recently in 1984 by which time they had received the data which they had requested, when they assigned it a full ADI of 10mg/kg bw on the basis of the results of a long-term study using mice.

When the SCF considered it in 1975 they felt they did not have sufficient data to provide an evaluation. By 1983 the SCF had been provided with more information, obtained with rats, rabbits and mice, and they ascribed an ADI of 10mg/kg bw. In the 1979 Colours review from the FACC this colour was classified on the 'B' list, which means that the substance is provisionally acceptable pending the receipt of further toxicological information within five years. The CoT reported in 1987 that they had received the data which they had requested, namely a chronic toxicity and carcinogenicity study on mice, and they were sufficiently satisfied that they promoted it into Group A. There is some direct evidence that it provokes intolerant symptoms in vulnerable human patients, even if it seems safe for laboratory animals.

Regulatory status Quinoline Yellow is permitted in the UK and the EEC, but is banned in Norway, Canada, Japan and the USA.

107: Yellow 2G
also known as Food Yellow 5 and Acid Yellow 17

Type It is a yellow colouring extracted from coal tar, chemically very similar to Tartrazine (see E102).

Foods added to It is used in some soft drinks, confectionery, dessert mixes, cakes and biscuits.

Toxicological evaluation and possible health hazards This chemical has been in use for many years without any adequate evidence of its safety. We know that different species metabolize Yellow 2G quite differently, yet governments are still relying solely on animals as an approximate guide to its effects on humans. In 1955 the experts who advised the British Food Standards Committee listed Yellow 2G in Group B, meaning that they did not have sufficient information to be certain of its safety. As recently as 1975, JECFA refused to evaluate its safety because its metabolism had not yet been satisfactorily examined and they just did not have sufficient information. They could report only eight partial studies on its toxicity using rats and pigs, at least three of them conducted at BIBRA, one of them 'private'. In spite of this fact it has remained in continuous use for over twenty years. More recently some evidence has indicated that it causes significant hazards (including the induction of lymphomas) to mice and rats when fed at high doses. Despite this information JECFA in 1981 were bold enough to specify a possible NEL and so a temporary ADI of 0.025mg/kg bw, even though there are

no grounds for assuming any safe threshold for a carcinogenic hazard.

In 1975 the SCF were marginally more careful and set a lower temporary ADI at 0.01mg/kg bw, calling for further studies which might help them interpret the incidence of mice lymphomas. By 1983 the SCF had apparently lost its patience with Yellow 2G and they refused to provide an evaluation, and they did so in a way which suggests that they believe it to be unsafe. Consequently it does not have an 'E' number; it is not E107, but just 107.

In 1979 the FACC listed this colour in Group B, stating that the substance was provisionally acceptable pending the receipt of further toxicological information within five years. The 1987 Colours' Report of the British FAC reveals that the data which they had requested in 1979 were never submitted, and so they demoted Yellow 2G to Group E, and recommended that its use should be banned. There is some direct evidence that it may provoke symptoms of intolerance among asthmatics and those who are sensitive to aspirin.

Regulatory status Before 1985 it was temporarily permitted in the EEC, but that permission was then withdrawn. It is used (though not widely) in the UK, but banned in Austria, Belgium, France, Greece, Italy, Japan, Norway, Spain, Sweden, Switzerland and the USA.

E110: Sunset Yellow FCF
also known as FD&C Yellow No. 6

Type It is an orange-yellow coal tar dye, which was first synthesized in 1878 for the textile industry. It is used very widely, especially in the USA and Western Europe where there are approximately fifteen manufacturers producing several thousand kilograms of it annually. It is predominantly used in foods, but also in drugs, cosmetics and inks.

Foods added to It is added to a very wide range of different kinds of food products such as confectionery, fish fingers, soft drinks, dessert powders, cereals, bakery goods, yoghurts and sauces, as well as some alcoholic beverages. In 1987 MAFF reported that it is used in no fewer than 1,215 different British products.

Toxicological evaluation and possible health hazards In 1966 JECFA established an ADI for Sunset Yellow of 5mg/kg bw based on the results of tests with rats and dogs, while calling for several further studies, including its combined effects with Tartrazine (see E102) and Amaranth (see E123). In 1975, the SCF of the EEC reviewed some more data and awarded it a lower ADI of 2.5mg/kg bw. In 1979 the CoT listed it in Group A, indicating that they considered it sufficiently safe to be used without specific restrictions. JECFA revised its judgement to come into line with the SCF in 1982.

In 1987, however, the CoT indicated that more recent evidence might indicate a hazard. The complication arose because, although ten long-term feeding studies had not suggested adverse effects, two more recent studies had indicated that Sunset Yellow damaged the kidneys and adrenal glands of laboratory rats. The results are difficult to interpret, partly because the background incidence of these conditions in ageing rats is rather high. At least four groups of pathologists have trawled through the tissue samples and records. Reviewing all the data and opinions, the CoT eventually concluded on balance that Sunset Yellow is sufficiently safe to remain in Group A.

There is some direct evidence that Sunset Yellow can provoke unpleasant acute symptoms in humans. People who are sensitive to aspirin, and/or who exhibit symptoms of azo-dye intolerance, such as hyperactive children, asthmatics, and urticaria sufferers, are advised to avoid this substance.

Regulatory status It is approved for use in many countries including the UK and the EEC, the USA and Cuba, but not Portugal. In Norway it is prohibited as are all other coal tar dyes.

E120: Cochineal
also known as Carminic acid

Type This red colouring occurs naturally in the tissue of the females of the insect *Coccus cacti* which is native to Central America but which has been introduced into the Canary Islands and Java. Strictly speaking the name Cochineal refers to the entire dried animal carcass, while Carminic acid is its coloured constituent. Some anxiety has been expressed within the food industry that if all other red dyes (see E122, E123, E124, E127 and E128) were banned it would be difficult to meet their requirements from natural Cochineal production. One guess attributed to the Natural History Museum estimates that to yield the quantity required would entail farming the insects across 130,000 square kilometres of Texas, New Mexico or California. Currently, the total world supply of Carmine would replace only 0.5 per cent of the world market for Amaranth (see E123).

Foods added to Cochineal is relatively scarce and expensive and so not widely used, although its use is more widely permitted. It may be found in some yoghurts, confectionery, meat products and sausage casings. Although it is expensive it is relatively stable when heated, and can therefore be found in some protein products which are heated during their manufacture.

Toxicological evaluation and possible health hazards JECFA reviewed Cochineal in 1974, 1975 and 1977, but on each occasion they concluded that it had been too poorly studied, and there was so much uncertainty about its toxicity that they were unable to provide an evaluation. In 1975 the SCF also felt unable to approve it for general use in foods, but restricted its use to some alcoholic beverages on a temporary basis. In spite of this fact it continued to be used in the UK. In 1981 JECFA was still calling for more information, but granted a temporary ADI of 2.5mg/kg bw on the basis of experiments with mice and rats. Later that year, the SCF reviewed the accumulated data, and despite the fact that they did not have all the data which they had previously requested, they did approve it and established an ADI of 5mg/kg bw, which was subsequently endorsed by JECFA in 1983. In 1979 the British FACC consigned Cochineal to Group B, meaning that it was temporarily acceptable pending further research, and the submission of results within five years. Results which have subsequently been provided to the CoT from a long-term feeding study have satisfied them that it is evidently safe for laboratory animals. On this basis the CoT promoted Cochineal to Group A in 1987.

Whatever the results of the animal tests may be, there is some anxiety that this is one of the colours which can provoke hyperactivity and other prob-lems of intolerance. There is a report from the USA that a consignment of Cochineal was carrying salmonella bacteria, and as a result all Cochineal should be pasteurized.

Special restrictions Since it is extracted from insects it is not acceptable to vegetarians or vegans, and it is not kosher.

Regulatory status Cochineal is currently permitted in the UK, the EEC, and in the USA. It is, however, banned in Norway and Spain.

E122: Carmoisine
also known as Azorubine

Type It is a red coal tar dye, not known to occur in nature. It was first synthesized in 1885 and then used by the textile trade.

Foods added to This colouring is quite widely used. In 1987 MAFF indicated that it is currently being used in at least 682 different products. It is permitted for use in eleven of the nineteen groups of food which were specified by the FACC in 1977. Food products containing Carmoisine include both sweets and savouries such as some savoury and fruit flavour sauces, desserts, chocolate products, confectionery, soup mixes, sausages, meat substitutes, soft drinks, cider and jams.

Toxicological evaluation and possible health hazards It was reviewed by JECFA in the 1950s and '60s, but it was not until 1974/75 that they eventually felt able to award it a temporary ADI of 0.5mg/kg bw, based on experiments with mice and rats and backed by calls for further research. Throughout this period the colour continued to be used, even though its safety or toxicity had yet to be determined. JECFA's reservations were due primarily to lack of complete and adequate rodent data rather than to evidence of toxicity in those animal tests which had been conducted and reported. In 1975 the SCF specified a temporary ADI of 2mg/kg bw, while also calling for several further studies. In 1978 JECFA raised its ADI to 1.25mg/kg bw, while maintaining its temporary character. In 1983, with results of some more tests, the SCF raised its ADI to 4mg/kg bw.

In Britain in 1955 it had been listed as Group A, but by 1979 the FACC had downgraded it into Group B, meaning that they were prepared provisionally to approve its use pending the submission of more data within five years. In 1987 the CoT reported that they had received sufficient supplementary data to enable them to promote it to Group A.

Despite the evidence that it is safe for rats, there is evidence that it may adversely affect those suffering from asthma, or sensitive to aspirin.

Regulatory status Carmoisine has been permitted in the UK and the EEC for many years, and currently it is permitted in Australia, Denmark, West Germany, India, South Africa, Spain and Switzerland. It is not permitted, however, in Norway, Sweden, Canada and the USA.

E123: Amaranth
also known as Red 2

Type It is a very widely-used red coal tar dye. It was first synthesized in 1878, and first produced on a large scale in the USA in 1914. There are approximately ten manufacturers in Western Europe producing more than 300 tonnes a year. It is used not merely in food products, but also in numerous drug preparations, cosmetics and inks.

Foods added to This is a widely-used colour in the UK. It can be found in many soft drinks, sweets, especially in products imitating cherries, strawberries, raspberries, or blackcurrants, in boiled sweets, confectionery, soft drinks, preserves, meat products, fruit fillings, biscuits and cider. In 1983, the British food industry incorporated about 50 tonnes of Amaranth into their products. It is also found in some toothpastes and is widely available from retailers in household dispensers as a food colour.

Toxicological evaluation and possible health hazards This chemical has been among the most controversial food chemicals during the last fifteen years. There have been some doubts about its safety since at least 1938. There is some direct human evidence that it can provoke hyperactivity and other symptoms of intolerance including asthma, eczema and urticaria.

In 1954 the British Food Standards Committee thought that the available evidence suggested that Amaranth was entirely safe for human use as a food additive. They confirmed this opinion in 1964, despite recognizing that it had not been fully tested, even by the relatively modest standards of the day. JECFA reviewed Amaranth during the 1950s and in 1966 assigned to it an ADI of 1.5mg/kg bw, while calling for further studies of possible effects on reproduction. The Russians conducted such tests and then promptly banned Amaranth in the light of their results. JECFA did not accept the Russian results or conclusions and merely revised their evaluation in 1972, when a temporary ADI of 0.75mg/kg bw was set on the basis of the results of tests on rats, mice, rabbits, cats and dogs. During the turbulent debates of the 1970s this was reconfirmed twice in the face of a complex welter of incomplete and sometimes paradoxical data. In 1975 the SCF endorsed an ADI at the same level as JECFA, while they too called for yet more studies. In 1976, in the midst of a heated controversy in the USA, the Food and Drug Administration banned Amaranth from use in food products.

Between 1975 and 1981 further studies produced yet more conflicting evidence, especially in relation to possible hazards to the foetus, while JECFA continued to set an ADI of 0.75mg/kg bw, although it remained temporary, as it had been for twelve years. In 1983 the SCF awarded a permanent ADI of 0.8mg/kg bw to Amaranth, even though they called for yet further research to try to resolve some puzzling anomalies. In 1984 JECFA pronounced themselves sufficiently satisfied with the accumulated data to set a full ADI at the slightly lower figure of 0.5mg/kg bw.

In Britain the 1979 report of the CoT demoted Amaranth to Group B, as they called for further studies. When they reported in 1987 they pronounced themselves sufficiently satisfied to promote it back into Group A. Anomalies remain but the benefit of doubt is being given to the chemical rather than to consumers.

The doubts about the long-term safety of Amaranth became particularly pronounced in 1970 when some work in the Soviet Union suggested that Amaranth is carcinogenic. This provoked an extensive discussion, particularly in the United States, where the scientists of the FDA concluded and then recommended that Amaranth (or Red 2 as it is known in America) should be banned. The US food industry put up an enormous fight to retain the use of Amaranth, which they eventually lost, and Amaranth was banned in the USA in January 1976. It was this decision which was responsible for the extraordinary occasion when the American importers of Smarties had to go to the customs shed and throw away all the red ones, so as to ensure that the remaining colours would be allowed into the USA. There are indications that the American food industry is on the verge of requesting the re-introduction of Amaranth into the USA.

One focus of the controversy has concerned the validity of the Russian work which had indicted Amaranth. One of the crucial studies was conducted by the Russian scientist Andrianova and showed that 2 per cent of Amaranth in the diet of rats caused cancer in 13 out of a test group of 50 rats. Other Russian studies indicated that it caused birth defects, stillbirths, sterility and early foetal deaths in rats at relatively low dose levels. Much of this Russian work was judged to be unreliable by the Western toxicological establishment because the control group of animals exhibited a very low background level of cancers. A judgement about the toxicity of a chemical is based on the difference between the rates of illness among animals in the test groups and those in the control. For any given rate of illness in the test group, the apparent toxicity of the test substance is inversely proportional to the rate of illness in the animals comprising the control group. The unusual feature of the Russian tests was that the cancer rate among the controls was so low, and this has frequently been used in the West as grounds for dismissing the Russian evidence. It is nowadays very rare for animals in control groups to be free of all cancers, but it does occasionally occur. Laboratory animals are nowadays prone to obesity, and as a result there are now higher background cancer rates in animals than were common twenty years ago. This might explain both why the Russian studies had low background rates, and why these are now so unusual. If this explanation were correct, however, then it would partly undermine the case for dismissing some of the evidence against Amaranth.

During the 1970s, and at the height of the American controversy about Amaranth, the FDA conducted its own series of tests to try to see whether they could confirm or refute the Russian findings. They investigated, for example, the effects of Amaranth on poultry chicks. This work readily suggested that the chemical produced defects in the chick embryos even at very low doses. The evidence was rather complicated because the dose-response curve was U-shaped. A high dose caused a strong effect, while a moderate dose caused less of an effect, but when the dose was reduced further the effect became stronger again. These results were then dismissed by industrial and government scientists because they did not conform to what most, but not all, toxicologists like to call 'a true dose-response relationship'. Data such as these should not be disregarded as unreliable; rather they imply a need for further investigations. This issue remains unresolved.

The Russians claimed that their tests had shown that chemically pure Amaranth is carcinogenic. Western toxicologists challenged this claim by suggesting that the substance tested was not chemically pure, and that the toxic effects may have resulted from the impurities. This was rejected by the Russians, but they never provided foreign scientists with a sample of the dye which they had tested. This remains one of the many sources of uncertainty. Since the Russians promptly banned Amaranth they have had no incentive to repeat their experiments.

Subsequent work conducted by scientists from both the FDA and the food industry indicated that Amaranth causes female rodents to reabsorb some of their foetuses. This is a curious and unpleasant phenomenon. In a healthy animal a fertilized egg implants on the wall of the womb, and the embryo then grows on a placenta connected to its mother by an umbilical cord until it is sufficiently mature to be born. One of the ways in which that process can go wrong is for the foetal tissue to be consumed back into the maternal womb, and for no foetus to develop. The evidence of reabsorption has been dismissed.

One of the reasons given for dismissing some of the results of this work is the method by which the test substance was administered. The animals did not receive it as part of an unlimited food supply; it was introduced into the animals by a technique known as 'gavage'. Gavage administration involves forcing a tube down the throat of the animals and pouring a liquid directly into their digestive tracts. Gavage has the advantage that scientists can control precisely the dose and the diet of the animals, and can even force them to digest materials which they would not otherwise choose to consume. It would almost undoubtedly be a mistake to rely heavily on this technique, but there is one set of circumstances in which it may be appropriate, and this is when trying to test the effect of chemicals to be used in drinks. Gavage models drinking, although it cannot model either eating or inhaling a chemical. Since Amaranth is often incorporated into soft drinks, and for that matter into red alcoholic drinks too, gavage is probably no less appropriate as a method of administration than incorporating it into solid food. On this occasion toxicologists dismissed the evidence although gavage data in other cases had been thought reliable.

Regulatory status Amaranth is banned in the USA, USSR, Greece, Yugoslavia, Norway, Sweden, Finland and Austria, but permitted and widely used in Britain and at least sixty-three other countries. The US food industry appears eager to reintroduce it into their market.

E124: Ponceau 4R
also known as Cochineal Red R

Type A red coal tar dye.

Foods added to It is used quite widely in both sweet and savoury products, for example in some tomato soups, strawberry jam, edible ices and packet mixes. In the UK it is permitted for use in thirteen of the nineteen food groups specified by the FACC in 1979. In 1987 MAFF reported that it is used in no fewer than 674 different products.

Toxicological evaluation and possible health hazards In the mid-1960s, when this colour was already in use, JECFA stated that insufficient data were then available to enable them to provide any evaluation of its safety or toxicity. In 1969, however, after continued use and further tests on cats, guinea-pigs and mice, they assigned to it a temporary ADI of 0.75mg/kg bw. On receipt of further information obtained from rats they revised this figure downwards in 1974 to 0.125 mg/kg bw, and it remained temporary. In 1975, when considering the same information, the SCF felt unable to provide any definite opinion, pending the availability of the results of further studies. In Britain, although it had previously been listed as Group A, the FACC demoted it to Group B in 1979, pending more information within five years. In spite of the uncertainty and ignorance, the colour continued in use. In 1983, however, both JECFA and the SCF were eventually satisfied that they had received sufficient animal information to assign Ponceau 4R a full ADI which they raised to 4mg/kg bw. In 1987 the CoT reported that the data which they had requested in 1979 had been provided, and were sufficient to satisfy them that Ponceau 4R can safely be consumed at the levels which currently prevail.

Whatever effects it may or may not have in laboratory animals, it appears to cause acute problems for human asthmatics and those sensitive to aspirin.

Regulatory status This colour has been banned in the USA since 1976, although they do permit two red colouring additives which are banned in the EEC (Ponceau SX and Allura Red AC, see E129). It has been permitted and used in the UK and the EEC for some years, and is currently also permitted in Australia, India and Switzerland, but banned along with all other synthetic colours in Norway.

E127: Erythrosine
also known as FD&C Red No. 3

Type It is a red coal tar dye. In the early 1970s the American food industry was using about 150,000lb of this dye annually. No comparative figures are available for either the UK or for other EEC countries.

Foods added to It is used on its own in some confectionery and other sweet products to provide rose and pink shades; and it is used in combination with other colours to give purple, mauve and violet. It can also be found in some biscuits, canned fruits, flavoured yoghurts, cherry pie mixes, meat products and fried snack foods. It is currently permitted for use in the UK in eleven of the FACC's nineteen food groups, but in April 1987 the CoT recommended that its use should be confined to cocktail and glacé cherries.

Toxicological evaluation and possible health hazards In the mid-1960s JECFA refused to evaluate its safety or toxicity because the available data were insufficient. In spite of this fact it continued to be used. After further tests on rats, they gave it a temporary ADI of 1.25mg/kg bw in 1969. They expressed several reservations, including worries that it might be converted into the chemical fluorescein which can poison the kidneys. By 1974, when they conducted a further review, some of these doubts had diminished, and JECFA set a new full ADI at 2.5mg/kg bw, even though it had been shown to be moderately mutagenic to some bacteria. JECFA again requested further studies and more data about how it is metabolized by both rats and humans. During the subsequent ten years substantial amounts of data accumulated which appeared either to indicate that Erythrosine might be hazardous, or which were equivocal. The most worrying aspect reported by JECFA in 1984 is that Erythrosine had been shown to provoke tumours in the thyroid glands of rats. Evidence was also available to indicate that the thyroid damage was not being caused by sodium iodide which is normally present as an impurity in commercial samples of the colour; this implied that the tumour data could not readily be dismissed. They interpreted much of the mutagenicity data, however, as grounds for supposing that there might be a commercially useful threshold level of use below which the risk of cancer would be negligible. JECFA's response was to reduce the ADI to 1.25mg/kg bw and to make it temporary, pending the receipt of further data.

In 1975 the SCF adopted an ADI in agreement with JECFA's figure, but specified that fluorescein should not be present as an impurity at levels of more than 0.1 per cent. In 1983, however, the SCF adopted a significantly more cautious approach. They had received much new data from tests in rats, mice and pigs but they too were unsure how these data should be interpreted. In particular they expressed concern about the recent American rat study indicating that it causes thyroid cancer at high doses. Their response was to withdraw the full ADI and to replace it with a temporary figure of 1.25mg/kg bw, along with a call for more information. In spite of the uncertainty it continues to be used.

In 1979 it was listed in Group B by the FACC, pending the receipt of more information within two years, and the CoT recommended that its use should be restricted, but the action required to implement that recommendation was not taken by ministers. When the FAC and CoT reported in 1987 they reviewed the issue in detail, and postulated a hormonal mechanism which might be responsible for the thyroid changes, and concluded that the levels at which humans might be consuming Erythrosine are unlikely to reach a threshold at which thyroid damage would occur. They promoted it to Group A, subject to the condition that consumption is kept to very low levels. In other words, they imply that it is safe to eat just as long as you hardly ever eat it. The FAC responded by recommending that its use should be permitted only in glacé and cocktail cherries where it is said to be 'particularly important'. Since at least one major manufacturer sells glacé and cocktail cherries which are free from Erythrosine, their latter claim is hard to sustain.

There is some direct evidence that Erythrosine can provoke hyperactivity and other symptoms of acute intolerance in humans. There are several fragments of biochemical evidence suggesting possible mechanisms through which Erythrosine might affect the brain, since it can partially block the uptake of dopamine in the brain cells of rats, and can irreversibly change the release of neurotransmitters from the brain cells of frogs.

Regulatory status It is permitted and used in the UK and in the EEC, In Australia, Canada, South Africa, Switzerland (but only for whole, stoned or halved fruit) and in the USA, but it is not permitted in Japan or Norway. In April 1987 the CoT recommended that its use should be confined to cocktail and glacé cherries.

E128: Red 2G

Type It is a red coal tar dye.

Foods added to In the UK it is permitted in seven out of the nineteen food groups specified by the FACC. It can be found in some confectionery, yoghurts, fish spreads, and in some meat products including minced meat, meat filling and sausages, as well as in vegetable protein products designed to resemble meat.

Toxicological evaluation and possible health hazards In 1955, the British experts who advised the Food Standards Committee listed Red 2G in Group B, because they did not have sufficient information to be confident of its safety. Red 2G has, however, remained in continuous use even though official toxicologists remain to be fully satisfied as to its safety.

In 1966 JECFA stated that the available data were still insufficient to provide the basis for any evaluation. During the 1960s BIBRA recommended to its members that they should cease using this colour because they were unable to establish any level of use in animals at which no adverse effects could be observed. They stopped testing it, and only renewed their interest after many other red dyes had been banned. Despite that advice, UK manufacturers have continued to use Red 2G.

In spite of JECFA's hesitations the SCF in 1975 judged its use to be acceptable and set an ADI of 0.1mg/kg bw. In 1977 the SCF confirmed this evaluation, but with the qualification that it should not be used in conditions, such as high temperature or acidity, in which it might hydrolyse to Red 10B, which is a colour whose safety they were not prepared to assess. In 1977, and on the basis of tests on rats fed Red 2G incorporated into sausage meat, JECFA agreed to a temporary ADI at the rather low figure of 0.006mg/kg bw, conditional upon several further tests. In 1979 the CoT listed it in Group B as temporarily permissible pending the receipt of further information within two years, especially concerning its possible effects on reproduction and offspring. The CoT also expressed concern about its possible effects on people deficient in the red blood cell enzyme called glucose-6-phosphate dehydrogenase, and requested MAFF and the DHSS to consider a special study of this matter. In 1981, however, even though not all suggested further studies had been completed, JECFA set a full ADI at the level specified by the SCF.

When the FAC and CoT reported in 1987 the CoT had promoted Red 2G to Group A despite the fact that they again requested yet further studies, and they set limits on the conditions in which its use should be approved. The worries they had cited in 1979 were still not entirely resolved. The CoT concluded, however, that problems should not occur as long as the levels of Red 2G were kept low, and confined to meat products. In other words, they implied that it was safe to eat just as long as you hardly ever ate it. In response to the comments of the CoT, the FAC recommended that Red 2G should continue to be permitted, but its use should be confined to meat products and vegetable protein meat analogues only, up to a maximum level of 20mg/kg of the product.

Regulatory status It is permitted in the UK, Denmark and South Africa, but it is banned in Austria, Australia, Belgium, Finland, France, India, Norway, West Germany, Sweden, Switzerland and the USA. It only received an 'E' number in 1985, and its use in the EEC is confined to products which are not subject to processing at high temperatures, and products which are not highly acidic.

E129: Allura Red
also known as FD&C Red No. 40

Type This orange-red coal tar dye was developed for use in the late 1960s specifically to extend the range of red colours available to food manufacturers.

Foods added to Its use was first approved in the USA in 1971, but it was only after Amaranth (see E123) was banned in the US that Allura Red gained a significant market share, and by the end of the 1970s it was being used very widely in the USA. Its use is not yet permitted in the UK, but it is used occasionally on the European continent. If and when Allura Red is introduced in the UK, it is likely to be found replacing the former uses of Erythrosine (see E127).

Toxicological evaluation and possible health hazards The FDA in the USA approved its use at the start of the 1970s, but when both JECFA and the SCF came to evaluate it they both refused to accept it. JECFA examined it initially in 1974. On that occasion they reviewed thirteen unpublished reports, twelve of them from the Allied Chemical Corporation, but concluded that too little information was available and that no evaluation was possible. The SCF endorsed that decision in December 1975.

In 1976, however, the FDA reported that they had been informed that after forty-one weeks of a seventy-eight-week feeding study in 400 mice there was evidence of the early signs of malignancy in the test groups which was not seen in the controls. When the study was completed the FDA reported that final results were rather equivocal, and depended on the statistical analyses which were applied to the results. Shortly after, a second feeding study in mice was also reported to show the same problem. By the end of 1977 the results of a long-term rat study were also available, but they indicated no carcinogenic activity in that species. The mouse studies remained a focus of controversy. Different statistical techniques imply differing interpretations, and there is no consensus on which methods are most appropriate.

When JECFA considered it next in 1977 they felt that the evidence was inadequate rather than indicative of a possible hazard, and a decision was postponed pending the receipt of the results of further long-term mouse and rat studies. Two years later, when rather more data had accumulated, JECFA decided that Allura Red did not possess a carcinogenic potential, and they set a full ADI at 7mg/kg bw. The FACC also reported in 1979, but on that occasion they cautiously consigned Allura Red to Group E, indicating that they had not been satisfied that the data were yet adequate. One year later, however, JECFA reviewed it again, and qualified their evaluation by demoting the ADI to a temporary status, pending yet another analysis on the results of the long-term mouse studies. When that analysis eventually arrived in 1981 they were satisfied once more and the full ADI was then restored. This judgement was eventually endorsed by the SCF in 1983, and in 1985 an 'E' number was assigned to this compound.

When the FAC reported in 1987, the CoT promoted Allura Red from Group E to Group B. The CoT recited many of the inadequacies in the data set, but also reported that there was direct evidence that it could provoke symptoms of acute intolerance in susceptible people. They judged it to be provisionally acceptable, pending the results of more careful studies in larger groups of animals, and a fuller understanding of the ways in which it was metabolized. The FAC rather coyly said that the provisional acceptance of this colour '. . . should not be opposed'.

Regulatory status It is permitted and used in the USA. It received an 'E' number only in 1985, but is not used widely in the EEC. At the time of writing its use is not permitted in the UK, but in April 1987 the CoT and FAC recommended that its use should be permitted.

E131: Patent Blue V
also known as Acid Blue 3

Type Blue-violet coal tar dye.

Foods added to It can be found on some Scotch eggs, in some ice creams, canned vegetables, desserts, soft drinks and confectionery products.

Toxicological evaluation and possible health hazards This was reviewed by JECFA in 1959 and 1964, but it was not until 1969 that they agreed to set a temporary ADI of 1mg/kg bw based on a rat study. The lack of toxicological confidence did not inhibit the use of this chemical in food products. In 1974 JECFA reviewed the old data, along with some new data, and withdrew their previous ADI because the evidence from rats and cats was then considered insufficient. They requested a long-term feeding study in a second rodent species, and a short-term study in a non-rodent species. In 1975, however, the SCF dissented from this judgement, and gave it a temporary ADI of 2.5mg/kg bw in humans, based on the same animal data; at the same time the SCF asked for even more studies than those requested by JECFA. In 1979 the FACC listed it in Group E, meaning that they did not consider that sufficient data were available for them to provide any evaluation. By 1983, however, the SCF concluded that they had received sufficient information about its effects on rats, cats and dogs to enable them to set a new ADI at the rather high level of 15mg/kg bw by reference specifically to a mouse study. In 1985 the EEC awarded it an 'E' number.

When the FAC reported in 1987 the CoT promoted Patent Blue V to Group A. They had received some new data, and although several parts of the data set were inadequate, they judged that the totality was sufficient to satisfy them as to its safety. Despite the fact that the CoT states that there is no direct evidence that it can provoke hyperactivity, some doctors and other authorities believe that there is a risk that it could provoke problems of intolerance including skin inflammations and occasional respiratory problems in sensitive people.

Regulatory status Although it had been listed in Group E since 1979 it none the less continued to be permitted in the UK. In 1987 the CoT promoted it to Group A, and so its continued use may be assumed. It is permitted but not widely used in the rest of the EEC, as well as in Austria, Sweden and Switzerland. It is banned in Canada, Israel, Japan, Norway and the USA.

E132: Indigo Carmine
also known as Indigotine, and as FD&C Blue No. 2 in the USA

Type It is a dark-blue coal tar dye often used in mixtures. For example, it can be mixed with Tartrazine (see E102) to produce a green, and with Amaranth (see E123) to give violet. In 1970, about 40,000lb was used in the American food industry, but no similar figures are available for the UK or other EEC countries.

Foods added to In the UK it can be used in ten of the nineteen food groups specified by the FACC. In the USA it can be used in sweets, confectionery products, drinks, dessert powders, baked goods and some dairy products. In the UK it is most likely to be found in confectionery, biscuits, fruit fillings, dessert powders, soups and gravy mixes.

Toxicological evaluation and possible health hazards JECFA considered it in 1964, and 1969, and on the second occasion assigned a temporary ADI of 2.5mg/kg bw, based primarily on studies using rats. At the same time they called for a further long-term study using a non-rodent mammalian species. JECFA were particularly puzzled by the results of injecting a dilute solution of this substance under the skin of rats. Fourteen out of eighty rats developed sarcomas (fibrous tumours) at the site of the injection. Further studies followed to try to illuminate the meaning of these growths, but JECFA concluded that whatever they might mean, the substance did not cause cancer in animals if they ingested it in food or drink. They reviewed it next in 1974 and, on the basis of further information mainly from rat studies, the ADI was doubled, and was made full rather than temporary. One of the pigs which was fed this substance at a low dose level was found to have liver abscesses, but this was not thought to be attributable to the test substance. A group of fifty mice was injected under the skin with a weak solution of Indigo Carmine dissolved in water, and many of them died from acute convulsion immediately after being injected, but these injection studies were not considered important for human consumption by the scientists on JECFA. Important sections of the vital data, however, remain unpublished.

In 1975 the SCF endorsed JECFA's judgement and confirmed the ADI of 5mg/kg bw, and by reference to rat data reaffirmed this view in 1983. In 1979 the FACC categorized it in Group A, which means that they were satisfied both that they had sufficient information, and that it is safe. Curiously, the 1987 Colours Report of the FAC entirely failed even to mention Indigo Carmine.

Despite official confidence in its safety, there are some doctors who recommend those who suffer from hyperactivity and other problems of intolerance to avoid this substance.

Regulatory status It is permitted for use in the UK and in EEC countries. It is also permitted in Austria, Australia, Canada, India, Switzerland, South Africa and the USA. It is banned, however, in Norway along with all other synthetic dyes.

133: Brilliant Blue FCF
also known in the USA as FD&C Blue No. 1

Type It is a blue coal tar dye, which yields a green when mixed with Tartrazine (see E102). There is a slight confusion about the identity of this substance. It is a triarylmethane compound, and has been used both as a diammonium and a disodium salt. The disodium salt is the one which is used in foods, while the diammonium salt is used in drugs and cosmetics. The diammonium salt is banned in the EEC and the USA from use in foods. In 1970, the US Food and Drug Administration estimated that more than 83,000lb of Blue No. 1 was used in food products.

Foods added to It can be found in some canned peas, canned fruit, jams, jellies, sweets, biscuits, soups, soft drinks and in some retail food colourings, as well as in certain alcoholic beverages.

Toxicological evaluation and possible health hazards In the mid-1960s JECFA concluded that the paucity of biochemical information made it impossible for them to provide any evaluation of its safety or toxicity, although some long-term tests in several species had failed to reveal any adverse effects. During this period it continued to be used. A concern persisted because repeated injections of this colour under the skin of rodents produced localized tumours called sarcomas. In 1964 the report of the UK Food Standards Committee (FSC) recommended that Brilliant Blue FCF be banned on the grounds of the 'probable toxicity' suggested by these experiments. The British Industrial Biological Research Association (BIBRA) then mounted a large-scale research effort in an attempt to show that the carcinogenic effects were due to the gross physical properties of the colour rather than any chemical carcinogenic potential. In the interim the FSC suspended its original judgement and the colour continued to be used.

In 1969 JECFA was willing to reconsider its position, and concluded that while the sarcomas were caused by the injection of the chemical, this was irrelevant to its consumption in food and drink. JECFA then ascribed to it an ADI of 12.5mg/kg bw, based on a no effect level in the rat of 2,500mg/kg bw. This means that they were using a safety factor of 200 rather than the more usual figure of 100, suggesting that they were intending to be cautious.

When the SCF first reviewed colouring additives in 1975 they did not endorse the JECFA ADI for Brilliant Blue, but on the basis of similar information, particularly that concerning possible reproductive hazards, set a lower ADI at 2.5mg/kg bw. In 1978, however, the World Health Organization in collaboration with the International Agency for Research on Cancer (IARC) stated that the disodium salt which is currently used in foods produces kidney tumours both by injection and by oral administration. The FACC in 1979 listed it in Group A, indicating that they believed it to be adequately investigated and safe. The report of the Committee on Toxicity of the DHSS, which is attached to the FACC report, is not properly referenced, but it appears that they did not consider the IARC judgement. In 1983 the SCF again reviewed this substance with some fresh information obtained with mice and rats and established a revised ADI of 10mg/kg bw, but their review also fails to make any reference to the IARC judgements. Curiously, the 1987 Colours Report of the FAC entirely failed even to mention Brilliant Blue FCF.

Whatever effects it may have on laboratory animals, there is some direct evidence that it provokes intolerance symptoms, especially urticaria, and contributes to hyperactivity. People who suffer from these conditions are advised to avoid this substance.

Regulatory status The disodium salt is permitted for food use in the USA, and since 1969 has been in the odd position of being 'permanently provisionally' listed. The EEC first published a Directive on food colours in 1962, before the UK became a member, and at that time Brilliant Blue FCF was excluded from that list. In 1978 it was added to the EEC list of permitted colours, but permission to use it is only temporary, and it is listed in Annex II. This means that member states may permit its use, but are not obliged to do so, as they would be if it was listed in Annex I. In 1985 the EEC Commission proposed to transfer it from Annex II to Annex I, along with the award of an 'E' number. It is currently permitted in the UK, but it is banned in Austria, Belgium, Denmark, France, Norway, Sweden, Switzerland and West Germany (among others).

E140: Chlorophyll
also known as Natural Green 3

Type This is a naturally-occurring green colouring found in, for example, grass as well as in many other plants.

It plays an essential part in processes of plant photosynthesis. For food use, it is generally extracted from alfalfa, nettles, lucerne, clover and spinach. Commercially available Chlorophyll colour usually contains a complex mixture of the basic ingredient with some of its degradation products, plus some impurities.

Foods added to Being insoluble in water, it is generally confined to fats and oils, but it is also added to some preserved fruits and vegetables.

Toxicological evaluation and possible health hazards This chemical has a long history of food use, but it has yet to be fully investigated even by the standards of toxicology which currently prevail. As the 1987 report of the FAC recognizes there is no reason for assuming that natural colours are any safer than those synthesized artificially. In recent years some doctors have come to appreciate that one breakdown product of Chlorophyll may provoke problems of intolerance in those people unfortunate enough to suffer from Refsum's disease. In 1969 JECFA reviewed it but did not allocate a specific ADI to this substance, rather it is approved for unlimited use. Similarly, in 1975 the SCF listed it as a colour for which an ADI cannot be established, but which nevertheless is acceptable for food use. In 1979 the FACC listed it in Group A, and in 1983 the SCF reasserted its previous position. Curiously, the 1987 Colours Report of the FAC entirely failed even to mention Chlorophyll. Apart from the qualification given above, it is generally presumed to be safe.

Regulatory status It has been permitted at least since the 1960s, and continues to be permitted, both in the UK and throughout the EEC, and in the USA.

E141: Copper Complexes of Chlorophyll and of Chlorophyllins, with Sodium and Potassium Salts

Type These are blue colourings which range from olive to greeny-blue shades, and are produced by chemical reactions primarily between copper and Chlorophyll. They are sometimes manufactured from nature-identical Chlorophyll rather than a natural derivative. The commercial products are complex mixtures of several components.

Foods added to They can be found in some confectionery and preserved green vegetables such as cucumber relishes, but they are not widely used.

Toxicological evaluation and possible health hazards In 1965, and again in 1970, JECFA took a rather tentative approach to these substances, because their chemical identity was not fully established. None the less, on the second occasion, a temporary ADI of 15mg/kg bw was allocated. They continued to be permitted and used throughout this period and subsequently. In 1975 the SCF endorsed JECFA's ADI of 15mg/kg bw for combinations of the Copper Complexes of both Chlorophyll and Chlorophyllins. In 1978 JECFA revised their chemical specifications, and a full ADI was set by reference to a long-term feeding study using rats. In 1983 the SCF repeated its previous opinion without any modifications. Curiously, the 1987 Colours Report of the FAC entirely failed even to mention Copper Complexes of Chlorophyll and of Chlorophyllins. They are generally presumed to be safe.

Regulatory status At present, these

substances are permitted in the UK and in the rest of the EEC.

E142: Green S (sometimes called Food Green S)

also known as Lissamine Green

Type It is a green coal tar dye. Under the name of Wool Green BS it is used in the textile trade.

Foods added to It is used in at least 592 different products in the UK, and can be found for example in some canned vegetables including peas, soups, sweets, biscuits, fruit pie-fillings, jams, ice cream and both lime- and lemon-flavour drinks, as well as cider, wines and spirits.

Toxicological evaluation and possible health hazards In 1955 the British experts who advised the FSC listed Green S in Class B, which meant that they did not have sufficient information to make a judgement. In the mid-1960s JECFA classified it as a colour for which there were not sufficient data for them to pronounce on its safety or toxicity. By 1970 they judged that they knew enough about its effects on rats and mice to allocate a temporary ADI of 5mg/kg bw. This was, however, based on an estimated NEL in the rat of 1,000mg/kg bw, so they were trying to be slightly cautious using a safety factor of 200. JECFA stated that they required further data, especially on its effects on reproduction and embryos. When in 1975 these data had not been provided, JECFA withdrew their ADI. In the same year, curiously enough, and on the basis of the same limited data, the SCF endorsed the ADI which JECFA had just withdrawn. Their justification appears to have been that they did not have any evidence of toxicity, even if the evidence of safety was incomplete. They did, perhaps inevitably, call for further studies and more data on long-term toxicity and embryotoxicity.

In 1979 the FACC demoted this substance from Group A where it had previously been categorized, placed it into Group B and requested data from further studies. Throughout these debates its use continued uninterrupted. In 1983, when more data had been provided, the SCF reasserted the ADI of 5mg/kg bw, based on an NEL of 500mg/kg bw in the rat. In 1987 the CoT returned this substance to Group A, following an eight-year sojourn in Group B. They had by then received data which they judged as sufficient. The complex collection of data includes an example where long-term feeding in mice indicated the possibility of weak carcinogenicity, and at high doses it stained the foetuses of rats. The CoT judged, however, that the likely levels of consumption would be significantly below what they took to be a threshold, and so they approved it for general use. Uniquely on this occasion they chose to criticize the ADI which the SCF had set at 5mg/kg bw, and recommend in its place a figure of 1mg/kg bw.

Whatever effects it may or may not have in laboratory animals, it is suspected by some experts of provoking intolerant symptoms including asthma and child hyperactivity. Despite the uncertainty and the doubts, this colour has remained continuously in use for over thirty-five years.

Regulatory status It is permitted and used in the UK and the EEC, but it is banned in Norway, Sweden and in the USA.

E150: Caramels

Type There are innumerable ways

of producing Caramel colours. A Caramel is basically a burnt sugar, but there are several different sugars and they can be burnt under a variety of conditions of temperature and pressure, and in the company of many different chemicals. These various combinations will produce many different Caramels with slightly different colours and flavours. Caramel colours are thick viscous liquids with colours ranging from dark brown to black. The accompanying reactants which are used in their manufacture include ammonium salts, sulphites, acids and alkalis, singly and in several combinations. The Caramels are collectively the most widely-used colour additives. There are so many Caramels, and they are such complex chemical mixtures, that their chemical identity remains only partly known. There are at least 100 different commercially available Caramels.

Foods added to This group of substances is used very widely. In Britain, Caramels can be found in at least 1,221 different products. They can be found especially in cola drinks, beers (especially in mild, pale, light, and stout), wines and whiskies, but also in malt vinegar, some pickles, sauces, meat fillings and other products, soups, yoghurts, bread, dessert mixes, chocolate and confectionery products, cakes and biscuits. So much Caramel is used that in terms of weight, these Caramels account for some 98 per cent of all colourings added to foods and drinks. Many people who drink a lot of cola, beer and/or whisky could easily consume Caramels at levels in excess of the ADI.

Toxicological evaluation and possible health hazards Their toxicological evaluation is extremely complex, partly because they are so numerous, and their identity is poorly defined. Life has been made especially difficult because there are at least four competing ways of categorizing them. In the course of negotiations for the preparation of their 1979 report, the FACC observed that the British food industry was using over 100 distinct Caramel formulations, and they complained, quite reasonably, because none of the formulations could be chemically defined, none of the available toxicological data could be referred accurately to the materials being used, and some of those data indicated that some Caramels might be hazardous.

In response the FACC proposed to divide Caramels into four groups: burnt sugar, caustic Caramels, ammonia Caramels and ammonium sulphite Caramels. The British Caramel Manufacturers Association countered, however, by proposing a division into six categories, namely: a caustic Caramel (CC1 – used in alcoholic spirits); two ammonia Caramels (AC1 for light-coloured beers and AC2 for darker beers), three ammoniated sulphite Caramels one of which would be double strength (DSAS1– for soft drinks including colas) and two of single strength (SSAS1 for vinegar and pickling onions, and SSAS2, also for colas and other soft drinks). In 1979 the FACC called for relevant toxicological data in support of these six groups. When the FAC and CoT reported in 1987 they repeated that request indicating that the data which they had received in the interim still failed to relate to the materials in use.

The entire debate is further complicated because the international caramel manufacturers' organization, the International Technical Caramel Association (ITCA), introduced yet a further proposal to divide Caramels into four groups: CCI – caustic Caramel; CCII – caustic sulphite Caramel; CCIII – ammonia Caramel; CCIV – ammonium sulphite Caramel. This is the categorization which was eventually adopted by JECFA in 1985. The SCF confused the issue even further because in 1983 it adopted a five-fold division of the Caramels, by decomposing CC1 into burnt sugar Caramels and plain spirit Caramels. In 1987 the CoT explained that it considered the approach of the BCMA to be more satisfactory than that used by the ITCA, JECFA and the SCF because the last did not involve any adequately precise specifications of the materials. None the less, the CoT had to review fourteen volumes of data which the ITCA submitted in 1985.

There are some reviews in the literature produced by industry arguing that all Caramels are unproblematically safe. The fact that such reviews frequently refer to unpublished as well as some published documents can do little to reassure the public. JECFA in 1971 and the SCF in 1975 both accepted the use of the non-ammoniated Caramels without setting any quantitative restrictions. Caustic sulphite Caramels have never been properly evaluated because of the comprehensive lack of data, but this omission passes almost unremarked because of the controversies about ammoniated and ammoniated sulphited Caramels.

One recurring problem about the safety of Caramels concerns the presence of an impurity called 4-Methylimidazole. This substance has been

shown to produce convulsions in rabbits, mice and chicks when fed to them at high doses. This impurity is found in Caramels produced by processes using ammonia. In 1971 JECFA considered all the other Caramels to be sufficiently safe that they could be used in foods and drinks without any specific limits needing to be set. At the same time, and by reference to a short-term test with rats, JECFA set a temporary ADI of 100mg/kg bw for ammoniated Caramels. This was quite unusual. At the time, no long-term carcinogenicity or mutagenicity studies were available, and yet an ADI was set. As a rule, ADIs are defined only by reference to an NEL in long-term tests. When this temporary ADI was set, further tests were requested, but that is unexceptional.

JECFA reconsidered ammoniated Caramels in 1974, when they extended the life of the temporary ADI and qualified it to limit the likely concentration of 4-Methylimidazole. By 1977 evidence had become available to indicate that, 4-Methylimidazole apart, ammoniated Caramels can adversely affect the levels of white blood cells and lymphocytes in laboratory animals, and so probably in humans too. Since it was not possible to establish a level of consumption at which no adverse effects could be observed, JECFA revoked the temporary ADI for ammoniated Caramels. There is one report suggesting that, by 1981, JECFA had received sufficient further information to persuade them to reinstate the temporary ADI at the previous level, but this is contradicted by all other sources. A study on rabbits which was published in 1982 provided evidence that even small doses of ammoniated Caramels act as Vitamin B6 antagonists, in the sense that they inhibit the ability of animals to absorb or to retain this essential nutrient. There is, furthermore, evidence that low levels of Vitamin B6 aggravate the lymphocyte problem, and make the entire issue more serious. In 1985 JECFA suggested that one impurity might be entirely responsible for the problems, but by 1987 when the CoT reported, further evidence has been provided indicating that hypothesis to be no longer tenable. In 1985, however, JECFA set an ADI for ammoniated Caramels at a level of 200mg/kg bw.

The SCF in 1975 followed JECFA in providing separate evaluations for ammoniated Caramels, and endorsed the JECFA position with a temporary ADI of 100mg/kg bw, while calling for the results of long-term and reproductive toxicity tests. In 1979 the SCF extended the temporary ADI for this group, and called for yet further information. In 1983 they again renewed temporary permission to use it but without specifying an ADI. They stated that it was temporarily acceptable at least until 1987 while they awaited some answers to a very complex web of toxicological questions. They did add that, even then, further questions might remain to be resolved.

When the CoT reviewed Caramels in 1987 they devoted most of their discussion to the problem of the lymphocytopenia in rats. They concluded that the problems may well be caused by several components of ammoniated Caramels, and that they could not be disregarded or explained away. They reaffirmed their Group B listing, which might be considered generous in view of their repeated assertion that none of the toxicological data which they had received could be matched with the specifications of any commercial products.

The toxicology of Caramels which are both ammoniated and sulphited is even more complex. In the mid-1970s neither JECFA nor the SCF felt that they had sufficient data to evaluate these, and it was not until 1977 that JECFA set a temporary ADI of 100mg/kg bw for this set of substances, while calling for further studies on possible chronic toxicity. In 1975 the SCF treated this group alongside ammoniated Caramels, in 1979 they evaluated them separately, but assigned a similar temporary ADI. The most recent opinion of the SCF, expressed in 1983, continued to identify unresolved puzzles, and no ADI was set, pending the results of further studies due in December 1987, and on the quite exceptional condition that they were provided with regular six-monthly reports. JECFA reconsidered this matter most recently in 1985 when they reported that new data had been received. They judged that this was sufficient to permit a higher ADI at 200mg/kg bw, in combination with revised purity standards.

We are hampered in our efforts to review the position, because all of the data which the SCF has received and evaluated since 1977 have been provided by the Caramel and cola industries, and remains unpublished. Both the SCF and the FAC have provided figures which indicate that Caramels are being consumed at such high levels that standard methods for specifying an ADI as 100th of the level at which no adverse effects are observed would not justify current practice. The SCF has represented this as a problem with the methodology of toxicology, but it may be more realistic just to say that people may be eating and drinking too much Caramel.

In 1979 the FACC report listed the Caramels in Group B, meaning that they were considered temporarily acceptable pending the receipt of further information. The 1987 report reaffirmed this status for all Caramels, but they also recognized that reductions in levels of consumption are desirable. Consequently they recommended that in general levels of permitted Caramels should be restricted to 1,000mg/kg of food though they were prepared, for example, to accept levels of 2,000mg/kg in bread and 5,000mg/kg in crisps, beers, wines and spirits.

The fact that there have been, and continue to be, serious doubts and uncertainties about the safety of at least some of the Caramels has not prevented their use from growing rapidly to the point at which their consumption by many people already exceeds the ADIs.

Regulatory status Caramels are permitted and widely used in the UK, the EEC and the USA. While manufacturers are often obliged to list Caramels as ingredients on labels, there is no requirement that they specify which Caramel(s) they are using. In the UK, adding Caramels to bread (other than to white or soda bread) is permitted, but this practice is banned in Austria, Denmark, France, Israel, Italy, Luxemburg, Norway, Portugal, Switzerland and the USA. Some brown bread sold in the UK is white bread dyed brown with Caramels.

E151: Black PN
also known as Brilliant Black BN and Food Black

Type It is a black coal tar dye.

Foods added to It can be used in four of the nineteen food groups specified by the FACC. It can be found in products containing or resembling blackcurrants and other dark fruits, as well as confectionery, ices, meat products, soups, soft drinks, cheese cake mixes, brown sauces, cider, wines and spirits.

Toxicological evaluation and possible health hazards When JECFA reviewed it in 1969 they did not consider that they had sufficient information to evaluate it. In spite of this fact it continued to be permitted and used. In 1974, on the basis primarily of partial and incomplete studies on rats, JECFA allocated a temporary ADI of 2.5mg/kg bw, by reference to an NEL in the rat of 500mg/kg bw. They commented at the time that the number of animals used in the experiment was rather slight. These facts account for their caution in using a safety factor of 200 rather than the nominal figure of 100. In 1975 the SCF, considering essentially similar data, allocated to it an ADI of only 0.75mg/kg bw, thereby exhibiting slightly greater caution. In 1978, JECFA considered a long-term mouse feeding study and a 90-day feeding study on pigs. In the pig study they noted that intestinal cysts were found at the highest dose levels. None the less, they did not modify the ADI, but they did call for further studies, especially to elucidate the causes of the cysts.

In 1979 the FACC categorized it in Group B, calling for further studies but not restricting its use further.

Throughout these debates it continued to be used in food products. By 1981 JECFA had received significantly more data and allocated a new ADI which JECFA's most recent publication stated to be 1mg/kg bw. In 1983, however, the SCF set an ADI of 5mg/kg bw by reference to new rat data, while claiming that this was JECFA's figure. This contradiction has yet to be resolved. In 1987 the CoT promoted it to Group A, having received most of the data which they had requested in 1979. They noted the absence of any data on how it is metabolized by humans, the lack of any bacterial mutagenicity tests, and some limitations in the conduct of the new tests, but judged that over all the available data were sufficient for them.

Whatever effects it might have on laboratory animals, some doctors suspect it of causing hyperactivity and some other allergic reactions in people.

Regulatory status Permitted and used in the EEC and the UK, as well as in Austria, Australia, India and Switzerland, but it is banned in Canada, Norway, Spain, South Africa and the USA.

E153: Carbon Blacks
also known as Vegetable Carbon

Type These substances are black colourings made from heated vegetable or other organic materials which could be of mineral or animal origin. The use of animal materials is unlikely, but not impossible. In so far as these additives come from an animal source they would be unacceptable to vegans and vegetarians, and they may not be kosher or halal. These substances have had a traditional role as medicinal therapeutic agents.

Foods added to These can be found in some confectionery, chocolate cake mixes, biscuits, jams, concentrated fruit juices and jellies. They can be used in two of the nineteen groups of food products listed by the FACC.

Toxicological evaluation and possible health hazards The toxicological tests which have been applied to Carbon Blacks have not been sufficient to enable JECFA to give any evaluation, even to this day. There have been some carcinogenicity tests, but there have been no adequate acute toxicity tests, nor long-term animal feeding tests. In spite of this fact they have been in continuous use in the UK and the EEC for many years. In 1975 the SCF decided that even though no ADI could be established, they would permit them for use on the external coatings of confectionery products. In 1977 the SCF reaffirmed its view that these materials should continue to be permitted, in part this was because the quantities used are not great, and in the light of our experience in using Vegetable Carbon for medicinal purposes. At the same time they commented that Carbon Blacks are the only products which complied with their earlier recommendations on limits to the levels of polycyclic aromatic hydrocarbons. These are substances thought to be carcinogenic which can occur in Carbon Blacks as impurities. Their remarks imply that levels of polycyclic aromatic hydrocarbon impurities in many other food products remain worryingly high. The 1983 Report of the SCF contains no modification of this position. In 1979 the FACC listed these substances in Group A, implying that it is their view that they had been adequately studied, and are safe. This judgement was based mainly on the long-standing use of Vegetable Carbon for medicinal purposes; they added, however, that non-vegetable Carbon Blacks should not be used.

Before 1976 Carbon Blacks were generally permitted for use in food products in the USA, but they were then re-evaluated by the FDA and promptly banned, because of suspicion that they might cause cancers. There is some evidence that when industrial workers handle large quantities of these substances they can act as a skin irritant, and may even cause skin cancer.

Special restrictions Since the production of these chemicals may depend upon animal sources, they might not be acceptable to vegetarians or vegans, and may not be kosher or halal.

Regulatory status They are permitted and used in the UK and in the EEC, but are banned in the USA. The 1987 report of the FAC recommended that Vegetable Carbon Blacks should be permitted in sugar confectionery up to a level of 400mg/kg of the product (which is four times the level generally recommended for similar colours), and that their use should not be permitted in chocolate confectionery.

154: Brown FK
also known as Brown for Kippers

Type This substance is a brown colouring, and is a mixture of six chemicals.

Foods added to Its name implies that its use might be confined to colouring kippers, but in practice it is used more widely, and can be found in other fish and meat products, as well as in some canned soup, soft drinks, confectionery, dessert and dry mixes. It is also used in the UK to mark some home produced carcass meats. In 1979 the FACC recommended that the use of Brown FK should be restricted to smoked and smoke flavoured fish products and to marking meat, but ministers failed to implement those recommendations. In 1987 they recommended that its use should be confined to smoked and cured fish.

Toxicological evaluation and possible health hazards There have been doubts about the safety of Brown FK for over thirty years, yet it has remained in continuous use throughout this period. JECFA has reviewed this substance on three occasions. In 1966 they complained that the data on reproductive toxicity and teratogenicity were inadequate. In 1978 they stated that two of the primary metabolites of Brown FK are cardiotoxic, that is to say they are poisonous to the heart. They also observed that in long-term feeding studies on mice it caused potentially hazardous nodules to form in the liver, and it also caused mutations in some bacteria. This latter fact is interpreted by many scientists as implying that it might therefore cause both mutations and cancer in humans. In spite of all of these reservations, the SCF gave Brown FK a temporary ADI at 0.05mg/kg bw, on the basis of tests on rats; at the same time they called for further studies, especially of its effects on reproduction and the embryo.

In 1979 the CoT listed Brown FK in Group B, because of the liver nodule problem and bacterial mutagenicity, commenting rather coyly that the data were 'not unequivocal'. The FACC responded by recommending that its use should be confined to smoked and smoke flavoured fish products and to marking meat, but ministers failed to implement those recommendations, and it continued in unrestricted use. In 1983 the SCF reported on further studies. By then they had received the results of some reproductive studies, and they were sufficiently satisfied to triple the ADI to 0.15mg/kg bw.

In 1985 JECFA reviewed some new data which provided a marginal improvement on what had previously been available, but these too were judged incomplete and inadequate. JECFA marginally revised its ADI up to a figure of 0.075mg/kg bw (which is half the SCF's figure), tightened the purity specifications, and demanded a more detailed analysis of the data from long-term rat feeding studies. In 1987 the CoT promoted Brown FK to Group A. They reviewed the data and noted the effects of Brown FK on animals seemed to be slight but inconsistent. The bacterial mutagenicity evidence is unchallenged, but the CoT doubts its significance in the absence of clear evidence that it causes cancer in animals. Despite its promotion of Brown FK to Group A, the CoT repeats its recommendation that its use should be restricted to smoked and smoke flavoured fish and to meat marking up to a maximum level of 20mg/kg of the product, a recommendation which has again been endorsed by the FAC. Almost all the toxicological data on Brown FK which have been submitted to JECFA, the SCF and the CoT have been provided by Unilever, and remain unpublished.

While the officials may be satisfied that Brown FK is safe for laboratory animals and humans (at the dose levels used) some doctors and other experts continue to suspect that it can provoke both hyperactivity and other problems of intolerance.

Regulatory status Brown FK is permitted and used in the UK, but it is banned in Austria, Belgium, Denmark, France, Norway, Sweden, Switzerland, West Germany and the USA. Even though the SCF of the EEC is prepared to allocate an ADI, the Council of Ministers have not approved it for general use, and so it does not have an 'E' number.

155: Brown HT

also known as Chocolate Brown HT

Type It is a brown coal tar dye.

Foods added to It is permitted for use in the UK in eight of the nineteen groups of food products identified by the FACC, and can be found in some chocolate and especially imitation chocolate products, but it can also be found in some dessert mixes, ice cream, yoghurts, preserves, pickles and soft drinks.

Toxicological evaluation and possible health hazards There have been doubts about the safety of Brown HT for over thirty years, yet it has remained in continuous use throughout this period. In 1966 JECFA refused to evaluate it because of serious deficiencies in the available data. In spite of this it continued to be used. By 1977, however, even though they still did not have proper data on how this substance is metabolized nor on its effects on animal or human reproduction, JECFA allocated a temporary ADI of 0.25mg/kg bw. This figure was based on a long-term feeding study on mice in which they found an NEL of 500mg/kg bw, indicating that they adopted the relatively cautious safety factor of 2,000. Inevitably this judgement was accompanied by requests for further studies. Meanwhile, in 1975 the SCF had awarded a temporary ADI at a figure ten times greater than JECFA's estimate, while also calling for further studies.

In 1979 the FACC listed it in Group B, indicating that they were not satisfied that they had sufficient data to establish its safety. In 1983 the SCF report revealed that the identity of about 20 per cent of the commercially used colour has yet to be established, and the new data on which they were relying had gone directly from BIBRA to the SCF and had not been published. The SCF appeared, however, to be entirely satisfied with the information which it had received, for it set a full ADI at 3mg/kg bw, basing the figure on a long-term feeding study in mice. JECFA evaluated it most recently in 1983, by which time they had received the data which they had requested six years earlier. They were sufficiently satisfied to set a full ADI of 1.5mg/kg bw, on the basis of an NEL of 150mg/kg bw, indicating that they now considered a standard safety factor of 100 to be adequate. In 1987 the CoT promoted it to Group A. Published mutagenicity studies were negative, while unpublished animal feeding studies on mice, rats and guinea-pigs indicated that Brown HT stains the tissues of the animals, but the changes were not thought to be pathological.

Whatever its effects in laboratory animals may be, it is suspected by some doctors of provoking hyperactivity and some allergic symptoms in people.

Regulatory status It is permitted and used in the UK, Australia and Denmark, but it is not permitted in most European countries, nor in Japan, South Africa or the USA.

E160(a): Alpha- Beta- and Gamma-Carotene

Type These are yellow, orange and red colouring substances which occur naturally in plant pigments. Their complex molecules can occur in several slightly different isomers. They are chemically related to Vitamin A. The main sources of Alpha-Carotene are red palm oil, green chestnut leaves, and mountain ash berries; Beta-Carotene is mainly extracted from alfalfa, carrots, green leaves and butter; Gamma-Carotene comes mainly from the leaves of lily-of-the-valley. Some Beta-Carotene is also manufactured synthetically and is sold as a red powder.

Foods added to Carotenes can be found occurring naturally in carrots, butter and egg yolks. These colourings are being used fairly widely and their use is increasing rapidly. Their increased use can be attributed to consumer pressure against the synthetic coal tar dyes, which is interpreted by many manufacturers and retailers as a preference for natural colouring additives. Their use in the UK more than doubled between 1971 and 1981, even though the Carotenes are rather expensive and provide relatively pale and unstable colours by comparison with coal tar dyes. They can be found in many edible fats and oils, non-dairy whiteners, low fat spreads, margarines, cheese products, soups, dessert mixes, cakes and biscuits. Carotenes can be found in nine of the nineteen groups of food products identified by the FACC.

Toxicological evaluation and possible

health hazards In 1978 JECFA judged that they did not have sufficient information to enable them to evaluate the safety or toxicity of natural Carotenes, and no ADI could be specified. In the late 1960s, however, JECFA were satisfied with the data available on synthetic Beta-Carotene. By reference to a feeding study in the rat and the role of Beta-Carotene as a precursor for Vitamin A they set a two-level ADI: a conditional figure of 5mg/kg bw and an unconditional ADI of 2.5mg/kg bw. By 1974 JECFA had revised their policy and decided not to employ the concept of a conditional ADI, so they allocated a full ADI of 5mg/kg bw, where this figure is intended to apply to the combined consumption of Beta-Carotene, along with Beta-apo-8'-Carotenal (see E160e) and the Ethyl and Methyl Esters of Beta-apo-8'-Carotenoic acid (see E160f). In 1975 the SCF endorsed the JECFA ADI, and reaffirmed this view in 1983. In 1979 the CoT listed these substances in Group A as being adequately tested and safe, and in 1987 had no occasion to comment on them again, other than to observe that Beta-Carotene should continue to be permitted in foods intended for babies and young children. These Carotenes are natural constituents of foods at levels significantly higher than their use as food additives and they are generally presumed to be safe, except when consumed in massive doses. There are some well-authenticated reports of people suffering ill effects from excess consumption of Carotenes, but the levels at which they are used as food additives would not make a significant contribution to such problems. It would be unwise, however, to try to live only by eating carrots.

Regulatory status These substances are widely permitted and used.

E160(b): Annatto
also known as Annatto Extracts, and as Bixin or Norbixin

Type These are naturally occurring colourings which vary from orange to peach colour. They are extracted from the pulp which surrounds the seeds of the Annatto tree.

Foods added to They can be found in two of the nineteen groups of food products listed by the FACC. Regulations permit the addition of Annatto to butter without its having to be listed on the label or packet, although many dairies probably do not take advantage of this option. These colourings can also be found in some cheeses and cheese products, creamed rice, margarines and pastry.

Toxicological evaluation and possible health hazards JECFA first evaluated Annatto in 1969 and specified a temporary ADI of 1.25mg/kg bw. Having received more data, they reviewed it again in 1974. On both occasions they did not have any information on how the material is metabolized, but they were satisfied with the results of the tests which had been conducted on rats, mice and dogs, and confirmed their previous ADI allocation, and in 1975 the SCF concurred with JECFA's judgement. The comments of both JECFA and the SCF referred specifically to Annatto which had been extracted using either edible oils or aqueous alkalis. When the CoT discussed this matter in 1979, they distinguished two broad categories of Annatto. They listed in Group A Annatto which had been extracted using either edible oils or aqueous alkalis, but they listed in

Group B those which are extracted with organic solvents, because the toxicological data only covered the former but not the latter. They failed to explain whether or not this latter class of compounds was in commercial use.

The SCF also reported in 1979, explaining that they had received further information, and set a new ADI of 2.5mg/kg bw for Annatto extracts. They did so on the assumption that the extracts contain about 2.6 per cent of carotenoids, and consequently the corresponding ADI for the carotenoids of Annatto is 0.065mg/kg bw. In 1982 JECFA endorsed this assessment and ADI. The 1987 CoT report explains that none of the information which they had requested in 1979 covering Annatto extracted by organic solvents had been provided, and so this group of compounds was consigned to Group E, and accordingly the FAC recommended that these specific Annatto extracts should be banned.

There is some direct evidence that Annatto even at very low levels can provoke symptoms of intolerance, especially among those people suffering from chronic urticaria and/or angioneurotic oedema. These conditions are unpleasant but affect a very small minority of the population. For most consumers Annatto is generally regarded as safe.

Regulatory status Permitted and used in the UK, and throughout the EEC.

E160(c): Capsanthin and Capsorubin
also known as Paprika Oleoresin
Type These are natural orange colours extracted from the spice paprika.

Foods added to They are used in some cheeses, fish products, savoury snack foods and confectionery.

Toxicological evaluation and possible health hazards JECFA has never evaluated these substances because their identity remains unspecified, nor have they been fully investigated toxicologically. Dried paprika powder has, however, a very long history of use in domestic and industrial food processing. In 1979 the CoT listed paprika powder in Group A, but assigned colouring extracts from paprika to Group B with a request for the results of a short-term rat feeding study within two years. When the CoT reported in 1987 they observed that the requisite information had not been provided and so these colours have been consigned to Group E, and accordingly the FAC recommended that these compounds should be banned. No adverse effects have been reported.

Regulatory status They have been permitted and used in the UK, and throughout the EEC, but an early review can be expected.

E160(d): Lycopene
Type This is a natural carotenoid, and it is a red colouring which is found in tomato extract. This substance has been investigated as a possible replacement for red coal tar dyes.

Foods added to No specific uses have been reported.

Toxicological evaluation and possible health hazards JECFA considered this substance in 1974, but concluded that insufficient data were available to permit any evaluation. They tried again in 1978 with slightly more information, but reached the same conclusion, mostly because they considered that it had been tested in too few animals. They had, in fact, received only one study and that had been conducted in 1958. In 1975, however, the SCF of the EEC stated that since Lycopene is prepared by a physical process from a natural food it is generally acceptable for use in foods, even though no ADI can be established. The CoT did not review this compound in 1979, but it remained on the permitted list, even though there was no evidence that UK manufacturers were using it. The FACC recommended its deletion, but ministers failed to implement that recommendation. The FAC referred the topic to the CoT. In 1985 it was deleted from the EEC list, but in 1987 the CoT listed it in Group B solely by reference to the 1958 study. They observed that it is not currently in use, and were it to come into use the CoT would require the results of metabolic studies. The FAC recommended that Lycopene should remain on the permitted list, even though it is not being used, and therefore cannot be said to be necessary. No adverse effects are known or suspected and it is presumed to be safe.

Regulatory status Permitted in the UK and the EEC.

E160(e): Beta-apo-8'-Carotenal
also known as Beta-apo-Carotenal

Type This substance is an orange-yellowish colouring which is widely and abundantly found in fruits and vegetables, especially in the pulp and skin of citrus fruits.

Foods added to It can be found in some biscuits, soups, confectionery and vegetable protein products.

Toxicological evaluation and possible health hazards As early as

1964 JECFA reviewed the results of some tests on rats and dogs and set an unconditional ADI of 2.5mg/kg bw (and a conditional ADI of 5mg/kg bw). In 1974, by reference to a small amount of supplementary data (provided by Hoffman-La Roche from an unnamed author, and unpublished) JECFA set a full ADI at 5mg/kg bw, where this figure is intended to apply to the combined consumption of Beta-Carotene (see E160a), Beta-apo-8'-Carotenal and the Ethyl Esters of Beta-apo-8'-Carotenoic Acid (see E160f) and the Methyl Ester which is not used in Britain. In 1975 the SCF endorsed JECFA's evaluation, and they did not re-evaluate it in 1983 because no further data were available. In 1979 the CoT listed it in Group A, and had no occasion to re-evaluate it in 1987. No adverse effects have been reported and it is generally presumed to be safe.

Regulatory status Permitted and used in the UK and the EEC.

E160(f): Ethyl Ester of Capsanthin
also known as Ethyl Esters of Beta-apo-8'-Carotenoic Acid

Type It is a yellow colouring, naturally occurring and derived from plants. It is also a normal metabolite of Apo-Carotenal.

Foods added to The only reported use in the UK is in butter oil, but Codex would permit it to be used in margarine and other edible oils and fats, jams, jellies and ices.

Toxicological evaluation and possible health hazards In 1964 JECFA established an unconditional ADI of 2.5mg/kg bw, as well as a conditional ADI of 5mg/kg bw, on the basis of only rather small amounts of data obtained using rats. In 1974 it was reviewed again, with a little more unpublished information supplied by Hoffman-La Roche without naming the author. This substance is evaluated on the same basis as Beta-Carotene (see E160a). In 1975 the SCF endorsed JECFA's evaluation and saw no reason to reconsider the matter in 1983 since they had received no new information. In 1979 the CoT listed it in Group A, and had no occasion to re-evaluate it in 1987. No adverse effects have been reported, and it is presumed to be safe.

Regulatory status Permitted and used in the UK and the EEC.

E161: Xanthophylls

Type These substances are yellow colourings which are derived from green leaves, and they constitute approximately 10 per cent of the colouring matter in commercial Chlorophyll (see E140). Chemically they are considered as belonging to the class of Carotenoids (see E160).

Foods added to These may be added to some chicken feeds to colour the egg yolks, but there is no specific evidence that they are currently in use.

Toxicological evaluation and possible health hazards JECFA and the SCF have made no attempt to provide toxicological evaluation of these substances because of a lack of knowledge of their composition, identity, method of preparation and biochemical effects. Nevertheless, the SCF recommended in 1975 that these substances should be accepted for use without further investigation. They reaffirmed this view in 1983, and no ADI has been set. The CoT did not consider these compounds in 1979, but the FACC recommended that E161-(a–f) should all be deleted from the

permitted list because no food manufacturers wanted to use them. Since these compounds were, however, on the EEC permitted list, the FAC referred them to the CoT. When the CoT reported in 1987 they listed these six colours in Group B, indicating that their continued presence on the permitted list is acceptable. The CoT did however request evidence concerning the extent of their use. The FAC recommended that their use should continue.

No adverse effects have been reported and Xanthophylls are generally presumed to be safe.

Regulatory status Permitted and used in the UK, and EEC, and the USA.

E161(a): Flavoxanthin

Type A specific type of Xanthophyll (see E161), it is a yellow colouring derived from green leaves.

Foods added to No specific uses have been reported.

Toxicological evaluation and possible health hazards Regarded by JECFA and the SCF in precisely the same manner as E161. The CoT did not consider this compound in 1979, but the FACC recommended that E161(a) should be deleted from the permitted list. Since it was, however, on the EEC permitted list, the FAC referred it to the CoT. When the CoT reported in 1987 they listed it in Group B, indicating that its continued presence on the permitted list is acceptable. The CoT did however request evidence concerning extent of its use. No adverse effects have been reported, and it is generally presumed to be safe.

Regulatory status Permitted in the UK and EEC.

E161(b): Lutein
also known as Vegetable Lutein

Type This is a reddish-yellow colouring.

Foods added to No specific uses have been reported.

Toxicological evaluation and possible health hazards Regarded by JECFA and the SCF in precisely the same manner as E161. The CoT did not consider this compound in 1979, but the FACC recommended that E161(b) should be deleted from the permitted list. Since it was, however, on the EEC permitted list, the FAC referred it to the CoT. When the CoT reported in 1987 they listed it in Group B, indicating that its continued presence on the permitted list is acceptable. The CoT did however request evidence concerning extent of its use. No adverse effects have been reported, and it is generally presumed to be safe.

Regulatory status Permitted in the UK and the EEC.

E161(c): Cryptoxanthin

Type A yellow colouring which is derived from corn and marigolds.

Foods added to No specific uses have been reported.

Toxicological evaluation and possible health hazards Regarded by JECFA and the SCF in precisely the same manner as E161. The CoT did not consider this compound in 1979, but the FACC recommended that E161(c) should be deleted from the permitted list. Since it was, however, on the EEC permitted list, the FAC referred it to the CoT. When the CoT reported in 1987 they listed it in Group B, indicating that its continued presence on the permitted list is acceptable. The CoT did however request evidence concerning extent of its use. No

adverse effects have been reported, and it is generally presumed to be safe.

Regulatory status Permitted in the UK and the EEC.

E161(d): Rubixanthin

Type A yellow colouring derived from Carotene and naturally occurring in rosehips.

Foods added to No specific uses have been reported.

Toxicological evaluation and possible health hazards Regarded by JECFA and the SCF in precisely the same manner as E161. The CoT did not consider this compound in 1979, but the FACC recommended that E161(d) should be deleted from the permitted list. Since it was, however, on the EEC permitted list, the FAC referred it to the CoT. When the CoT reported in 1987 they listed it in Group B, indicating that its continued presence on the permitted list is acceptable. The CoT did however request evidence concerning extent of its use. No adverse effects have been reported, and it is generally presumed to be safe.

Regulatory status Permitted in the UK and the EEC.

E161(e): Violoxanthin

Type A natural orange-red colouring which is derived from yellow pansies and from some orange peel.

Foods added to No specific uses have been reported.

Toxicological evaluation and possible health hazards Regarded by JECFA and the SCF in precisely the same manner as E161. The CoT did not consider this compound in 1979, but the FACC recommended that E161(e) should be deleted from the permitted list. Since it was, however, on the EEC permitted list, the FAC referred it to the CoT. When the CoT reported in 1987 they listed it in Group B, indicating that its continued presence on the permitted list is acceptable. The CoT did however request evidence concerning extent of its use. No adverse effects have been reported, and it is generally presumed to be safe.

Regulatory status Permitted in the UK and the EEC.

E161(f): Rhodoxanthin

Type A yellow colouring which is isolated from yew tree seeds.

Foods added to No specific uses have been reported.

Toxicological evaluation and possible health hazards Regarded by JECFA and the SCF in precisely the same manner as E161. The CoT did not consider this compound in 1979, but the FACC recommended that E161(f) should be deleted from the permitted list. Since it was, however, on the EEC permitted list, the FAC referred it to the CoT. When the CoT reported in 1987 they listed it in Group B, indicating that its continued presence on the permitted list is acceptable. The CoT did however request evidence concerning extent of its use. No adverse effects have been reported, and it is generally presumed to be safe.

Regulatory status Permitted in the UK and the EEC.

E161(g): Canthaxanthin

Type It is a natural orange colouring present in some mushrooms, crustaceans and fish, and in the plumage and organs of flamingos and roscato spoonbills. It is a type of Beta-Carotenoid (cf. E160a).

Foods added to The UN Food and Agriculture Organization recommends that this compound be permitted in margarine and other edible oils and fats, canned shellfish, jams, jellies and ices. It can be found in the UK in biscuits, preserves, sauces, dressings and in edible sun-tan capsules. It is also used as an additive to fish feed for farmed salmon and trout to darken the colour of the flesh.

Toxicological evaluation and possible health hazards It was evaluated by JECFA in 1966 when an unconditional ADI of 12.5mg/kg bw was set (along with a conditional ADI of 25mg/kg bw), on the basis of a short-term study on eighteen dogs, and two long-term studies on between two and three hundred rats. In 1974 JECFA restated their position because no new data had been forthcoming. In line with their new policy, however, they abandoned the concept of a conditional ADI, and set a full ADI at 25mg/kg bw. The SCF endorsed this view in 1975 and again in 1983 without any supplementary data having been requested or provided. The CoT did not consider this compound in 1979, but the FACC recommended that E161(g) should be deleted from the permitted list because they had received no indications that any manufacturers wanted to use it. Ministers failed to implement this recommendation, and subsequently the FAC received a considerable number of representations from food manufacturers wishing to continue to use this compound, consequently the FAC referred it to the CoT.

When the CoT reported in 1987 they explained that in 1981 they had listed it in Group A (by reference to some unpublished data provided by Hoffman-La Roche from an unnamed author), but had subsequently received reports that people who consumed large amounts of this colouring, especially from artificial skin-tanning capsules, developed bright yellow patches on the retinas of their eyes. These changes can, for example, impair vision especially at twilight, and increase sensitivity to glare. With uncharacteristic boldness, the CoT commented that the new data entailed that the ADI set by JECFA was significantly too high, and they recommended a substantially lower figure, and that the use of Canthaxanthin should be confined to the feed of farmed salmon and trout. By leaving it in Group A, they implied that they considered it safe to eat, just as long as you hardly ever ate any. It is not entirely clear from the 1987 FAC report whether or not they have endorsed the restrictions proposed by the CoT, but they did recommend that when fish which has received artificially coloured feed is offered for sale it should be labelled accordingly.

Regulatory status Permitted in the UK, the EEC and the USA.

E162: Beetroot Red
also known as Betanin

Type It is a natural reddish-purple colouring which is found in beetroots.

Foods added to It is not used widely, although the UN Food and Agriculture Organization recommends that this compound be permitted in flavoured yoghurts, edible ices and ice mixes. In the UK it can be found in some oxtail soups.

Toxicological evaluation and possible health hazards In 1974 JECFA evaluated it on a rather limited data base, namely one unpublished report compiled in 1959 of work conducted on rats, which was supplied to JECFA on a personal basis by H. Druckrey. Although long-term feeding and reproductive studies had been conducted and reported, JECFA stated that too few parameters had been examined and essential observations had not been reported. They pointed out, however, that far higher levels of this substance would be consumed in beetroot than could be consumed from its use as a food additive, and so they judged it to be acceptable for use as an additive with what is termed an 'unspecified' ADI, but they did call for further studies of human metabolism and of long-term consumption in an 'acceptable species'. In 1975 the SCF did not endorse JECFA's view precisely, but given the available information they did agree to the use of this colouring additive without any ADI. They did, however, state that they, too, would require more information if this substance continued to be used into the future. JECFA reviewed the position in 1978 and noted that increasing use was being made of this substance. Their requirements for further data were increased substantially. In 1979 the FACC listed it in Group A, meaning that they were satisfied that they had sufficient information, and they assume it is safe. In 1982 JECFA explained that they had received no indication that the studies which they had requested had even been initiated, and so withdrew their previous unspecified ADI and called for proper studies. Subsequently the 1983 SCF report and the 1987 report of the FAC and CoT have both failed even to mention it.

No adverse effects have been reported, and it is generally presumed to be safe.

Regulatory status Permitted in the UK and the EEC.

E163: Anthocyanins

Type A group of at least six naturally occurring, intensely coloured, water-soluble pigments. They are extracted from the flowers to which they give their colours.

Foods added to They are rather expensive and thus rarely used, but they can be found, for example, in some biscuits, confectionery, soft drinks and in some fruit sorbets.

Toxicological evaluation and possible health hazards This group of compounds was first considered by JECFA in the mid-1960s but they were not evaluated because there was insufficient information about their source, preparation, composition and toxicology. In spite of this they continued to be used, albeit rather sparingly. The amount of toxicological information available on these compounds is very slight, and although JECFA reconsidered them in 1977 and 1982, they were still unable to set an ADI. In 1975 the SCF decided that since these substances are naturally occurring and extracted from plants by physical processes they can be accepted for use in foods without any ADI and without any further investigations. The SCF re-affirmed this view in 1983. The CoT did not review them in 1979, and the FACC recommended that they should be deleted from the positive list. This proposal was not implemented, but the FAC subsequently received numerous representations from food manufacturers wishing to continue to use these compounds, and the CoT was asked to comment. The CoT responded by listing them in Group A on the basis of three unpublished reports. The FAC therefore recommended their continued acceptance.

No adverse effects are known, and they are generally presumed to be safe.

Regulatory status Permitted in the UK and the EEC.

E163(a): Cyanidin

Type This is a natural red colouring derived from plants.

Foods added to No specific uses have been reported.

Toxicological evaluation and possible health hazards See E163.

Regulatory status Permitted in the UK and the EEC.

E163(b): Delphinidin

Type This is a natural blue colouring derived from plants.

Foods added to No specific uses have been reported.

Toxicological evaluation and possible health hazards See E163.

Regulatory status Permitted in the UK and the EEC, but banned in the USA and Sweden.

E163(c): Malvidin

Type It is a naturally occurring purple colouring derived from plants.

Foods added to No specific uses have been reported.

Toxicological evaluation and possible health hazards See E163.

Regulatory status Permitted in the UK and the EEC.

E163(d): Pelargonidin

Type It is a naturally occurring brown colouring derived from plants.

Foods added to No specific uses have been reported.

Toxicological evaluation and possible health hazards See E163.

Regulatory status Permitted in the UK and the EEC.

E163(e): Peonidin
Type It is a naturally occurring red colouring derived from plants.

Foods added to No specific uses have been reported.

Toxicological evaluation and possible health hazards See E163.

Regulatory status Permitted in the UK and the EEC.

E163(f): Petunidin
Type It is a naturally occurring red colouring derived from plants.

Foods added to No specific uses have been reported.

Toxicological evaluation and possible health hazards See E163.

Regulatory status Permitted in the UK and the EEC.

E170: Calcium Carbonate
also known as Chalk

Type This is a familiar white-coloured, naturally occurring material. It is tasteless and odourless, and is found in chalk rock, marble and coral. It has several uses for the food industry, since it can be used not just as a colour but also as an anti-caking agent and as an alkaline neutralizer.

Foods added to It can be found in some white flour, bakery products, evaporated milk, sweetened condensed milk and confections. It is also often used in the manufacture of pills, and it can be found, for example, in some vitamin pills.

Toxicological evaluation and possible health hazards JECFA considered it in 1965 and approved it for general use with an unlimited ADI, and re-iterated this view without reservations in 1973. The CoT did not consider it necessary to review this compound in either 1979 or 1987. It is generally presumed to be safe, except that at very high doses it can cause constipation.

Regulatory status Permitted in the UK and the EEC and listed in the USA as GRAS, but apparently is banned in Canada, Israel and Sweden because of its historical role in adulteration. The EEC has proposed to restrict the use of Calcium Carbonate to surface colouring only.

E171: Titanium Dioxide
Type It is a white, surface colourant made from a naturally occurring mineral.

Foods added to It can be found on some biscuits, ices and confectionery products as a surface colourant, as well as in some sweets and cottage- and mozzarella-type cheeses. It can be used in three of the nineteen groups of food products listed by the FACC.

Toxicological evaluation and possible health hazards JECFA considered this substance in 1966, but declined to evaluate it because of insufficient data. In 1969 they reconsidered the position because, although the data were still incomplete, they had some information on the metabolism of this chemical, and a couple of short-term feeding studies on rats. JECFA did not allocate a specific ADI, but judged that given its likely uses no significant health hazard would be posed, and so an ADI was not required. In 1975 the SCF also considered that its use for surface and mass colouring of sugar confectionery was acceptable without an ADI and without further investigation. In 1977 they modified this position to recommend it for general food use, again without an ADI or further investigation. This position was reiterated in 1983. In 1979 the CoT listed it in Group A despite the poverty of toxicological data, because industrial exposure had not indicated any hazard, and by 1987 they had not reconsidered it.

No adverse health effects have been reported and it is generally presumed to be safe when used as an additive, although it may be hazardous when inhaled in large doses because it may irritate the lungs.

Regulatory status Permitted in the UK and the EEC, but banned in Japan, Portugal and Spain. The 1987 report of the FAC recommended that while Titanium Dioxide should be permitted for use in mozzarella-like cheese made from cows' milk so that it more closely resembled the original product made from buffalo milk, they recommended against its use for similar purposes in feta-type cheese made from cows' milk. The FAC also recommended that this compound should be permitted up to the relatively high level of 400mg/kg in sugar and chocolate confectionery products.

E172: Iron Oxides and Hydroxides

Type There are three substances under this heading. One is a black powder called ferroso ferric oxide, the second is anhydrous ferric oxide, which is red, and the third hydrated ferric oxide, which is yellow. Some organic compounds are used as mixtures.

Foods added to They can be found in some fish, shellfish and meat pastes, as well as in some dessert packet mixes. It is also being used at high levels in fungal-based imitation meat products. The FACC recommended that these substances should be used in only

one of their nineteen groups of food products.

Toxicological evaluation and possible health hazards The human biochemistry of iron is well understood. In a normal healthy person, more than 70 per cent of the body's iron is carried in the blood as haemoglobin. A lack of iron exhibits itself as anaemia. In 1974 JECFA judged that although these substances had not been specifically subjected to extensive toxicological testing in animals, and despite the fact that what was known about them could not be directly extrapolated to their use as food additives, they could be considered as sufficiently safe so that their use as food additives need not be restricted, even though no ADI could be allocated. They did, however, request more information on the metabolism of ingested iron oxides by June 1978. In 1978 they reconfirmed their basic position on these substances. In 1979 the FACC listed these chemicals in Group A, meaning that they believed that they have sufficient information and that they are safe. In 1987 the FAC reported that some fungal-based imitation meat products contained Iron Oxides and Hydroxides at levels of up to 4,000mg/kg. Since the Group A categorization by the CoT in 1979 had been predicated on the assumption that use of these compounds would not rise significantly, the FAC recommended that the permitted total level of colouring in these products should not exceed 100mg/kg. They were, however, prepared to sanction levels of 500mg/kg in fish and shellfish pastes, spreads and pâtés.

No toxic hazards have been reported or suspected and they are generally presumed to be safe.

Regulatory status These are permitted in the UK and the EEC, but in the USA they are only permitted in pet food products, not in foods for people.

E173: Aluminium

Type This silvery colourant occurs naturally in bauxite ore, and can also be found in tea because the plant absorbs it from the soil.

Foods added to In a powdered form this metal is used to decorate some sugar-coated confectionery products.

Toxicological evaluation and possible health hazards In 1975 the SCF listed this colour as one for which an ADI could not be established, but which is none the less acceptable for limited use as external colouring and decoration. They did, however, recommend a more general study of the total intake of Aluminium from all sources. JECFA considered this metallic powder in 1977 and judged that sufficient data were available on its effects in both humans and animals. They did not consider it necessary to establish any ADI because the quantities in which it is used are so slight. It is not clear, however, if they would have been able to set an ADI were they so to have wished. The CoT did not evaluate Aluminium in 1979, and the FACC recommended its deletion from the positive list, but ministers failed to implement this recommendation. Subsequently the FAC received representations from firms proposing its continued use, and so the matter was referred to the CoT. In 1987 they listed Aluminium in Group A, just so long as its use is confined to the surface coating of confectionery decorations known as

dragées. In particular they recommended that the recently introduced practice of coating large items of sugar confectionery should be discontinued. The FAC endorsed these recommendations.

There has been a long-standing but low-level controversy about the safety of Aluminium. Many authorities presume Aluminium to be safe at low doses, but there is some evidence that this metal plays a part in causing premature senility in the form of Alzheimer's disease. The contribution to levels of bodily Aluminium from its use as a food additive are likely to be very slight, especially by comparison with the contributions from cereals, vegetables, tea and from the use of Aluminium cooking pans. There are certainly grounds for further studies and caution in the meantime.

Regulatory status Permitted in the UK and the EEC, but only for surface colouring.

E174: Silver

Type This metal occurs naturally. Occasionally it is found naturally in its metallic state, but more generally it occurs in metallic ores in combination with other metals.

Foods added to It is used occasionally as a surface colouring for some sugar-coated confectionery products.

Toxicological evaluation and possible health hazards JECFA considered Silver in 1966, but made no attempt to evaluate it toxicologically. Silver is known to be toxic to humans when consumed at sufficiently high doses, but JECFA believed that its use as a food additive is so minimal as not to pose any significant hazard. When consumed in toxic doses it can cause a wide range of problems, including gastrointestinal irritation and lesions in the kidneys and lungs, as well as inflicting a slate-blue colour on the skin and in the eyes of people exposed to it, and it is also suspected of provoking arteriosclerosis. The metal is used only very rarely in foods, and given that JECFA was unable to establish precisely the nature of the Silver used in foods, and since they know that Silver can accumulate in the body, they have postponed making any decision; meanwhile it continues to be used. The SCF, on the other hand, decided in 1975 that although no ADI could be established, the use of Silver for surface colouring and decoration of foods is acceptable without any further investigation.

The CoT did not evaluate Silver in 1979, and the FACC recommended its deletion from the positive list, but ministers failed to implement this recommendation. Subsequently the FAC received representations from firms proposing its continued use, and so the matter was referred to the CoT. In 1987 they listed Silver in Group A, just so long as its use is confined to the surface coating of confectionery decorations known as dragées, and to occasional sugar-coated flour and chocolate confectionery.

The extensive use of Silver as a food additive cannot be presumed to be entirely safe because it accumulates and can be toxic when it is accumulated, but this practice would certainly be uneconomic.

Regulatory status Permitted in the UK and the EEC, but not approved for use in the USA. The EEC has proposed to restrict the use of Silver to surface colouring only.

E175: Gold

Type It is a rare, naturally occurring metal which is chemically rather inactive.

Foods added to It is used occasionally as a surface colourant on some sugar-coated confectionery products.

Toxicological evaluation and possible health hazards JECFA considered Gold as a food colouring additive in the mid-1960s, but they did not even attempt to provide a toxicological evaluation. In 1975 the SCF, recognizing the comprehensive lack of proper toxicological information, concluded that no ADI could be established. They judged, none the less, that the use of metallic Gold for surface colouring and decoration could be accepted without any further investigation. JECFA considered the matter in 1978 and noted that Gold salts are used in the treatment of rheumatoid arthritis and that such treatment has provoked numerous undesirable side effects, including skin rashes and gastrointestinal disturbances. It is also known that Gold can accumulate in the kidney. In the light of the fact that this metal is used only very occasionally and in microscopic quantities, JECFA concluded that such use would pose no significant hazard to human health. The CoT listed Gold in Group A in 1979, and in 1987 this judgement was reiterated, just so long as its use was confined to the surface coating of confectionery decoration known as dragées, and to occasional sugar-coated flour and chocolate confectionery. Despite the poverty of information the current usage of Gold as a food additive is generally presumed to be safe.

Regulatory status Permitted in the UK and the EEC, but not approved for use in the USA. The EEC has proposed to restrict the use of Gold to surface colouring only.

E180: Pigment Rubine
also known as Lithol Rubine BK, and as D&C Red No. 7 in the USA

Type This is a synthetic red coal tar dye.

Foods added to Its use is restricted to the rinds of some cheeses such as Edam, but is also used in some drugs and cosmetics, especially in the USA.

Toxicological evaluation and possible health hazards In the mid-1960s JECFA considered this colour, but refused to evaluate it because of a lack of data, and particularly a complete lack of information about its long-term toxicity. In spite of this fact the use of this colour persisted. In 1975 the SCF listed it as one for which no ADI could be provided because of a chronic lack of information, yet they approved its continued use in cheese rinds. In 1977 JECFA considered the matter again. They reviewed all the data available to them (which were entirely unpublished) and reported that the tests on rats and rabbits revealed no worrying toxicity, but that mink which had been fed on cheese rind containing this colouring showed a reduced number of offspring in their litters. The CoT did not evaluate Pigment Rubine in 1979, and the FACC recommended its deletion from the positive list, but ministers failed to implement this recommendation. Subsequently the FAC received representations from firms proposing its continued use, and so the matter was referred to the CoT.

Pigment Rubine had been placed on JECFA's agenda for its meeting in 1982, but as so little new data had been provided they would not evaluate it; and they have not subsequently returned to the topic. In 1983, however, sufficient data were presented to the SCF to persuade them to set an ADI of 1.5mg/kg bw, on the basis of a long-term feeding study on rats. In 1987 the CoT listed this colour in Group B, pending the receipt of long-term and metabolic studies within two years.

Whatever effects this chemical may or may not have on laboratory animals, it is suspected by some doctors of provoking allergenic symptoms and child hyperactivity. It is possible, no doubt, to remove the rind from a cheese before eating it, but there remains a possibility of the colouring's migrating into the cheese itself and contaminating it.

Regulatory status Permitted in the UK and the EEC for the colouring of cheese rind only, but banned for use in foods in the USA.

E200: Sorbic Acid

Type It is a white powder which can be obtained from the berries of the mountain ash tree, and also synthesized industrially. It can function to inhibit the growth of bacteria, moulds and yeasts. Food manufacturers have been using Sorbic Acid since the 1950s.

Foods added to This is one of the most commonly used preservative agents. It can be found in some salads, chocolate syrup, cheese, cheesecake, prunes, flour confectionery, soft drinks, fruit yoghurts, cakes and beer. It can also be added to solutions of food colours for commercial sale.

Toxicological evaluation and possible health hazards JECFA first evaluated this chemical in 1961, and allocated to it an ADI of 12.5mg/kg bw. It must have been one of the first chemicals to receive this accolade, since the concept of the ADI was only invented in 1958, and first used institutionally in the early 1960s. They reviewed it again in 1965, in 1973 (when the ADI was raised to 25mg/kg bw) and in 1976. The FACC listed Sorbic Acid and the Sorbates in Group B in 1972, but answers to some of their doubts have been provided since then. Sorbic Acid is generally evaluated along with Sodium, Potassium and Calcium Sorbates (see E201, E202 and E203). These are among the better studied and understood food chemicals. There is some direct evidence that humans and rats metabolize them in similar ways. Studies in rats and mice have been quite extensive, and

the level of consumption which provokes no observable adverse effects is 2,500mg/kg bw for Sorbic Acid and the Sorbates, singly and in combination. There is some evidence, however, that at high concentrations, for example at the levels at which it is used in food processing plants, it can irritate the eyes, nose, throat and skin of industrial workers.

Regulatory status Permitted and widely used in the UK, the EEC, and categorized in the USA as GRAS. In Austria and Israel it is not permitted to add Sorbic Acid to processed fruit.

E201: Sodium Sorbate

Type It is a widely used food preservative.

Foods added to It can be found in some baked goods, soft drinks, dried fruit, and cheese products.

Toxicological evaluation and possible health hazards It has been evaluated with Sorbic Acid (see E200). No adverse effects have been reported, and it is presumed to be safe at the levels at which it is used as a food additive.

Regulatory status Permitted and widely used in the UK, the EEC, and categorized in the USA as GRAS.

E202: Potassium Sorbate

Type A white crystalline powder which is used as a preservative to inhibit the growth of bacteria.

Foods added to It can be found in some chocolate products, baked goods, soft drinks, pie fillings and glacé cherries.

Toxicological evaluation and possible

health hazards It has been evaluated with Sorbic Acid (see E200). No adverse effects have been reported, and it is presumed to be safe at the levels at which it is used as a food additive.

Regulatory status Permitted and widely used in the UK, the EEC, and categorized in the USA as GRAS.

E203: Calcium Sorbate

Type It is a preservative and antifungal agent.

Foods added to It can be found in some chocolate syrup, salads, cheese cake, pie fillings, baked goods and soft drinks.

Toxicological evaluation and possible health hazards It has been evaluated with Sorbic Acid (see E200). No adverse effects have been reported, and it is presumed to be safe at the levels at which it is used as a food additive.

Regulatory status Permitted and widely used in the UK, the EEC, and categorized in the USA as GRAS.

E210: Benzoic Acid

Type This is used in the UK and the EEC as a preservative, but it can also be used as a flavouring. It occurs naturally in many berries, tea and cherry bark. It was first described in 1608 when it was found in gum benzoin. Commercial Benzoic Acid is usually synthesized industrially.

Foods added to In the UK, it is permitted in twenty-four different kinds of food, and it can be found, for example, in some salad dressings, reduced sugar jams, fruit juices and soft drinks, alcoholic beverages, fruit yoghurts and pickles. It is also often used as a preservative with other classes of additive such as colours, artificial sweeteners and flavours. When used in these contexts its presence does not have to be labelled.

Toxicological evaluation and possible health hazards JECFA first evaluated Benzoic Acid, and the Benzoates (see E211, E212, and E213), in 1961 when they set an unconditional ADI of 5mg/kg bw, with a conditional ADI up to 10mg/kg bw , but in 1973 they revised this judgement to set a full ADI at the lower figure. The ADI is intended to apply jointly to Benzoic Acid and the Benzoates either singly or in combination. These evaluations were based on quite an extensive collection of data on metabolism, acute and long-term toxicity tests in mice, rats, rabbits, guinea-pigs and cats, as well as on metabolic studies on a few humans. Toxic effects in most species have been demonstrated at high doses, but it was possible to identify levels of use at which no adverse effects could be observed, and it was from these levels that the ADI was set. Both JECFA and the SCF have noted, however, that there is some direct evidence that Benzoic Acid and the Benzoates can provoke symptoms of allergy and intolerance in some people, and this finding is widely confirmed in the literature. People who are sensitive to aspirin, and/or who suffer from asthma or chronic urticaria or hyperactivity are advised to avoid Benzoic Acid and the Benzoates. There have been reports that some food industry workers have suffered mouth and skin irritations from handling Benzoic Acid and Benzoates in large quantities, and therefore they should be handled industrially with caution and with protective equipment or clothing. There has been at least one report that Benzoic Acid may have a synergistic effect in combination with Sodium Bisulphite (see E222), and the two in combination may cause far more severe problems to asthmatics than either might on its own. Tests in the USSR on mice, which were subjected to stress and exposed to a known carcinogen, have suggested that Benzoic Acid might enhance the action of the carcinogen, and for that reason its use in the USSR has been substantially restricted.

Regulatory status Permitted and widely used in the UK and the EEC. Despite an extensive controversy it remains GRAS in the USA. Benzoic acid is not permitted to be added to processed fruit in Austria, Luxemburg and Israel, but this use is permitted in the UK.

E211: Sodium Benzoate
also known as Benzoate of Soda

Type It is the sodium salt of Benzoic Acid (see E210), and it is widely used as a preservative and as an antifungal agent. It occurs naturally in many fruits (such as cranberries and prunes) and vegetables. It has been used as a preservative for over seventy years.

Foods added to It is widely used, and can be found for example in some carbonated and other soft drinks, fruit juices, bottled sauces, margarines and cheesecake mixes. It is also often used as a preservative with other classes of additives such as colours, artificial sweeteners and flavours. When used in these contexts its presence does not have to be labelled.

Toxicological evaluation and possible health hazards It has been evaluated by JECFA alongside Benzoic Acid (see E210). In 1961 and 1964 they set an unconditional ADI of 5mg/kg bw, and a conditional ADI up to 10mg/kg bw. In 1973, a full ADI was set at 5mg/kg bw for Sodium Benzoate on its own or in combination with Benzoic Acid and/or Potassium Benzoate (see E212). The amount of toxico-

logical information on this substance is quite extensive, and it has been obtained using rats, mice, rabbits and dogs. Observations have also been made on its effects in humans. In all the species studied, levels of consumption have been found which provoke ill health including (in some cases) foetal damage. It has, however, been possible to identify sufficiently low doses in laboratory animals to establish a level at which no adverse effects can be observed, and hence an ADI has been set. Despite this fact, there is plenty of direct evidence that Sodium Benzoate can provoke a wide range of symptoms of acute intolerance including hyperactivity, asthma and urticaria. People who suffer from these conditions are therefore advised to avoid this substance.

Regulatory status Permitted and widely used in the UK and the EEC, and despite some controversy it remains GRAS in the USA.

E212: Potassium Benzoate
Type This is the potassium salt of Benzoic Acid (see E210), and is used as an antimicrobial preservative.

Foods added to It can be found in a wide range of products including soft drinks, fruit juices, bottled sauces, margarines and cheesecake mixes. It is also used as a preservative with other classes of additive such as colours, artificial sweeteners and flavours. When used in these contexts its presence does not have to be labelled.

Toxicological evaluation and possible health hazards It has been evaluated by JECFA alongside Benzoic Acid and Sodium Benzoate (see E210 and E211). In 1964 they set an unconditional ADI of 5mg/kg bw, and a conditional ADI up to 10mg/kg bw.

In 1973, a full ADI was set at 5mg/kg bw for Potassium Benzoate on its own or in combination with Benzoic Acid and/or Sodium Benzoate (see E211). The amount of toxicological information on this substance is rather slim, but it is treated by JECFA (apparently without any experimental evidence) as toxicologically indistinguishable from Sodium Benzoate. There is some evidence that, like Sodium Benzoate, Potassium Benzoate can provoke a wide range of symptoms of acute intolerance including hyperactivity, asthma and urticaria. People who suffer from these conditions are therefore advised to avoid this substance.

Regulatory status Permitted and widely used in the UK and the EEC. Although Sodium Benzoate (E211) is permitted in the USA, Potassium Benzoate is not a permitted food additive there.

E213: Calcium Benzoate
also known as Monocalcium Benzoate
Type It is the calcium salt of Benzoic Acid (see E210), and is used as a preservative.

Foods added to It can be found, for example, in some soft drinks, fruit juices, bottled sauces, margarines and cheesecake mixes. It is also used as a preservative with other classes of additive such as colours, artificial sweeteners and flavours. When used in these contexts its presence does not have to be labelled.

Toxicological evaluation and possible health hazards JECFA first evaluated this chemical as recently as 1983, when an ADI of 5mg/kg bw was set. There have been few direct studies of this chemical, and its evaluation is based primarily on extrapolations

from studies on Benzoic Acid (see E210) and Sodium Benzoate (see E211). Like other Benzoates, it may adversely affect hyperactive children, asthmatics and those sensitive to aspirin or with recurrent urticaria; it is otherwise presumed to be safe.

Regulatory status It is permitted and used in the UK and the EEC, but is banned in the USA.

E214: Ethyl 4-hydroxybenzoate
also known as Ethyl Para-hydroxybenzoate
Type It is a synthetic antimicrobial preservative.

Foods added to It is used in a wide range of products and some of the products in which it can be found include processed fruits, jams, jellies, soft drinks and coffee essences. It can also be used as a preservative with other classes of additive such as colours, artificial sweeteners and other flavourings. When used in this role its presence does not have to be labelled.

Toxicological evaluation and possible health hazards It was first evaluated by JECFA in 1961, and again in 1965 and 1973. These evaluations covered this chemical (214) as well as Propyl 4-hydroxybenzoate (see E216) and Methyl 4-hydroxybenzoate (see E218) and their three corresponding sodium salts (see E215, E217 and E219). In 1961 an unconditional ADI of 2 mg/kg bw was established with a conditional ADI of up to 7mg/kg bw). In 1973 a full ADI was set at 10mg/kg bw, where this figure is intended to apply to all of the hydroxybenzoates singly or in combinations (see E214–E219). These judgements were based on fairly extensive studies of metabolism, acute and long-term toxicity using mainly dogs, rats, rabbits and mice. At sufficiently high doses these chemicals can be variously lethal and/or toxic to laboratory animals, but in each case dosing levels have been found at which no adverse effects were observed, and this information has provided the basis for the ADIs which have been set. Some of the hydroxybenzoates have been studied more thoroughly than others, and in 1973 JECFA called for further studies on the biochemistry of Ethyl 4-hydroxybenzoate in humans and animals, and on the ways in which humans metabolize Methyl 4-hydroxybenzoate (see E218). There is, however, no evidence that such work has been conducted, or at any rate, reported. JECFA has been aware since the 1960s that these substances can provoke intolerant symptoms in a small minority of people, but this is not reflected in their over-all evaluations.

The SCF of the EEC has not had occasion to evaluate these preservatives, and when the Council of Ministers allocated 'E' numbers to these substances they have relied on the evaluations provided by JECFA and their national regulatory agencies.

The 1972 report on preservatives of the FACC indicated that until that time this additive had not been permitted in the UK, but on that occasion they listed it in Group A, and it has subsequently been permitted and used in Britain.

Like the inorganic benzoates (E210–E213) these substances may adversely affect hyperactive children and asthmatics and those people who are intolerant of aspirin.

Regulatory status Permitted and used in the UK (since 1972) and the EEC, but banned in the USA.

E215: Ethyl 4-hydroxybenzoate, Sodium Salt

also known as Sodium Ethyl Para-hydroxybenzoate

Type It is a synthetic preservative.

Foods added to It is used in a wide range of products and some of the products in which it can be found include processed fruits, jams, soft drinks and coffee essences. It can also be used as a preservative with other classes of additive such as colours, artificial sweeteners and other flavourings. When used in this role its presence does not have to be labelled.

Toxicological evaluation and possible health hazards It was first evaluated by JECFA in 1961, and again in 1965 and 1973. These evaluations covered Ethyl 4-hydroxybenzoate (E214), Propyl 4-hydroxybenzoate (see E216) and Methyl 4-hydroxybenzoate (see E218) and their three corresponding sodium salts (E215, E217 and E219). In 1961 an unconditional ADI of 2mg/kg bw was established (with a conditional ADI of up to 7mg/kg bw). In 1973 a full ADI was set at 10mg/kg bw, where this figure is intended to apply to all of the hydroxybenzoates singly or in combinations (see E214–E219). These judgements were based on fairly extensive studies of metabolism, acute and long-term toxicity using mainly dogs, rats, rabbits and mice. At sufficiently high doses these chemicals can be variously lethal and/or toxic to laboratory animals, but in each case dosing levels have been found at which no adverse effects were observed, and this information has provided the basis for the ADIs which have been set. Some of the hydroxybenzoates have been studied more thoroughly than others, and in 1973 JECFA called for further studies on the biochemistry of Ethyl 4-hydroxybenzoate in man and animals, and on the ways in which humans metabolize Methyl 4-hydroxybenzoate (see E218). There is, however, no evidence that such work has been conducted, or at any rate, reported. JECFA has been aware since the 1960s that these substances can provoke intolerant symptoms in a small minority of people, but this is not reflected in their over-all evaluations.

The SCF of the EEC has not had occasion to evaluate these preservatives, and when the Council of Ministers allocated 'E' numbers to these substances they have relied on the evaluations provided by JECFA and their national regulatory agencies.

Like the inorganic benzoates (E210–E213) these substances may adversely affect hyperactive children and asthmatics and those people who are intolerant of aspirin.

Regulatory status Permitted and used in the UK and the EEC, but banned in the USA.

E216: Propyl 4-hydroxybenzoate
also known in the USA as Propylparaben

Type It is a synthetic preservative.

Foods added to It is used in a wide range of products and some of the products in which it can be found include processed fruits, jams, soft drinks and coffee essences. It can also be used as a preservative with other classes of additives such as colours, artificial sweeteners and other flavourings. When used in this role its presence does not have to be labelled.

Toxicological evaluation and possible health hazards It was first evaluated by JECFA in 1961, and again in 1965 and 1973. These evaluations covered Ethyl 4-hydroxybenzoate (see E214), Propyl 4-hydroxybenzoate (E216) and Methyl 4-hydroxybenzoate (see E218) and their three corresponding sodium salts (E215, E217 and E219). In 1961 an unconditional ADI of 2mg/kg bw was established (along with conditional ADI of up to 7mg/kg bw). In 1973 a full ADI was set at 10mg/kg bw, where this figure is intended to apply to all of the hydroxybenzoates singly or in combination (see E214–E219). These judgements were based on fairly extensive studies of metabolism, acute and long-term toxicity using mainly dogs, rats, rabbits and mice. At sufficiently high doses these chemicals can be variously lethal and/or toxic to laboratory animals, but in each case dosing levels have been found at which no adverse effects were observed, and this information has provided the basis for the ADIs which have been set. Some of the hydroxybenzoates have been studied more thoroughly than others, and in 1973 JECFA called for further studies on the biochemistry of Ethyl 4-hydroxybenzoate in man and animals, and on the ways in which humans metabolize Methyl 4-hydroxybenzoate (see E218). There is, however, no evidence that such work has been reported. JECFA has been aware since the 1960s that these substances can provoke intolerant symptoms in a small minority of people, but this is not reflected in their over-all evaluations.

The SCF of the EEC has not had occasion to evaluate these preservatives, and when the Council of Ministers allocated 'E' numbers to these substances they have relied on the evaluations provided by JECFA and their national regulatory agencies.

Like the inorganic benzoates (E210–E213) these substances may adversely affect hyperactive children and asthmatics and those people who are intolerant of aspirin.

Regulatory status Permitted and used in the UK and the EEC, and permitted for use as a preservative (in concentrations up to 1 per cent) in the USA where it is classified as GRAS.

E217: Propyl 4-hydroxybenzoate Sodium Salt
also known as Sodium Propyl Para-hydroxybenzoate

Type It is a synthetic preservative.

Foods added to It is used in a wide range of products and some of those in which it can be found include processed fruits, jams, soft drinks and coffee essences. It can also be used as a preservative with other classes of additive such as colours, artificial sweeteners and other flavourings. When used in this role its presence does not have to be labelled.

Toxicological evaluation and possible health hazards It was first evaluated by JECFA in 1961, and again in 1965 and 1973. These evaluations covered Ethyl 4-hydroxybenzoate (E214), Propyl 4-hydroxybenzoate (see E216) and Methyl 4-hydroxybenzoate (see E218) and their three corresponding sodium salts (E215, E217 and E219). In 1961 an unconditional ADI of 2mg/kg bw was established (along with a conditional ADI of up to 7mg/kg bw). In 1973 a full ADI was set at 10mg/kg bw, where this figure is intended to apply to all the hydroxy-benzoates singly or in combinations (see E214–E219). These judgements were based on fairly extensive studies of metabolism, acute and long-term toxicity using mainly dogs, rats, rabbits and mice. At sufficiently high doses these chemicals can be variously lethal and/or toxic to laboratory animals, but in each case dosing levels have been found at which no adverse effects were observed, and this information has provided the basis for the ADIs which have been set. Some of the hydroxybenzoates have been studied more thoroughly than others, and in 1973 JECFA called for further studies on the biochemistry of Ethyl 4-hydroxybenzoate in man and animals, and on the ways in which humans metabolize Methyl 4-hydroxybenzoate (see E218). There is, however, no evidence that such work has been reported. JECFA has been aware since the 1960s that these substances can provoke intolerant symptoms in a small minority of people, but this is not reflected in their over-all evaluations.

The SCF of the EEC has not had occasion to evaluate these preservatives, and when the Council of Ministers allocated 'E' numbers to these substances they have relied on the evaluations provided by JECFA and their national regulatory agencies.

Like the inorganic benzoates (E210–E213) these substances may adversely affect hyperactive children and asthmatics and those people who are intolerant of aspirin.

Regulatory status Permitted and used in the UK and the EEC, but banned in the USA.

E218: Methyl 4-hydroxybenzoate
also known as Methyl Para-hydroxy-benzoate, and known in the USA as Methylparaben

Type It is a synthetic antimicrobial preservative.

Foods added to It is used in a wide range of products and some of the products in which it can be found include processed fruits, jams, soft drinks and coffee essences. It can also be used as a preservative with other classes of additive such as colours, artificial sweeteners and other flavourings. When used in this role its presence does not have to be labelled.

Toxicological evaluation and possible health hazards It was first evaluated by JECFA in 1961, and again in 1965 and 1973. These evaluations covered Ethyl 4-hydroxybenzoate (see E214), Propyl 4-hydroxybenzoate (see E216) and Methyl 4-hydroxybenzoate (E218) and their three corresponding sodium salts (E215, E217 and E219). In 1961 an unconditional ADI of 2mg/kg bw was established (along with a conditional ADI of up to 7mg/kg bw). In 1973 a full ADI was set at 10mg/kg bw, where this figure is intended to apply to all of the hydroxybenzoates singly or in combinations (see E214–E219). These judgements were based on fairly extensive studies of metabolism, acute and long-term toxicity using mainly dogs, rats, rabbits, guinea-pigs and mice. At sufficiently high doses these chemicals can be variously lethal and/or toxic to laboratory animals, but in each case dosing levels have been found at which no adverse effects were observed, and this information has provided the basis for the ADIs which have been set. Some of the hydroxybenzoates have been studied more thoroughly than others, and in 1973 JECFA called for further studies on the biochemistry of Ethyl 4-hydroxybenzoate in man and animals, and on the ways in which humans metabolize Methyl 4-hydroxybenzoate. There is, however, no evidence that such work has been reported. JECFA has been aware since the 1960s that these substances can provoke intolerant symptoms in a small minority of people, but this is not reflected in their over-all evaluations.

The SCF of the EEC has not had occasion to evaluate these preservatives, and when the Council of Ministers allocated 'E' numbers to these substances they have relied on the evaluations provided by JECFA and their national regulatory agencies.

Like the inorganic benzoates (E210–E213) these substances may adversely affect hyperactive children and asthmatics and those people who are intolerant of aspirin.

Regulatory status It is permitted and used in the UK and the EEC, and it is permitted as a preservative (up to concentrations of 0.1 per cent) in the USA where it is categorized as GRAS.

E219: Methyl 4-hydroxybenzoate, Sodium Salt
also known as Sodium Methyl Parahydroxybenzoate

Type It is a synthetic preservative.

Foods added to It is used in a wide range of products, some of which include processed fruits, jams, some soups, salad cream, beverages, pickles and fish, soft drinks and coffee essences. It can also be used as a preservative with other classes of additive such as colours, artificial sweeteners and other flavourings. When used in this role its presence does not have to be labelled.

Toxicological evaluation and possible health hazards It was first evaluated by JECFA in 1961, and again in 1965 and 1973. These evaluations covered

Ethyl 4-hydroxybenzoate (E214), Propyl 4-hydroxybenzoate (see E216) and Methyl 4-hydroxybenzoate (see E218) and their three corresponding sodium salts (E215, E217 and E219). In 1961 an unconditional ADI of 2mg/kg bw was established (along with a conditional ADI of up to 7mg/kg bw). In 1973 a full ADI was set at 10mg/kg bw, where this figure is intended to apply to all of the hydroxybenzoates singly or in combinations (see E214–E219). These judgements were based on fairly extensive studies of metabolism, acute and long-term toxicity using mainly dogs, rats, rabbits and mice. At sufficiently high doses these chemicals can be variously lethal and/or toxic to laboratory animals, but in each case dosing levels have been found at which no adverse effects were observed, and this information has provided the basis for the ADIs which have been set. Some of the hydroxybenzoates have been studied more thoroughly than others, and in 1973 JECFA called for further studies on the biochemistry of Ethyl 4-hydroxybenzoate in man and animals, and on the ways in which humans metabolize Methyl 4-hydroxybenzoate (see E218). There is, however, no evidence that such work has been reported. JECFA has been aware since the 1960s that these substances can provoke intolerant symptoms in a small minority of people, but this is not reflected in their over-all evaluations.

The SCF considered this preservative in 1974 when the UK, Denmark and Ireland joined the EEC. They considered this preservative, with two others, because until that time it had not been permitted for use in the EEC, but it was being used in the UK.

At the time the EEC was already permitting the use of E214, E215, E216, E217 and E218. The SCF asserts that there is a technical need for this hydroxybenzoate (E219) as a substitute for one or more of the others, but this point is not properly explained. As to toxicology, the SCF simply refers to the judgement of JECFA.

Like the inorganic benzoates (E210–E213) these substances may adversely affect hyperactive children and asthmatics and those people who are intolerant of aspirin.

Regulatory status Permitted and used in the UK and the EEC, but banned in the USA.

E220: Sulphur Dioxide, and the sulphiting agents (E221–E227)

Type Sulphur Dioxide is the most widely used antimicrobial preservative. It can also function as an antioxidant preventing oils and fats from turning rancid, it will preserve the flavour and appearance of food, can be used to inhibit enzyme activity and to control both enzymic and non-enzymic browning reactions, and it can be used to modify the structure and behaviour of some proteins. Frequently Sulphur Dioxide and the sulphites are used to perform two or more functions, and there are several mechanisms by which Sulphur Dioxide acts as a preservative. Sulphur Dioxide occurs naturally, but it is produced industrially by a simple chemical process. The fact that it can perform all these functions and is simple and cheap to produce and use accounts for its popularity with food manufacturers and for the fact that it has been in use for hundreds of years. There are several continuous-flow and automated food-product manufacturing processes used, for example, to make biscuits, which could not continue without sulphiting agents. Sulphur Dioxide is a gas at room temperature and this limits the scope of its direct use. There are six solid sulphite salts (see E221–E227) which are used because they release Sulphur Dioxide.

Foods added to Given that Sulphur Dioxide is the most widely used preservative it would be easier to list the food products in which it is not used rather than those in which it is used. It is permitted for use in the UK in no fewer than fifty-two different kinds of food. The foods in which it can be found include sausage meat, wine, beer, dried fruit (at the relatively very high level of 2,000 parts per million (ppm)), sauces, soups, flour, dried vegetables (including instant mash potatoes), glucose syrup and vinegar to mention but a few. It can also be added to commercial supplies of other kinds of food additive to preserve them. It can be added, for example, to colours, flavours and modified starches. Under current regulations it is not permitted in fresh minced meat. Some trading standards officers and other researchers believe that this rule is widely disregarded, but the offenders are very rarely caught and prosecutions even rarer. There is also a rule that fresh salads in restaurant salad bars must not be sprayed with sulphite solution. This is important because a handful of deaths was caused in the USA as a result of such spraying. What little evidence there is suggests that in the UK this rule is being observed.

Toxicological evaluation and possible health hazards The toxicological, commercial and regulatory history of this substance is fascinating. In summary, it is of enormous technological, industrial and commercial value, but we know that it is directly harmful to at least a few people, and it may be harmful to many people. It has been in use since antiquity and even then there was no room for doubt that at high concentrations it is a very noxious substance. There have been doubts about its safety as a food additive for nearly a hundred years. There have been innumerable expert committees to review and report, and all take an essentially similar form. They summarize the ever-increasing body of data which details the harm Sulphur Dioxide can do to many different species and at a wide range of doses, and then they attempt to show why none (or only a little) of the data is relevant to human exposure at plausible doses. To put it mildly, the arguments are incomplete; to be direct, they are full of holes.

JECFA has evaluated the safety and toxicity of Sulphur Dioxide and the sulphiting agents (E221–E227) five times, the first time in 1961 and most recently in 1973. Over this period the ADI for Sulphur Dioxide has risen from 0.35mg/kg bw to 0.7mg/kg bw. Its biochemistry, metabolism, mutagenicity, acute and chronic toxicity have all been studied in a very wide range of species including some studies on humans, although there have been no studies of its known interaction products. In every case, though not in every sub-department of toxicology, some hazard from Sulphur Dioxide has been identified. There are dose levels and species at which it reduces levels of calcium in the body making teeth and bones brittle. At moderate doses it causes mutations in bacteria, which means that it might cause mutations and cancer in mammals, including humans. There is no evidence that sulphur dioxide on its own can cause cancer or mutations in laboratory animals, but then there are serious doubts about the adequacy of laboratory animals to predict effects on humans. A sulphite solution can, however, enhance the carcinogenic action of a known carcinogen. It destroys Vitamin B1 down to levels which can be hazardous for anyone eating a diet that is poor in vitamins. At high doses it causes nausea and headaches in all people, and at very low doses the effects persist for a few. The levels at which Sulphur Dioxide is currently used in wines and other alcoholic beverages can provoke asthma attacks in susceptible individuals.

When JECFA set an ADI for Sulphur Dioxide and the sulphiting agents they relied heavily on a long-term feeding study in which Sodium Metabisulphite (E223) was fed to three generations of rats which were simultaneously receiving a diet enriched with Vitamin B1. The fact that the diets were enriched in this manner means that the results are unrepresentative of the normal human situation, and the validity of this test is further undermined by the fact that we know that rats can metabolize sulphites far more rapidly than can humans.

When they set an ADI for Sulphur Dioxide and sulphiting agents, JECFA and the SCF, and national regulatory agencies too, fail to take into account the fact that we are all exposed to varying concentrations of Sulphur Dioxide as atmospheric industrial pollution. Obviously, those living in industrial cities endure highest levels of exposure while those in remote rural areas receive relatively less. Even if it were possible to establish a genuine NEL for all humans, and a level of daily intake which is genuinely acceptable, we should deduct the background level from the total exposure before specifying levels at which it could be used in food and drink. This calculation is never done. In part, this is because the levels of atmospheric Sulphur Dioxide are inadequately recorded, and partly because we do not have accurate estimates of the amounts of Sulphur Dioxide which people are consuming with their food and drink. Average intake is estimated in the UK at 15mg per day, but there are no proper estimates of extreme, but realistic, diets.

In 1907, and in order to avoid their embarrassment, the United States Department of Agriculture refused to publish a report of experiments to find ways to replace Sulphur Dioxide. The USDA had previously tried to restrict the use of Sulphur Dioxide on dried fruit, but political pressure from the California fruit interests had forced the Secretary of Agriculture to exercise his discretion, and to take no action. In 1979 the SCF of the EEC was examining a report on how to reduce the food industry's reliance on Sulphur Dioxide and sulphiting agents. This shows how little progress is made in protecting public health when the relationship between industry and official regulators is so close for so long.

The most that JECFA should conclude from their data on Sulphur Dioxide and the sulphites is that they present no demonstrable severe hazard to the majority of the population (if they consume no more than the ADI), and the best that the SCF can say is that they present no hazard to the great majority. One obvious problem is that there is uncontested evidence that the Sulphur Dioxide intake of a significant number of consumers exceeds the ADI.

There is direct evidence that it can provoke asthmatic attacks in sensitive individuals and cause allergic or nervous reactions in asthmatics, those sensitive to aspirin, and those suffering with eczema, hypertension and ulcers. Regulatory agencies repeatedly announce that the incidence and severity of these problems are so slight that no special precautions need to be taken, but they simply do not have sufficient information to support that view, and it may be little more than wishful thinking.

Decisions about the control of Sulphur Dioxide and the sulphites are complicated by the fact that if we wanted to avoid these substances entirely, but perform the same technological functions, then we should have to use a larger number of different chemicals, including Benzoic Acid and the hydroxybenzoates see E210–E219), which may pose at least as great a risk to human health.

Regulatory status Sulphur Dioxide is permitted and widely used in the UK and the EEC. The UK and the EEC also permit the use of Sodium Sulphite (E221), Sodium Bisulphite (E222), Sodium Metabisulphite (E223), Potassium Metabisulphite (E224), Calcium Bisulphite (E226) and Calcium Bisulphite (E227) for the Sulphur Dioxide which they release. In the USA Sulphur Dioxide is categorized as GRAS as long as it is not used in meats or in foods which are recognized as a source of Vitamin B1, but there the sulphites, E226 and E227, are not

permitted, while Potassium Bisulphite is permitted, although it is banned in the EEC. Sulphur Dioxide and the sulphites can be used in the UK in various food products from which they are banned in Austria, Finland, Israel, Luxembourg and Spain, among others.

E221: Sodium Sulphite
Type This is a slightly pink, odourless powder with a salty taste.

Foods added to See E220. It can be found particularly in cut fruits, fruit juices, fruit-pie mixes, shellfish, quick-frozen fried potato products, wine and beer.

Toxicological evaluation and possible health hazards See E220.

Regulatory status Permitted and used in the UK and the EEC, and GRAS in the USA.

E222: Sodium Hydrogen Sulphite
also known as Sodium Bisulphite

Type It is a white powder with a disagreeable taste, and is used as an antimicrobial preservative.

Foods added to It is used particularly as a preservative on shellfish, quick-frozen fried potato products and fruit juice, and as a bleaching agent in wine, ale and beer.

Toxicological evaluation and possible health hazards See E220.

Regulatory status Permitted and used in the UK and the EEC, and GRAS in the USA.

E223: Sodium Metabisulphite
Type It is an antibacterial preservative, and it is also used to inhibit fermentation.

Foods added to It can be used on shellfish, quick-frozen fried potato products, fruit and vegetable juices, dried fruits, sauces, sausages, dehydrated vegetables and jams. It is also used to discourage sugars and syrups from fermenting.

Toxicological evaluation and possible health hazards See E220.

Regulatory status Permitted and used in the UK and the EEC, and GRAS in the USA.

E224: Potassium Metabisulphite

Type It is a white or colourless powder which smells of Sulphur Dioxide (see E220). It is used as a preservative and as an anti-browning agent.

Foods added to It is widely used in wine, beer and ale. It may also be found in fruit juices and dehydrated vegetables, quick-frozen shellfish, and quick-frozen fried potato products.

Toxicological evaluation and possible health hazards See E220.

Regulatory status Permitted and used in the UK and the EEC, and GRAS in the USA.

E226: Calcium Sulphite

Type Synthetically manufactured preservative, which can also be used as a firming agent.

Foods added to It can be found, for example, in some ciders.

Toxicological evaluation and possible health hazards See E220.

Regulatory status Permitted and used in the UK and the EEC, but it is not permitted in the USA.

E227: Calcium Bisulphite
also known as Calcium Hydrogen Sulphite

Type It is a synthetically manufactured preservative, and it can also be used as a firming agent.

Foods added to It can be found, for example, in jams, jellies and some beers.

Toxicological evaluation and possible health hazards See E220.

Regulatory status Permitted and used in the UK and the EEC, but banned in the USA.

E230: Diphenyl
also known as Biphenyl, and as Phenyl Benzene

Type It is a preservative and antifungal agent.

Foods added to It is used on both wrapping materials surrounding citrus fruits, and on the skins of citrus fruits themselves, to inhibit the development of moulds. This chemical can therefore contaminate cooked fruit products such as marmalades which contain the peel as well as the fruit.

Toxicological evaluation and possible health hazards JECFA evaluated this substance in 1961, and again in 1964. On both occasions they set an unconditional ADI of 0.05mg/kg bw (with a conditional ADI up to 0.25mg/kg bw). They have not evaluated it since, and the SCF has not published any review of this substance. The FACC's 1972 report listed Diphenyl in Group B. This was because they had evidence that this compound can be toxic to rats at moderate doses, and they asked for the results of a lifetime feeding study in another species of laboratory animal. This substance has still not been extensively tested, and such tests as have been conducted have examined it on its own, and not in combinations with fruit. Even so, the results of these tests indicate that it might cause bacteria to mutate and it may induce cancer in laboratory animals. There is also some direct evidence that it causes nausea, vomiting and irritations to workers in food processing plants. American produce which is shipped to West Germany and Italy must be labelled with the warning 'with diphenyl, peel unsuitable for consumption', but no such provision applies in the USA or the UK.

Regulatory status It is permitted and used in the UK and the EEC. It is permitted in the USA on citrus fruit skins, and in a small group of foods at low levels as a flavouring.

E231: Orthophenylphenol
also known as 2-Hydroxybiphenyl and as Orthoxenol

Type It is a synthetic preservative.

Foods added to It is used on the skins of citrus fruits, and on wrapping materials for citrus fruits, to inhibit the development of moulds. This chemical can therefore contaminate cooked fruit products such as marmalades which contain the peel as well as the fruit.

Toxicological evaluation and possible health hazards It was evaluated by JECFA in 1961 and in 1964. On both occasions an unconditional ADI was set at 0.2mg/kg bw, supplemented with a conditional ADI of 0.2–1mg/kg bw. Since that time, JECFA has abandoned the concept of the conditional ADI, and new information has emerged indicating that this substance may be both a mutagen and carcinogen; none the less JECFA has not re-evaluated this additive. The 1972 FACC report listed this chemical in Group B, and called for further studies, which indicates that they did not have sufficient information to be confident about its safety. They ask that a new information should be available in time for their next review.

There is no evidence that the required data have yet been generated, supplied and/or reviewed. There is, furthermore, some direct evidence that industrial workers who handle this chemical in bulk quantities can suffer from nausea and irritation to eyes and nose.

Regulatory status Permitted and used in the UK and the EEC.

E232: Sodium Orthophenylphenate
also known as Sodium Orthophenylphenol and as Sodium Biphenyl-2-yl Oxide

Type It is a synthetic preservative with an antifungal action, and a strong and distinctive soapy smell.

Foods added to It is used on the skins of citrus fruits, and on wrapping materials for citrus fruits, to inhibit the development of moulds. In the USA it can also be used on the skins of cherries. This chemical can therefore contaminate cooked fruit products such as marmalade which contain the peel as well as the fruit.

Toxicological evaluation and possible health hazards This substance was evaluated by JECFA in 1961 and 1964. On both occasions an unconditional ADI was set at 0.2mg/kg bw, supplemented with a conditional ADI of 0.2–1mg/kg bw. Since that time, JECFA has abandoned the concept of the conditional ADI, and new information has emerged indicating that at large doses this substance is acutely toxic and can even be fatal when as little as 1.5g are ingested. At some doses and in some test systems it can cause destruction of chromosomes and can lead to genetic mutations. It may cause nausea, convulsions and vomiting, and it may irritate the eyes and nose. The 1972 FACC report listed this chemical in Group B, and called for further studies, which indicates that they did not have sufficient information to be confident about its safety. They asked that the new information should be available in time for their next review. There is no evidence that the required data have yet been generated, supplied and/or reviewed.

Regulatory status Permitted and used in the UK and the EEC.

E233: Thiabendazole
also known as 2-(Thiazol-4-yl) Benzimidazole

Type It is a synthetic fungicide.

Foods added to It is applied to the skins of some bananas and citrus fruits. It is also used as an agricultural pesticide, as a pre-planting seed treatment and also for post-harvest treatment of a variety of crops. In some cases it is used both pre-harvest and post-harvest on the same crops, such as apples, pears, bananas, citrus fruits, grapes, sugar-beet and tomatoes. It is used occasionally in medicines for humans, and furthermore as a veterinary medicine on animals intended for human consumption. When Thiabendazole is used in commercial agricultural fungicide preparations it is generally incorporated into products along with other fungicides.

Toxicological evaluation and possible health hazards This substance has not been evaluated by JECFA, but in 1970 it was examined by its close relative the WHO/FAO Joint Expert Committee on Pesticide Residues which set an ADI of 0.3mg/kg bw. Permission to use this substance as a fungicide was given in a 1967 Community Directive on Preservatives in Foodstuffs. In 1976 the SCF were asked by the EEC Commission to comment on a proposal from commercial users of this substance to raise the level at which this substance may be used so that residues on citrus fruit could rise from 6mg/kg to 10mg/kg of the whole fruit. At that time the SCF did not have sufficient information on over-all levels of consumption. On several occasions the SCF had stated that they did not believe it to be desirable to permit a chemical to be used as a food additive or agricultural chemical if it is also used in human medicines or as a veterinary medicine in animals intended for human consumption. Between 1976 and 1978, the SCF received some supplementary data, so that by 1978 they were ready to report. They concluded, on this occasion, that since its use in human medicine in Europe is quite limited, and since veterinary residues are low (around 0.1mg/kg bw) they are prepared to accept its continued use on fruit, but they insisted against commercial pressure that levels of use should not increase above 6mg/kg of whole fruit. At the same time, the SCF endorsed the ADI of 0.3mg/kg bw.

Regulatory status This substance is permitted and used in the UK and the EEC, but it is not permitted as a direct food additive in the USA.

234: Nisin
Type It is a polypeptide antibiotic which is particularly effective at inhibiting the growth of some (but not all) of those bacteria which are known as *Clostridia* and *Lactobacillae*. It is manufactured by isolating it from the secretions of a bacterium called *Streptococcus lactis*.

Foods added to Since it is a natural

constituent of some cheeses, it is often used as a preservative in certain cheeses and cream products such as clotted cream. It can also be found in some canned foods if they are vulnerable to spoilage by clostridial bacteria.

Toxicological evaluation and possible health hazards JECFA evaluated it just once in 1969, and set a full ADI at 3.3mg/kg bw. There is some evidence that this substance is degraded harmlessly in the intestinal tract. No adverse effects have been reported, and it is presumed to be safe.

Regulatory status Permitted and used in the UK, and in some other European countries, but the Council of Ministers of the EEC have not allocated an 'E' number to it. It is not permitted in the USA.

E236: Formic Acid
also known as Methanoic Acid

Type This substance is not permitted in the UK, but is used elsewhere in the EEC as a preservative. In the USA it cannot be used as a preservative, but it is permitted as a flavouring. Commercial grade Formic Acid is produced synthetically. It is a colourless liquid which occurs naturally in apples, mace oil, peaches, raspberries, strawberries and tobacco leaves; it can also be found in the tissue of ants. When in a concentrated form it is highly corrosive. This substance used to be used in dilute concentrations as a diuretic, but this is no longer recommended practice.

Foods added to It is not permitted in the UK, but it may be imported in foods including baked goods, beverages, and ice cream.

Toxicological evaluation and possible health hazards JECFA first evaluated this substance in 1961 when it set a maximum conditional ADI of 5mg/kg bw. They confirmed this figure next in 1964, but in 1973 they revised their judgement and set a full ADI of 3mg/kg bw. The data on which these judgements were based are extremely thin. They had the results of some acute toxicity studies in dogs and rabbits, but no long-term studies, carcinogenicity studies or reproductive studies. They had received a small amount of metabolic data obtained from humans as well as from dogs and rabbits. One report published in 1917 suggested that between 2g and 4g of Sodium Formate (see E237) could be consumed daily by humans without any untoward effects. In large doses this substance is known to be corrosive and an irritant. The effects of long-term low dose consumption are not really understood.

Regulatory status This substance is not permitted as a food additive in the UK, but is permitted and used in some other EEC countries. It is permitted in the USA as a flavouring.

E237: Sodium Formate

Type This preservative is manufactured from Formic Acid, see E236.

Foods added to It is not permitted in the UK, but it may be imported in foods including baked goods (other than bread), beverages, and ice cream.

Toxicological evaluation and possible health hazards This substance has been evaluated as part of the evaluation of Formic Acid, see E236. JECFA first evaluated this substance in 1961 when it set a maximum conditional ADI of 5mg/kg bw. They confirmed this figure next in 1964, but in

1973 they revised their judgement and set a full ADI of 3mg/kg bw. The data on which these judgements were based are extremely thin. They had the results of some acute toxicity studies in dogs and rabbits, but no long-term studies, carcinogenicity studies or reproductive studies. They had received a small amount of metabolic data obtained from humans as well as from dogs and rabbits. One report published in 1917 suggested that between 2g and 4g of Sodium Formate could be consumed daily by humans without any untoward effects. In large doses this substance is known to be corrosive and an irritant, and may lead to kidney disorders. The effects of long-term low dose consumption are not really understood.

Regulatory status It is not permitted in the UK, but it may be imported in some foods including baked goods (other than bread), beverages, and ice cream.

E238: Calcium Formate

Type It is a synthetic preservative.

Foods added to It is not permitted in the UK, but it is permitted and used in some other EEC countries in bakery products.

Toxicological evaluation and possible health hazards JECFA has not provided any specific evaluation, but their evaluation is likely to be similar to that for Formic Acid (see E236) and for Sodium Formate (see E237).

Regulatory status Not permitted in the UK or the USA, but permitted and used in some EEC countries.

E239: Hexamine

also abbreviated to HMT, Hexa-methylene Tetramine, and also sometimes called Methenamine

Type It is a synthetic preservative and fungicide. It is used because, under acid conditions, it decays into formaldehyde, which is a powerful preservative, and ammonia.

Foods added to The use of this substance is restricted quite tightly. It can be used in provolone cheese which is popular in some continental European countries, and in the USA, but not in the UK. It can also be found in some marinaded fish products, especially herrings and mackerel.

Toxicological evaluation and possible health hazards JECFA has looked at this substance four times. In 1961 they were not prepared to set any ADI. In 1964 they decided to postpone making any decision. In 1971 they set a temporary ADI of 5mg/kg bw, while in 1973 they set a full ADI but reduced the figure substantially to 0.15mg/kg bw. Since HMT decays into formaldehyde and since this can be metabolized into Formic Acid (see E236), it is necessary that these substances be evaluated together. HMT, Formic Acid and formaldehyde are known to cause mutations in bacteria, and so potentially may cause mutation and cancer in humans. In the course of a reproductive study in rats, tumours were observed in a statistically significant proportion of animals fed on high doses. Specific carcinogenicity studies, however, have not confirmed this finding. In a reproductive study using dogs, a high proportion of stillbirths and defective pups was found. Injections under the skin of rats using both HMT and formaldehyde produced cancers at the site of injections, but corresponding rat feeding studies did not confirm the apparent carcinogenicity. On the other hand, in one long-term feeding study with mice, H M T did provoke cancers, but this effect was not seen in other such tests. It has been shown, too, that in strongly acidic solutions H M T can interact with nitrites (see e.g. E249 and E250) to produce nitrosamines, which are notoriously carcinogenic. When setting the ADI, JECFA based its evaluation on an NEL in dogs of 15mg/kg bw, and so reached an ADI of 0.15mg/kg bw, using a standard 100-fold safety factor. Whatever effects H M T may have on laboratory animals, the formaldehyde it produces could lead to inflammations, irritations and gastrointestinal disturbances in humans. We cannot be certain, moreover, that it does not cause cancer, and therefore we cannot assume that there is a threshold at which it can safely be used. The concept of the ADI is therefore inappropriate to this substance, as it is for all suspected carcinogens.

Regulatory status It is permitted and used in the UK and the EEC in a limited number of foods. It is not permitted in the USA.

E249: Potassium Nitrite

Type See E250

Foods added to It can be found in some cooked meat and sausage products including salami, pâtés and liver sausage, but Sodium Nitrite (E250) is more frequently used in all of these products.

Toxological and possible health hazards See E250

Regulatory status It is permitted in the UK and the EEC, and in the USA. Before 1976 this substance was not permitted in the EEC, but at the end of 1975 the SCF recommended

that if Sodium Nitrate was permitted then Potassium Nitrate should be permitted too. They reached this conclusion without apparently addressing the question of the safety of them both. They endorsed the call, however, for further studies on the problem of nitrosamines and carcinogenicity. Eleven years later they have not returned to the outstanding questions.

In the UK and in some other countries this substance is not permitted in foods intended for babies and young children because it is known to be toxic to them, although this provision has only been in force in the UK since the late 1970s. For a brief period in the 1970s the use of nitrites in meat products was entirely banned in Norway. After intense industrial pressure, including threats to use even less desirable additives, the Norwegian government relented and re-permitted the use of nitrites, albeit under tight restraints. Many countries restrict the levels at which the nitrates and nitrites can be used far more severely than does the UK.

E250: Sodium Nitrite

Type A white granular or crystalline powder. It is categorized as a preservative in the UK, but JECFA, the FDA and the regulatory agencies of many countries, including the USSR, more accurately call it a colour fixative. It can be used as a preservative agent primarily to inhibit the growth of the bacterium (*Clostridium botulinum*) responsible for botulism, but at the levels at which it is used its primary role is to maintain the colour of the processed foods to which it is added, and thus should be considered to be a cosmetic additive.

Foods added to It can be found in

virtually all cooked meat and sausage products including bacon, ham, salami, pâtés and liver sausage. It can also be found in many fish and cheese products.

Toxicological evaluation and possible health hazards The debate about the safety of the nitrites, and so by implication the nitrates too (see E251 and E252), is focused on two clearly defined problems. First, when nitrites enter the blood supply they interfere with the mechanism for distributing oxygen around the body. Oxygen is carried in the blood supply with the assistance of a substance in the red corpuscles called haemoglobin. Nitrites interfere with this process by interacting directly with the haemoglobin so as to prevent it from carrying oxygen. The younger we are, the more susceptible we are to this problem. Children are vulnerable to far smaller doses than adults, but babies are especially vulnerable to relatively small doses. This is partly because infant haemoglobin is different from and more susceptible than adult haemoglobin, and partly because infants can absorb the nitrite more rapidly in their stomachs. As a result Potassium and Sodium Nitrite are banned from food specifically intended for babies. Infants and children should therefore never be given foods containing these additives.

Second, the nitrites can combine with some basic chemicals called amines which are in our foods, and together they can produce a group of chemicals call nitrosamines which are among the most carcinogenic substances that scientists have ever identified. In so far as there is an argument about safety, the question is not whether nitrite consumption can contribute to cancer, but how much cancer is being caused by current rates of consumption. There is no evidence that there is some safe threshold, the question is just: is the number of cancers being caused acceptably small, given that we do want safe ways of preserving foods from bacterial spoilage? When it comes to the question of how much cancer might nitrites be causing, the honest answer has to be: no one knows. To the question: is the hazard acceptable, given the over-all balance of possible benefits and risks? the expert scientists say: yes, but no one has bothered to ask consumers for their crucial opinion.

There is a slight sub-plot to the issue of carcinogenicity. In 1979, an American scientist reported that his research had suggested that nitrites can be carcinogenic in rats directly and on their own even without first generating nitrosamines. This finding has not been repeated in other tests using different kinds of rat, but though the debate on this topic has subsided, the problem has not been solved, and this extra worry has not gone away.

One crucial question is: are there any alternatives? To this, the answer is yes and no. There are perfectly safe alternative ways of preserving meats and fish. We can freeze it or we can use alternative safe chemicals such as Vitamin C. The problem with these alternatives is that they do not fulfil the cosmetic function referred to above. The products would be just as safe in the short term, and safer by far in the long term, but their colour, flavour and odour would deteriorate far more rapidly than would happen if nitrites were used. For this reason, these safe alternatives are not acceptable to the food industry.

JECFA has evaluated this substance four times. In 1961 they set an unconditional ADI of 0.4mg/kg bw (with a conditional ADI of up to 0.4mg/kg bw). This judgement was confirmed in 1964, but in 1973 they revised their approach and set a full ADI at the lower figure of 0.2mg/kg bw. In 1976 they revised their view again, and set the same ADI but re-categorized it as temporary, pending the results of further studies. A re-evaluation by JECFA is long overdue. On each occasion Potassium Nitrite has been considered alongside its more popular cousin Sodium Nitrite (see E250). Almost all the data discussed were obtained with Sodium Nitrite, and they are treated as indistinguishable toxicologically. Food manufacturers find Potassium Nitrite less technologically advantageous than Sodium Nitrite.

When the FACC discussed the nitrites and nitrates in 1972 their report included a frank list of the two major hazards which are posed by this class of chemical. They listed them in Group B, and called urgently for further studies on the nitrosamine problem, and to find ways of reducing their use. They reported again in 1978, and laid it on the line saying: '. . . every effort should continue to be made to eliminate the use of nitrate and reduce nitrite levels as soon as practicable . . .', and they specified that the matter should be urgently reviewed within two years. There is no evidence that such a review has yet taken place.

Regulatory status It is permitted in the UK and the EEC, and in the USA. In these countries it is very

widely used. In the UK, as in other countries, this substance is not permitted in foods intended for babies and young children because it is known to be toxic to them, although this provision has only been in force in the UK since the late 1970s. For a brief period in the 1970s the use of nitrites in meat products was entirely banned in Norway. After intense industrial pressure, including threats to use even less desirable additives, the Norwegian government relented and re-permitted the use of nitrites, albeit under tight restraints. Many countries restrict the levels at which the nitrates and nitrites can be used far more severely than does the UK.

E251: Sodium Nitrate
also known as Saltpetre or Nitre

Type Like Sodium Nitrite (see E250) it is a preservative and a colour fixative. It is used essentially because it decays into Sodium Nitrite which is the effective chemical agent. It acts therefore to provide a buffer stock of nitrite.

Foods added to It can be found in many processed meat, fish and cheese products.

Toxicological evaluation and possible health hazards Sodium Nitrate decays into Sodium Nitrite (see E250), and so poses identical hazards (see E250). When JECFA reviewed Sodium Nitrite on the first three occasions it dealt with Sodium Nitrate too, but most recently in 1976 JECFA dealt only with the nitrite and did not specifically mention the nitrate. JECFA judged that Sodium Nitrate is safe in itself, and its potential toxicity arises only in so far as it decays into the nitrite. In order to provide a buffer stock of the nitrite a full ADI of 5mg/kg bw was set in 1973 by JECFA. By virtue of its decaying into nitrite, it is especially unsafe for infants and young children. It may be contributing to the incidence of cancer.

Regulatory status Permitted and widely used in the UK, the EEC and the USA. Many countries restrict the levels at which the nitrates and nitrites can be used far more severely than does the UK.

E252: Potassium Nitrate

Type Like Potassium Nitrite (see E249) it is a preservative and a colour fixative. It is used essentially because it decays into Potassium Nitrite which is the effective chemical agent. It acts therefore to provide a buffer stock of nitrite.

Foods added to It can be found in some processed meat, fish and cheese products.

Toxicological evaluation and possible health hazards Potassium Nitrate decays into Potassium Nitrite (see E249), and so poses identical hazards (see E249). When JECFA reviewed Potassium Nitrite on the first three occasions it dealt with Potassium Nitrate too, but most recently in 1976 JECFA dealt only with the nitrite and did not specifically mention the nitrate. JECFA judged that Potassium Nitrate is safe in itself, and its potential toxicity arises only in so far as it decays into the nitrite. In order to provide a buffer stock of the nitrite a full ADI of 5mg/kg bw was set in 1973 by JECFA. By virtue of its decaying into nitrite, it is especially unsafe for infants and young children. It may be contributing to the incidence of cancer.

Regulatory status Permitted and used in the UK, the EEC and the USA. Many countries restrict the levels at which the nitrates and nitrites can be used far more severely than does the UK.

E260: Acetic Acid

Type Acetic Acid is the main ingredient in vinegar, and as such is one of the oldest known preservatives and food additives. It is also used as an acidifier, as a flavouring and more recently to dilute commercial preparations of colour additives. Pure Acetic Acid is a colourless liquid. Ordinary vinegar contains approximately 4–6 per cent of Acetic Acid, while vinegar essence is about 14 per cent Acetic Acid. Alcohol can (all too readily) be converted into Acetic Acid. Acetic Acid occurs naturally at low concentrations in apples, grapes, peaches, raspberries, among other foods.

Foods added to It can be found in a very wide range of foods including some breads, in many pickles, savoury and fruit sauces, ketchup and processed cheeses. Acetic Acid is found as a diluent in commercial preparations of food colourings, and it is also used to manufacture some Caramels (see E150).

Toxicological evaluation and possible health hazards JECFA has evaluated Acetic Acid and its sodium and potassium salts (see E261, E262 and 262) twice in 1965 and in 1973. The amount of direct data available was relatively slight, but since vinegar is a normal constituent of many diets, JECFA were able to conclude that its use as an additive was acceptable without there being any need to set any limits. There is a clear consensus that concentrated Acetic Acid is corrosive and toxic to laboratory animals and to humans. It can not only irritate tissues, it can also damage the central nervous system and the kidneys. There is some evidence that long-term consumption of large doses of even dilute Acetic Acid can damage a person's liver, and so it may be wise to be careful if you use a lot of vinegar and have a damaged liver. When used as an additive it is not known to cause any adverse effects, and is generally regarded as safe.

Regulatory status Permitted and used very widely in the UK, the EEC and in innumerable other countries. It is categorized in the USA as GRAS.

E261: Potassium Acetate

Type It is the potassium salt of Acetic Acid (see E260), and is a colourless powder. It is either odourless, or else has a slight acetic odour depending on purity, and it has a slightly saline taste. It is used to preserve the natural colour of food products and as an acidic buffering agent.

Foods added to It is used, for example, on some frozen vegetables, and soups. It is used occasionally as a medicinal treatment for irregular heart beat, and as a diuretic.

Toxicological evaluation and possible health hazards It was evaluated by JECFA in 1973 in the context of their discussion of Acetic Acid (see E260). They judged it to be sufficiently safe that no ADI needed to be set, and it could be used as an additive without a specific limitation. The evidence suggests that if it is consumed by a healthy person then it poses no health hazard, but people who are suffering from damaged or failing kidneys should avoid this substance as it may aggravate their condition.

Regulatory status Permitted and used in the UK and the EEC. It is

permitted in the USA, but only as a synthetic flavouring, and not for use as a preservative.

E262: Sodium Diacetate

also known as Sodium Hydrogen Diacetate

Type It is a synthetic preservative which is used mainly to prevent the development of a group of microbes which can otherwise spoil bread.

Foods added to It can be found in some breads, and in some fried potato products.

Toxicological evaluation and possible health hazards JECFA evaluated this substance in 1961 and again in 1973. The report of their 1973 discussion is particularly curious. They imply that they have received some data since their previous consideration in 1961, but the only three sources of data which they cite were published between 1920 and 1951. They frankly state that they have no specific information whatsoever about this substance, and that they have treated it as if it were neutralized Acetic Acid (see E260). In the absence of any data whatsoever on this substance they pull out of the air an ADI of 15mg/kg bw. No adverse effects have been reported, and it is generally presumed to be safe.

Regulatory status Permitted and used in the UK, the EEC and the USA.

262: Sodium Acetate

Type The sodium salt of Acetic Acid (see E260). It is used mainly to stabilize the acidity of solutions, but it is also used, for example, as a preservative with liquorice. It also has commercial uses in photographic and dyeing processes.

Foods added to It can be found in

some packet soups, and also in some breads.

Toxicological evaluation and possible health hazards This substance has been evaluated by JECFA alongside Acetic Acid (see E260) and Potassium Acetate (see E261) in 1965 and in 1973. The amount of direct data available was relatively slight, but since Acetic Acid in the form of vinegar is a normal constituent of many diets, JECFA were able to conclude that its use as an additive is acceptable without there being any need to set any limits. It is used occasionally, and in doses significantly higher than when used in foods, in medical practice as a diuretic to reduce fluid retention, and as an expectorant. If it were used in large concentrations then it should be used with care, but when used at the levels appropriate to an additive it is not known to cause any adverse effects, and is generally regarded as safe.

Regulatory status Permitted and used in the UK. The Council of Ministers of the EEC have yet to assign an 'E' number to it, and therefore it can be listed simply as 262. In the USA it is categorized as a general purpose additive which is GRAS.

E263: Calcium Acetate

Type The calcium salt of Acetic Acid (see E260). It is a preservative, anti-mould agent, buffer, firming agent and sequestrant. It is used mainly to prevent the development of a group of microbes which can otherwise spoil bread.

Foods added to It has been found, for example, in packet mixes such as cheesecakes and jelly. It is also often added to caseinates which are by-products from milk proteins.

Toxicological evaluation and possible

health hazards JECFA considered this substance in 1963, and again ten years later. On both occasions they did not make their own evaluation or refer to any specific toxicological data on this substance. Instead they referred to a 1962 report from the Joint FAO/WHO Expert Group on Calcium Requirements, and stated that our daily intake of Calcium may safely vary between 400mg and 2g daily. They observed, however, that Calcium is an essential nutrient, and that the acetate is toxicologically insignificant. No adverse effects have been reported and it is presumed to be safe.

Regulatory status Permitted and used in the UK and the EEC. In the USA it is considered to be a sequestrant and GRAS.

E270: Lactic Acid
also known as DL-Lactic Acid

Type This is a colourless and nearly odourless liquid which can be found, for example, in sour milk. It can also be found naturally occurring in molasses, apples and other fruits, and in fermented drinks such as beer and wine. It is produced commercially by fermenting a range of carbohydrate materials including whey, corn starch and potatoes. It is used for a variety of reasons, partly as a preservative but also because it can act to enhance the antioxidant effects of other additives. It is also used as an acid and as a flavouring. The chemical structure of Lactic Acid is such that it can, and does, exist in two distinct forms (or isomers), one is L-Lactic Acid which is normally encountered in nature, and D-Lactic Acid which has a molecular structure that is the mirror image of its twin, and which does not normally occur in nature. Commercial DL-Lactic Acid is normally a 50-50 mixture of the two isomers.

Foods added to This chemical can be found in a wide range of food and drink products including beer, carbonated fruit beverages, white bread, rolls, margarine, jams, marmalade, confectionery, pickled vegetables and salad dressings.

Toxicological evaluation and possible health hazards JECFA evaluated this substance in 1965 and in 1973, with its ammonium, calcium (see E327), potassium (see E326) and sodium (see E325) salts. They observed that laboratory animals and humans are generally able to metabolize L-Lactic Acid, and indeed it is an integral part of a healthy biology. At very high doses this substance provokes a range of toxic symptoms, but such doses would not arise from the consumption of any realistic diet. D-Lactic Acid and commercially produced DL-Lactic Acid are more problematic, but concern is mainly for infants up to three months old (and especially premature babies) who may well have difficulties in metabolizing this substance. JECFA concluded that it is sufficiently safe for it to be approved for use as an additive without limit.

Special restrictions Since it may be produced from animal sources it is not acceptable to vegans.

Regulatory status It is permitted and used in the UK for a variety of purposes, and under a variety of different regulations. In the USA it is permitted, widely used and categorized as GRAS. It is permitted and used in many European countries, but not in all the contexts which are permitted in the UK and the USA.

E280: Propionic Acid
also known as Propanoic Acid

Type It is used as an anti-mould agent, especially against a type of microbe which causes bread to become 'ropey'. In the absence of a suitable preservative, the bread may become contaminated with a population of micro-organisms which cause the material to break up into strands or become 'ropey'. Propionic Acid is also used, especially in the USA, as a synthetic flavouring. It is a fatty acid which occurs naturally, and in small quantities, in dairy products, apples, strawberries, tea and woodpulp liquor. In a pure and concentrated form it is an oily liquid with a slightly pungent and rancid smell.

Foods added to It is a natural constituent of some Swiss cheeses, and it can also be found, in larger quantities, added to some breads and baked goods, including Christmas puddings, some processed cheeses and in flour confectionery.

Toxicological evaluation and possible health hazards It has been evaluated by JECFA in 1961, 1965, and in 1973, with its sodium, calcium and potassium salts (see E281–3). JECFA judged that this chemical is sufficiently safe, when used as a food additive, that no quantitative restrictions need be placed on its use. When the SCF considered Propionic Acid in 1978 they concurred with this judgement. This fatty acid is not a natural component of edible oils and fats, but it is a natural intermediate breakdown product of our digestion of edible oils and fats. Its subsequent metabolic fate is also well understood in both humans and animals. At high concentrations which are not found in food products, but can occur in chemical plants and at the mixing bins of food processing factories it is known to be a skin irritant. When used in low doses as a food additive it is presumed to be safe.

Regulatory status It is permitted and used in the UK and the EEC, and furthermore is listed as GRAS in the USA.

E281: Sodium Propionate
also known as Sodium Propanoate

Type It is a synthetic antimicrobial preservative which is used as an anti-mould and anti-rope agent. In the absence of suitable preservative, the bread may become contaminated with a population of micro-organisms which cause the material to break up into strands or become 'ropey'. Sodium Propionate is produced in the form of colourless crystals. It is also found as an active ingredient in powders and ointments intended for treating athlete's foot.

Foods added to It is added to some breads and baked goods, including Christmas puddings, some processed cheeses and in flour confectionery.

Toxicological evaluation and possible health hazards It has been evaluated by JECFA in 1961, 1965, and in 1973, with Propionic Acid (E280) and its other salts (see E282, E283). JECFA judged that this chemical is sufficiently safe, when used as a food additive, that no quantitative restrictions need be placed on its use. The SCF also approved it without restrictions, in 1978. Despite this, there are several reports that Sodium Propionate can cause allergenic reactions such as migraine attacks or skin irritation.

Regulatory status It is permitted and used in the UK, and is listed as GRAS in the USA.

E282: Calcium Propionate
also known as Calcium Propanoate

Type This chemical is a natural constituent of some Swiss cheeses, but the commercial additive is synthesized from Propionic Acid (see E280). It is used as an antimicrobial preservative which is used as an anti-mould agent and anti-rope agent. In the absence of a suitable preservative, the bread may become contaminated with a population of micro-organisms which cause the material to break up into strands or become 'ropey'. Calcium Propionate is produced in the form of white crystals, which have a faint odour of its acid precursor. It is also found as an active ingredient in antifungal medications intended for the skin.

Foods added to It is used in some rolls, breads and baked goods, including Christmas puddings, some processed cheeses and in flour confectionery.

Toxicological evaluation and possible health hazards It has been evaluated by JECFA in 1961, 1965, and in 1973, along with Propionic Acid (see E280) and its sodium and potassium salts (see E281, E283). JECFA judged that this chemical is sufficiently safe, when used as a food additive, that no quantitative restrictions need be placed on its use. The SCF also approved it without restrictions, in 1978. There are several reports, mostly from the USA, that it can cause allergic reactions with gastro-intestinal symptoms similar to gall-bladder attack. It may also contribute to migraine headaches. Another report which also emerged in the USA suggests that Calcium Propionate destroys the enzyme in our bodies that normally enables us to assimilate the calcium which is present naturally, or added through enrichment, in bread.

Regulatory status It is permitted in the UK and the EEC, but in Britain it is the policy of the Bakers' Union that it should not be used, so as to avoid the irritations and inflammations which it has been shown to cause. It remains on the GRAS list in the USA.

E283: Potassium Propionate

Type It is a synthetic preservative, and it is used as an anti-mould agent and anti-rope agent. In the absence of a suitable preservative, the bread may become contaminated with a population of micro-organisms which cause the material to break up into strands or become 'ropey'.

Foods added to It is added to some breads and baked goods, including Christmas puddings, some processed cheeses and in flour confectionery.

Toxicological evaluation and possible health hazards It has been evaluated by JECFA in 1961, 1965, and in 1973, along with Propionic Acid (see E280) and its Sodium and Calcium Salts (see E281, E282). JECFA judged that this chemical is sufficiently safe, when used as a food additive, that no quantitative restrictions need be placed on its use. The SCF also approved it without restrictions, in 1974 and again in 1978. No adverse effects have been reported, and it is presumed to be safe.

Regulatory status It is permitted and used in the UK and the EEC (since 1974), but is not on the permitted list in the USA.

E290: Carbon Dioxide

Type It is a colourless and odourless gas with a faintly acidic taste. It is used as a preservative, carbonating agent, packaging agent and as a pressure dispersing agent in gassed creams in aerosols. It is a natural product of yeast fermentation, but it is also manufactured synthetically. As we breathe, we take in oxygen, and breathe out Carbon Dioxide.

Foods added to It can be found in fruit juices, gassed creams, but most commonly it is found in fizzy drinks.

Toxicological evaluation and possible health hazards JECFA considered this substance just once, in 1979, and concluded that it is sufficiently safe that no quantitative restrictions on its use are required. In high concentrations it is known to cause shortness of breath, high blood pressure and vomiting, but it is unlikely to be consumed in such high doses when it is used as a food additive. Carbon Dioxide does affect the stomach by increasing the rate at which digestive acids are secreted, and it also accelerates the rate at which fluids, including particularly alcohol, are absorbed. It is generally regarded as safe.

Regulatory status Permitted and widely used in the UK, the EEC, the USA and most other countries.

296: DL-Malic Acid and L-Malic Acid

also known as Apple Acid

Type This is an acidifier and a flavouring agent. It occurs naturally, and at levels of 0.4 to 0.7 per cent in apples. It is present in all living cells as a natural and important metabolite. The food industry has been using it as an additive for some 40 years. It exists in two distinct but closely related forms D-Malic Acid and L-Malic Acid. The commercially available product is a mixture of the two.

Foods added to It can be found in some canned tomatoes and apples, frozen vegetables, soups, fried potato snack products, soft drinks, jam, marmalade, grape juice and wine.

Toxicological evaluation and possible health hazards When JECFA reviewed it in 1965 they specified that, subject to a few conditions, it could be used at levels of up to 100mg/kg bw. Since it is a natural constituent of all living cells, it is generally considered to be entirely safe. A few commentators point out, however, that while adults are probably perfectly able to metabolize both D-Malic Acid and the L-form, we can't be sure that infants can. As a result these commentators argue that it should not be added to foods intended for babies or young children. This is not a restriction which is imposed by the British government.

Regulatory status Permitted and used in the UK, but the Council of Ministers of the EEC have not yet given it an 'E' number. It is on the GRAS list in the USA. The UK permits Malic Acid to be added to many products which other EEC countries do not approve.

297: Fumaric Acid

Type It is an acidifier which is also used as a flavouring agent, is found in many plants and is essential to the life of vegetable and animal tissue. Commercial supplies are synthesized industrially.

Foods added to It can be found in some dessert powders, confections, soft drinks, baked goods, jams, cheesecake mix and sweets.

Toxicological evaluation and possible health hazards JECFA considered this substance in 1965 and 1974. The more recent report is puzzling because they say that they have some new information, and then list only the old information. Even so, Fumaric Acid and sodium fumarate have been studied fairly thoroughly in both humans and laboratory animals, and JECFA set a full ADI of 6mg/kg bw. At high doses it is known to act as a laxative, and is sometimes prescribed for that reason. It is generally presumed to be safe.

Regulatory status It is permitted and widely used in the UK, but the Council of Ministers have not yet given it an 'E' number. It is on the GRAS list in the USA.

THE ANTIOXIDANTS
E300–E321

E300: Ascorbic Acid
also known as Vitamin C

Type This is a naturally occurring chemical which is vital to a healthy life. We need it, but we cannot synthesize it within our own bodies, and so it must be in our diet. It is also manufactured synthetically and used as a preservative and an antioxidant. When it occurs naturally, Vitamin C is always found in combinations with other vitamins, minerals, trace elements and enzymes, whereas synthetic Vitamin C is a pure crystalline powder. Some commentators argue that we are better nourished by it if we consume it as one element in a rich mixture of nutrients than if we eat the pure but isolated chemical. The Vitamin C which goes into vitamin pills is almost always the pure synthetic powder. This suggests that if you are going to take vitamin supplements they should be eaten with food, rather than instead of it. The levels at which this chemical is used as a food additive are, fortunately, fairly close to the levels at which they occur naturally in fresh foods.

Foods added to It can be added, for example, to beer, potato flakes, breakfast foods, cut fruits, meats, flour, stock cubes, bread and baked products. Ascorbic Acid is used as an antioxidant on its own, and in combinations with some of the synthetic antioxidants (e.g. with E310, E320 and E321), because it can enhance their action.

Toxicological evaluation and possible health hazards JECFA has evaluated Vitamin C as a food additive on three occasions: 1961, 1966 and 1973. The metabolism of this chemical is well understood, and JECFA most recently set a full ADI of 15mg/kg bw. It was classified in Group A by the FACC report of 1974. In the early 1930s, a German scientist fed massive doses of Vitamin C to twenty adults, ninety-three children and twenty-nine infants for over three and a half years. Eventually he did provoke some diarrhoea, nausea, vomiting, flushing of the face, headache and fatigue, which suggests that it was the experiment rather than the substance which provided the hazard. Some authorities argue that massive doses of Vitamin C can provide substantial health benefits. The benefits which have been claimed range from preventing colds to preventing cancer and heart disease. Most of these claims have yet to be either proved or refuted.

Regulatory status Permitted and used in the UK, the EEC, and listed as GRAS in the USA.

E301: Sodium L-Ascorbate

Type This is mainly an antioxidant but it is also used to preserve the colour in some food products.

Foods added to It can be found in concentrated milk products, cured meats, smoked turkey and frozen vegetables, baby foods and stock cubes.

Toxicological evaluation and possible health hazards JECFA evaluates this substance alongside its parent Ascorbic Acid (see E300), and it has a full ADI of 15mg/kg bw. It was classified in Group A by the FACC report of 1974. It is generally presumed to be equally safe. Some researchers speculate that this substance might act as protection from some potential carcinogens. No adverse effects have been reported or suspected.

Regulatory status It is permitted and widely used in the UK, the EEC and the USA, where it is listed as GRAS.

E302: Calcium L-Ascorbate

Type It is a synthetic antioxidant but it is also used to preserve the colour in some food products.

Foods added to It is added to some concentrated milk products, cured meat products, Scotch eggs, baby foods and stock cubes.

Toxicological evaluation and possible health hazards JECFA considered this substance only once, in 1981, but they did not set any ADI. It is generally considered to be as safe as its parent Ascorbic Acid and it was classified in Group A by the FACC report of 1974. It is generally presumed to be equally safe. No adverse effects have been reported or suspected.

Regulatory status Permitted and used in the UK, the EEC and the USA, where it is listed as GRAS.

E304: 6-O-Palmitoyl-L-Ascorbic Acid
also known as Ascorbyl Palmitate

Type It is a synthetic antioxidant but it is also used to preserve the colour in some food products. Ascorbic Acid (E300) is a good antioxidant, but it will not dissolve in fats, whereas this synthetic chemical is a fat-soluble relative.

Foods added to It can be found in some sausage and cured meats and chicken stock cubes.

Toxicological evaluation and possible health hazards JECFA first considered this compound in 1961, and most recently in 1973. The amount of information available to them was relatively slight. There have been only two partial tests on this chemical, and none for carcinogenicity or reproductive hazards. The substance which was used in the only long-term rat test was assumed to be mixed with Ascorbyl Stearate, and that study was conducted over thirty years ago. None the less, JECFA set an ADI for the two substances at 1.25mg/kg bw. In 1974, the FACC report listed this substance in Group A even though there are insufficient data available to demonstrate its safety. No adverse effects have been reported, and it is generally presumed to be safe.

Regulatory status It is permitted and widely used in the UK, the EEC and the USA where it is listed as GRAS.

E306: Tocopherols
also known as Vitamin E

Type This is a naturally occurring group of substances which act as antioxidants. They are distilled from natural sources including soya bean oil, wheatgerm and green leaves. Vitamin E is a vital ingredient of a healthy diet.

Foods added to They can be found in innumerable fats and oils and dessert toppings.

Toxicological evaluation and possible health hazards Vitamin E is an essential nutrient, and is used in foods at levels similar to those at which it occurs naturally. JECFA reviewed the Tocopherols, alongside Alpha-Tocopherol (see E307) in 1961 and 1973. As they explain, by the standards of most additives this substance has not been fully tested, but the knowledge which we have from clinical experience is sufficient to establish the safety of this substance when used as an additive. JECFA set an ADI of 2mg/kg bw. They were listed in Group A by the 1974 report of the FACC. There are some reports that at massive doses they can cause problems, but when used as an additive they are presumed to be safe.

Regulatory status It is permitted and widely used in the UK, the EEC and the USA where it is listed as GRAS.

E307: Alpha-Tocopherol
also known as Vitamin E

Type This is a naturally occurring vitamin and it is used as an antioxidant. It can be found in wheat and rice germ, and in vegetable oils.

Foods added to It is added to some white flour, enriched white bread and enriched white rice, margarine and sausages.

Toxicological evaluation and possible health hazards Vitamin E is an essential nutrient, and is used in foods at levels similar to those at which it occurs naturally. JECFA reviewed the Alpha-Tocopherol, alongside the other Tocopherols (see E306) in 1961 and 1973. As they explain, by the standards of most additives this substance has not been fully tested, but the knowledge which we have from clinical experience is sufficient to establish the safety of this substance when used as an additive. JECFA set an ADI of 2mg/kg bw. They were listed in Group A by the 1974 report of the FACC. There are some reports that at massive doses they can cause problems, but when used as an additive they are to be presumed to be safe. There is some evidence that its

addition to white bread as an 'enrichment' plays a significant role in reducing the extent of malnutrition among the poor and the elderly.

Regulatory status It is permitted and widely used in the UK, the EEC and the USA where it is listed as GRAS.

E308: Gamma Tocopherol
Type It is a synthetically produced antioxidant and vitamin.

Foods added to It can be found in some edible oils and sausages.

Toxicological evaluation and possible health hazards JECFA has not evaluated this substance, but in the 1974 report of the FACC it is listed in Group A alongside the rest of the Tocopherols. It has not been thoroughly tested by the standards of many additives, but on the basis of extensive clinical evidence it is presumed to be safe.

Regulatory status It is permitted and widely used in the UK, the EEC and the USA where it is listed as GRAS.

E309: Delta Tocopherol
Type It is a synthetic antioxidant and vitamin.

Foods added to It is frequently found in sausages.

Toxicological evaluation and possible health hazards See E308.

Regulatory status It is permitted and widely used in the UK, the EEC and the USA where it is listed as GRAS.

E310: Propyl Gallate
also known as Propyl Ester of Gallic Acid

Type It is a synthetic antioxidant. It is marketed as an odourless white powder which has a bitter taste.

Foods added to It can be found in many edible fats and oils, some fried foods, lemon juices, baked goods and gelatin desserts.

Toxicological evaluation and possible health hazards JECFA evaluated this substance several times, along with the other gallates (see E311– E312), first in 1961 and most recently in 1980. By 1973 JECFA could list the results of nineteen studies on the gallates, but seven of the most recent reports were unpublished, and four of those were from the company called IBT which was subsequently charged with falsifying results, and this casts doubt on the value of all of their work. If we take that evidence at face value, it shows that even though a commercially useful NEL has been found in a rat study, there are relatively modest doses at which this substance causes evident toxicity. There is clear evidence that it causes contact dermatitis in bakery and other food workers. JECFA also admits that it is known to provoke symptoms of acute intolerance in some sensitive individuals. In 1973 JECFA set a temporary ADI of 0.2mg/kg bw, but asked for further studies of potential effects on animal reproduction which might arise from a mixture of Propyl Gallate with BHA (see E320) and BHT (see E321). This particular concern arose because some Russian evidence suggested this combination might have undesirable reproductive effects. The 1974 report of the FACC attributes any potential problem to BHA and BHT, and lists the gallates in Group A. In 1976 the SCF endorsed JECFA's judgement without reservations, and agreed about the ADI. In 1980 JECFA was sufficiently satisfied to change the ADI from 'temporary' to 'full'. There remains, however, direct evidence that it may cause adverse symptoms to asthmatics, those sensitive to aspirin, and hyperactive children, as well as to those handling the material in industrial concentrations.

Regulatory status It is permitted in virtually every country in the world, with the exception of Poland, Romania and the USSR. It is permitted in the UK, but not in foods intended for babies.

E311: Octyl Gallate

Type It is a synthetic antioxidant.

Foods added to It is added to many edible oils and fats, and so can be found in some margarine, chewing gum and breakfast cereals.

Toxicological evaluation and possible health hazards JECFA evaluated this substance several times, with the other gallates (see E310 and E312), first in 1961 and most recently in 1980. By 1973 JECFA could list the results of nineteen studies on the gallates, but seven of the most recent reports were unpublished, and four of those were from the company called IBT which was subsequently charged with falsifying results, and this casts doubt on the value of all of their work. If we take that evidence at face value, it shows that even though a commercially useful NEL has been found in a rat study, there are relatively modest doses at which this substance causes evident toxicity. There is clear evidence that it causes contact dermatitis in bakery and other food workers. JECFA also admits that it is known to provoke symptoms of acute intolerance in some sensitive individuals. It is Octyl Gallate, especially in drinks, which is particularly thought to trigger the acute symptoms of intolerance, and so JECFA recommended that it should not be permitted or used in drinks. In 1973 JECFA set a temporary ADI of 0.2mg/kg bw, but asked for further studies specifically on potential effects on animal reproduction which might arise from a mixture of Propyl Gallate with BHA (see E320) and BHT (see E321). This particular concern arose because some Russian evidence suggested this combination might have undesirable reproductive effects. The 1974 report of the FACC attributes any potential problem to BHA and BHT, and lists the gallates in Group A. In 1976 the SCF endorsed JECFA's judgement without reservations, and agreed about the ADI. In 1980 JECFA was sufficiently satisfied to change the ADI from 'temporary' to 'full'. There remains, however, direct evidence that it may cause adverse symptoms to asthmatics, those sensitive to aspirin, and hyperactive children, as well as to those handling the material in industrial concentrations.

Regulatory status It is permitted and used in the UK (but not in foods intended for babies), and in many other countries too, but not in the USA.

E312: Dodecyl Gallate

Type It is a synthetic antioxidant.

Foods added to It is added to many edible oils and fats, and so can be found, for example, in margarine and rendered pork fat.

Toxicological evaluation and possible health hazards JECFA evaluated this substance several times, along with the other gallates (see E311–E312), first in 1961 and most recently in 1982. By 1973 JECFA could list the results of nineteen studies on the gallates, but seven of the most recent

reports were unpublished, and four of those were from the company called IBT which was subsequently charged with falsifying results, and this casts doubt on the value of all of their work. If we take that evidence at face value, it shows that even though a commercially useful NEL has been found in a rat study, there are relatively modest doses at which this substance causes evident toxicity. There is clear evidence that it causes contact dermatitis in bakery and other food workers. JECFA also admits that it is known to provoke symptoms of acute intolerance in some sensitive individuals. In 1973 JECFA set a temporary ADI of 0.2mg/kg bw, but asked for further studies specifically on potential effects on animal reproduction which might arise from a mixture of Propyl Gallate with BHA (see E320) and BHT (see E321). This particular concern arose because some Russian evidence suggested this combination might have undesirable reproductive effects. The 1974 report of the FACC attributes any potential problem to BHA and BHT, and lists the gallates in Group A. In 1976 the SCF endorsed JECFA's judgement without reservations, and agreed about the ADI. In 1982 JECFA was sufficiently satisfied to change the ADI from 'temporary' to 'full'. There remains, however, direct evidence that it may cause adverse symptoms to asthmatics, those sensitive to aspirin, hyperactive children, and those handling the material in industrial concentrations.

Regulatory status It is permitted and used in the UK (but not in foods intended for babies), and in many other countries too, but not in the USA.

E320: Butylated Hydroxyanisole
also known as BHA

Type It is a synthetic antioxidant.

Foods added to It is often added to oils and fats because it retards the process of going rancid, and thereby extends the shelf life of the products. BHA (and BHT, see E321) may also protect the fat-soluble vitamins A, D, and E. BHA alone is not particularly effective as an antioxidant when used in fats, and so is often used in combination with BHT, the gallates (see E310–E312) and other synergists. It is used very widely, especially in frying oils and fats, and so can be found, for example, in crisps and fried snack foods as well as in almost every type of processed food which contains fat or oil, such as chips, biscuits and pastries. It should not be found in packets of butter sold by retailers but can be incorporated into butter sold to food manufacturers. It is also used in beverages, chewing gum, ice cream, baked goods such as fruit pies, dry breakfast cereals, cheese spreads and margarine. It is also incorporated into food packaging materials, and into animal feeds. BHA can be added to compensate for poor standards of manufacture and distribution.

Toxicological evaluation and possible health hazards The two related substances – Butylated Hydroxyanisole (BHA or E320) and Butylated Hydroxytoluene (BHT or E321) – have been subject to particular scrutiny and criticism. As so often happens, these two additives were permitted long before anything resembling adequate testing had been conducted. Doubts were raised about the safety of these chemicals quite early on in the testing programme. In 1958 and again in 1963 the British government was recommended to ban BHT by the official committee of experts. On each occasion the industry asked for, and was given, the benefit of the doubt. The government permitted continued use of the chemical on condition that further studies were conducted. Industry organized and completed some further defensive research the results of which served to defuse and deflect some of the criticism but not eliminate it.

Of all the different additives the safety and toxicity of these antioxidants is the most complex and problematic. This is because, while some people claim that there is evidence that these antioxidants may cause chronic illness, others claim that they may also protect us from some chronic illnesses.

JECFA has published six evaluations of BHA. The first was in 1961, the most recent in 1983. From 1961 to 1973 JECFA set a conditional ADI up to 2mg/kg bw, with an unconditional ADI of 0.5mg/kg bw. Since 1973 the ADI has been 0.5mg/kg bw and it has been only temporary. This is simply a reflection of the extent and persistence of doubts about its safety.

There is clear evidence that BHA and BHT can trigger hyperactive and other intolerance symptoms, but the most serious concerns relate to their putative chronic toxicity and particularly their carcinogenicity. One reason why it is particularly difficult to evaluate these substances is that we know that humans and laboratory animals metabolize them in quite different ways. There is some evidence that they interfere with reproductive and embryonic processes in animals at moderate dose levels. There have been several studies over the years which have shown carcinogenic effects in some species at some doses, while other studies have failed to demonstrate any effect. Similarly some have claimed to have discovered circumstances in which each of these chemicals at some dose levels and in some animals can both inhibit and promote cancers from other toxins. The most serious evidence that BHA may be carcinogenic comes from one of the best conducted and most recent studies, carried out in Japan by Professor Ito and his colleagues.

In 1982 the Japanese team reported the results of what is generally conceded to be a particularly well-conducted study of the chronic toxicity of BHA. They showed that BHA, when fed at a level of 2 per cent in the diet, causes cancer to the forestomachs of rats of both sexes, and even more so to hamsters. As a result of this work, BHA has effectively been banned from food use in Japan. The Japanese have provided clear evidence that BHA is carcinogenic to laboratory animals, yet no further restrictions have been placed on its use in the UK, the USA or in the EEC.

In 1983 the SCF reported that, in response to the Japanese results, the EEC had created a Working Party which met with Ito in Heidelberg in October 1982. The Report of the Working Party is a very revealing document. The Working Party identified at least eight possible reasons for concluding that the animal data may be irrelevant to human consumption. The Report stated that BHA is considered indispensable *by the food industry*, but there is no claim that it is vital to consumers. It suggests that BHA may protect consumers against poisoning from oxidized toxins, but there is no evidence that the absence of BHA (e.g. in some brands of Austrian crisps) has ever constituted any hazard to consumers. In total, eight possible devices for disregarding the Japanese results are attempted, but none is successful. In other words, the Working Party cannot see anything wrong with the studies but, instead of recommending regulatory restrictions, they recommend further research in the hope of finding some adequate reason for overriding the negative implications of the evidence. The Report states that although Ito's study gives cause for concern there is no 'short-term risk to health'. But nobody ever said there was; just the risk of a long-term hazard. The Working Party called for further studies and more evidence before action is taken in Europe. We can all applaud the call for further research, but this should not be used as a tactic for failing to take any action in the short term, nor as a means for avoiding action in the long term.

The SCF stated that '... research ... should be undertaken rapidly so that any doubts on the immediate effects on health of BHA in food can be dissipated'. In other words the SCF were not calling for research to establish whether or not BHA can cause cancer in humans, but merely for defensive research to provide reasons for disregarding the human implications of Ito's work. If the purpose of the further research were to ensure maximum consumer safety rather than to enable industry to continue to use BHA, the programme of research would be substantially different. The FAC responded to the controversy in March 1986 by demoting BHA and BHT to Group B while they wait for the results of the defensive studies. They are presuming it to be safe until they have definitive evidence to the contrary. In May 1987 it was reported that work conducted at BIBRA had shown that, under certain conditions, BHA can be mutagenic. This is a vital piece of evidence since it implies that even one molecule of BHA might be sufficient to induce or promote a tumour, and therefore that there can be no safe level.

One notable study indicated that mice fed with modest doses of BHA or BHT during mating and gestation will produce offspring which themselves suffer when fed antioxidants once they are weaned. This result has prompted the customary call for further studies, but no regulatory action. In the meantime, parents might choose to avoid this substance, and not to feed it to their children.

Discussions of the acceptability of BHA and BHT are made even more complicated by the fact that some people claim that these antioxidants may serve to protect consumers. The mechanisms by which consumers may be protected are not well understood, and comprise both theoretical possibilities and extrapolations from animal data. There are theoretical reasons for fearing that oxidized oils may be toxic to humans, although attempts to 'confirm' this in animal studies have been inconclusive. There is, furthermore, some evidence from tests with some species of animals at various doses of both antioxidants and known animal carcinogens to suggest that these antioxidants can in some circumstances both promote and inhibit the formation of tumours. One reason why both these processes can occur, albeit at different doses and in com-

bination with different carcinogens, is because when they reach the liver the antioxidants stimulate the development of highly reactive enzymes. These enzymes can then play an active role in transforming other chemicals as they pass through the organ. In this way they may contribute to the detoxification of some chemicals which might otherwise do harm, but equally they can contribute to the synthesis of yet further chemicals which might themselves be poisonous.

For the most part, it is different people who work on different aspects of the problem, and each group emphasizes the significance of its own results and underplays the importance of the rest. No one is really in a position to judge the over-all net effect on humans of consuming BHA and BHT. We have innumerable fragments of information from different laboratory species, using different doses and different chemical agents, but we do not know how to extrapolate either from the doses which have been studied to the doses which humans consume, nor how to compare the animal species with each other, let alone how to relate all that data to human experience. The use of these antioxidants, therefore, amounts to a particularly mysterious and dramatic form of chemical roulette. We may be doing ourselves harm by eating them, or we may be doing harm by eating oils and fats free of synthetic antioxidants. We do not know, and we may never know. Perhaps the safest course of action would be to reduce our over-all consumption of oils and fats in line with the best nutritional advice, and to rely on vegetable oils which naturally contain their own antioxidants such as Vitamin E.

Regulatory status BHA is permitted and widely used in the UK, but it is used far more rarely and sparingly in some other EEC countries such as France and Germany. BHA may not be used in foods intended for babies in the UK. BHA has been used in the USA since 1947, and its use continues there too. The food distribution system of the USSR is said to rely on BHA and BHT, but this might be a reflection of their industrial problems as much as their confidence in its complete safety. BHA is banned in Japan.

E321: Butylated Hydroxytoluene
also known as BHT

Type It is a synthetic antioxidant.

Foods added to It is often added to oils and fats because it retards the process of going rancid, and thereby extends the shelf life of the products. BHT (and BHA, see E320) may also protect the fat-soluble vitamins A, D and E. BHT is often used in combination with BHA, the gallates (see E310–E312) and other synergists. It is used very widely, especially in frying oils and fats, and so can be found, for example, in crisps and fried snack foods as well as in almost every type of processed food which contains fat or oil, such as chips, biscuits and pastries. It should not be found in packets of butter sold by retailers but can be incorporated into butter which is sold to food manufacturers. It is also used in beverages, chewing gum, ice cream, baked goods such as fruit pies, dry breakfast cereals, cheese spreads and margarine. It is also incorporated into food packaging materials, and into animal feeds. BHT, like BHA, can be added to compensate for poor standards of manufacture and distribu-

tion. When fishmeal intended for animal feed is loaded on to ships, the maritime insurance companies often require it to be treated with BHT (and/or Ethoxyquin) to reduce the risk that the cargo will spontaneously ignite.

Toxicological evaluation and possible health hazards The two related substances – Butylated Hydroxytoluene (BHT or E321) and Butylated Hydroxyanisole (BHA or E320) – have been subjected to particular scrutiny and criticism. As so often happens, these two additives were permitted long before anything resembling adequate testing had been conducted. Doubts were raised about the safety of these chemicals quite early on in the testing programme. In 1958 and again in 1963 the British government was recommended to ban BHT by the official committee of experts. On each occasion the industry asked for, and was given, the benefit of the doubt. The government permitted continued use of the chemical on condition that further studies were conducted. Industry organized and completed some further defensive research the results of which served to defuse and deflect some of the criticism but not eliminate it.

Of all the different additives, the safety and toxicity of these antioxidants is the most complex and problematic. This is because, while some people claim that there is evidence that these antioxidants may cause chronic illness, others claim that they may also protect us from some chronic illnesses.

JECFA has published seven evaluations of BHT. The first was in 1961, the most recent in 1983. The magnitude of the ADI has been constant at 0.5mg/kg bw, and it has remained throughout either 'conditional' or 'temporary' and this is simply a reflection of the extent and persistence of doubts about its safety. In their most recent report, the SCF cut the ADI of BHT to 0.05mg/kg bw, which is to say they reduced it by a factor of 10.

There is clear evidence that BHA and BHT can trigger hyperactive and other intolerance symptoms, but the most serious concerns relate to their putative chronic toxicity and particularly their carcinogenicity. One reason why it is particularly difficult to evaluate these substances is that we know that humans and laboratory animals metabolize them in quite different ways. There is some evidence that they interfere with reproductive and embryonic processes in animals at moderate dose levels. There have been several studies over the years which have shown carcinogenic effects in some species at some doses, while other studies have failed to demonstrate any effect. Similarly some have claimed to have discovered circumstances in which each of these chemicals at some dose levels and in some animals can both inhibit and promote cancers from other toxins. The FAC responded to the controversy in March 1986 by demoting BHA and BHT to Group B while they wait for the results of the defensive studies. They are presuming it to be safe until they have definitive evidence to the contrary.

One notable study showed that modest doses of BHT are far more harmful to rats when they are on protein deficient diets than if they are well fed. This might imply that poorly nourished humans are also far more vulnerable than are those who are well fed. A further study indicated that mice fed with modest doses of BHA or BHT during mating and gestation will produce offspring which themselves suffer when fed antioxidants once they are weaned. This result has prompted the customary call for further studies, but no regulatory action. In the meantime, parents might choose to avoid this substance, and not to feed it to their children.

Discussions of the acceptability of BHA and BHT are made even more complicated by the fact that some people claim that these antioxidants may serve to protect consumers. The mechanisms by which consumers may be protected are not well understood, and comprise both theoretical possibilities and extrapolations from animal data. There are theoretical reasons for fearing that oxidized oils may be toxic to humans, although attempts to 'confirm' this in animal studies have been inconclusive. There is, furthermore, some evidence from tests with some species of animals at various doses of both antioxidants and known animal carcinogens to suggest that these antioxidants can in some circumstances both promote and inhibit the formation of tumours. One reason why both these processes can occur, albeit at different doses and in combination with different carcinogens, is because when they reach the liver the antioxidants stimulate the development of highly reactive enzymes. These enzymes can then play an active role in transforming other chemicals as they pass through the organ. In this way they may contribute to the detoxification of some chemicals which might otherwise do harm, but equally they can contribute to the synthesis of yet further chemicals which might themselves be poisonous.

For the most part, it is different people who work on different aspects of the problem, and each group emphasizes the significance of its own results and underplays the importance of the rest. No one is really in a position to judge the over-all net effect on humans of consuming BHA and BHT. We have innumerable fragments of information from different laboratory species, using different doses and different chemical agents, but we do not know how to extrapolate either from the doses which have been studied to the doses which humans consume, nor how to compare the animal species with each other, let alone how to relate all that data to human experience. The use of these antioxidants therefore amounts to a particularly mysterious and dramatic form of chemical roulette. We may be doing ourselves harm by eating them, or we may be doing harm by eating oils and fats free of synthetic antioxidants. We do not know, and we may never know. Perhaps the safest course of action would be to reduce our over-all consumption of oils and fats in line with the best nutritional advice, and to rely on vegetable oils which naturally contain their own antioxidants such as Vitamin E.

Regulatory status BHT is permitted and widely used in the UK, but it is used far more rarely and sparingly in some other EEC countries such as France and Germany. BHT may not be used in foods intended for babies in the UK; it has been used in the USA since 1954, and its use continues there too. The food distribution system of the USSR is said to rely on BHA and BHT, but this might be a reflection of their industrial problems as much as their confidence in its complete safety.

EMULSIFIERS, STABILIZERS, THICKENERS AND THEIR AUXILIARY COMPONENTS
E322–E495

E322: Lecithins
also known as Phosphatids and as Phospholipids

Type This refers to a mixed group of closely related substances which are widespread in the natural world. They are essential constituents of all living organisms and they are found in all the cells in the human body. Significant amounts are to be found especially in eggs, milk, fish, liver and vegetable oils. Most commercial Lecithins are extracted from soya beans and are used as emulsifiers and antioxidants.

Foods added to These can be found in some chocolate, milk powder, margarine, breakfast cereal, bread, rolls, cakes and biscuits.

Toxicological evaluation and possible health hazards JECFA evaluated this chemical group in 1963 and in 1973. By the standards of many food additives, there have been very few tests on animals with this group. On the other hand, we know that Lecithins are essential constituents of living cells, and we have extensive clinical experience with them. For this reason, JECFA judged them to be sufficiently safe to be used without a limiting ADI. Nobody dissents from this judgement. There are no reports of adverse effects, and they are presumed to be safe.

Special restrictions Since Lecithins may be extracted from animal sources they may not be acceptable to vegans.

Regulatory status Permitted and widely used in the UK and the EEC, but there are several uses which are allowed in the UK and not in some other industrialized countries. In the USA they are listed as GRAS.

E325: Sodium Lactate
Type This is the sodium salt of Lactic Acid (see E270). It is used as a synergist to enhance the effect of antioxidants. It can also be used as a humectant and bulking agent. It is a colourless, transparent salt of Lactic Acid, and is almost odourless.

Foods added to It can be used in some cheeses, low fat spreads, soup mixes and confectionery.

Toxicological evaluation and possible health hazards JECFA evaluated this substance in 1973 alongside Lactic Acid (see E270) and Potassium and Calcium Lactates (see E326 and E327). Lactates are naturally found as normal intermediate products when carbohydrates are metabolized. Sodium Lactate is sometimes used in medical practice to reduce the acidity of urine. By the standards of many food additives, there have been few tests on animals with this chemical. On the other hand, we know that Lactates are normally found in the human digestive system, and we have extensive clinical experience with them. For this reason, JECFA judged Sodium Lactate to be sufficiently safe for it to be used without a limiting ADI, although there remains a possibility that infants might find it hard to cope with this material. There are no reports of adverse effects, and it is generally presumed to be safe.

Special restrictions Since it is produced from Lactic Acid (see E270) which comes from animal sources it is not acceptable to vegans.

Regulatory status Permitted and used in the UK and the EEC.

E326: Potassium Lactate

Type It is an antioxidant synergist, and an acidity regulator.

Foods added to It is used in some cheeses, low fat spreads, soup mixes and confectionery.

Toxicological evaluation and possible health hazards JECFA evaluated this substance in 1973 alongside Lactic Acid (see E270) and Sodium and Calcium Lactates (see E325 and E327). Lactates are naturally found as normal intermediate products when carbohydrates are metabolized. By the standards of many food additives, there have been few tests on animals with this chemical. On the other hand, we know that Lactates are normally found in the human digestive system, and we have extensive clinical experience with them. For this reason, JECFA judged Potassium Lactate to be sufficiently safe for it to be used without a limiting ADI, although there remains a possibility that infants might find it hard to cope with this material. There are no reports of adverse effects, and it is generally presumed to be safe.

Special restrictions Since it is produced from Lactic Acid (see E270) which comes from animal sources it is not acceptable to vegans.

Regulatory status Permitted and used in the UK and the EEC.

E327: Calcium Lactate

Type It is used as a buffering agent, a yeast food, and a dough conditioner. In its commercial form, it is a white crystalline powder, which is almost odourless. It is sometimes used to inhibit discoloration of fruits and vegetables, and to improve the properties of dry milk powders and condensed milk.

Foods added to It can be found in some low fat spreads, baking powder, baked goods, jams and confectionery products.

Toxicological evaluation and possible health hazards In 1970, the FACC report listed Calcium Lactate in Group A. JECFA evaluated this substance in 1973 alongside Lactic Acid (see E270) and Sodium and Potassium Lactates (see E325 and E326). Lactates are naturally found as normal intermediate products when carbohydrates are metabolized. By the standards of many food additives, there have been few tests on animals with this chemical. On the other hand, we know that Lactates are normally found in the human digestive system, and we have extensive clinical experience with them. For this reason, JECFA judged Calcium Lactate to be sufficiently safe for it to be used without a limiting ADI, although there remains a possibility that infants might find it hard to cope with this material. There are no reports of adverse effects, and it is generally presumed to be safe.

Special restrictions Since it is produced from Lactic Acid (see E270) which comes from animal sources it is not acceptable to vegans.

Regulatory status Permitted and used in the UK and the EEC, and in the USA it is listed as GRAS.

E330: Citric Acid

Type This naturally occurring substance is used as an antioxidant and acidifier, as well as a sequestrant and flavouring agent. It can be found in many foods, most commonly in lemons and other citrus fruits. In a pure state it is a colourless liquid with a strongly acidic taste. It can be extracted from citrus fruits, but it can also be manufactured by fermenting crude sugars such as those found, for example, in sugar-beet.

Foods added to This is a very widely used substance. It can be found, for example, in dairy and baked products, jams, marmalade, jellies, pickles, carbonated beverages and bottled sauces.

Toxicological evaluation and possible health hazards JECFA has evaluated this substance four times, first in 1961 and most recently in 1973. The evaluations cover the acid along with its Sodium, Potassium and Calcium Salts (see E331–E333). They point out that Citric Acid and the Citrates are natural constituents of many foods, and normal metabolites of the body. There has been a handful of experiments feeding these chemicals to animals, but the information they provide is seen as supplementing what is known about their metabolism in humans. Citric Acid is considered sufficiently safe for its use to be approved without quantitative restrictions or an ADI. The FACC report of 1970 lists it in Group A. It is known that at high doses, however, Citric Acid can erode the enamel on our teeth. This apart, no adverse effects have been reported, nor are they suspected. It is generally assumed to be safe.

Regulatory status It is permitted and widely used in the UK, the EEC and many other countries. In the USA it is listed as GRAS.

E331: Sodium Citrates: Sodium Dihydrogen Citrate,
also known as Monosodium Citrate,

Disodium Citrate and Trisodium Citrate

Type The first and second are used as buffering agents and emulsifiers, while the third also acts as a sequestrant and as an emulsion stabilizer.

Foods added to They are very widely used, and can be found for example in processed milk and dairy products, ice cream confectionery, wines, fruit jellies, pickles, bottled sauces and frozen fruit drinks.

Toxicological evaluation and possible health hazards JECFA has on several occasions evaluated the sodium salts of Citric Acid (see E330) along with its Potassium and Calcium Salts (see E332 and E333). Sodium Dihydrogen Citrate was most recently evaluated in 1979, while Trisodium Citrate's latest evaluation was in 1973. JECFA does not deal specifically with Disodium Citrate. Sodium and Potassium Citrates have been used in medicines for many years. There has been a handful of experiments feeding these chemicals to animals, but the information they provide is seen as supplementing what is known about their metabolism in humans. Sodium Citrates are considered sufficiently safe for their use to be approved without quantitative restrictions or an ADI. No adverse effects have been reported, nor are they suspected. They are generally assumed to be safe, although there has been one report that they can alter the urinary excretion of other drugs thus making them either less effective or more toxic.

Regulatory status They are permitted and widely used in the UK, the EEC and many other countries, listed as GRAS in the USA.

E332: Potassium Citrates: Potassium Dihydrogen Citrate and Tripotassium Citrate

Type Both are used as alkaline buffering agents and emulsifiers, while the former can also act as a yeast food, and the latter can also act as an emulsion stabilizer.

Foods added to They are added to some processed dairy products, processed fruits, confections, and artificially sweetened jellies.

Toxicological evaluation and possible health hazards JECFA has on several occasions evaluated the Potassium Salts of Citric Acid along with its Sodium and Calcium Salts (see E331 and E333). Potassium Dihydrogen Citrate was most recently evaluated in 1979, while Tripotassium Citrate's latest evaluation was in 1973. Sodium and Potassium Citrates have been used in medicines for many years. There has been a handful of experiments feeding these chemicals to animals, but the information they provide is seen as supplementing what is known about their metabolism in humans. Potassium Citrate is considered sufficiently safe for its use to be approved without quantitative restrictions or an ADI. No adverse effects have been recorded, nor are they suspected. They are generally assumed to be safe.

Regulatory status They are permitted and widely used in the UK, the EEC and many other countries, listed as GRAS in the USA.

E333: Calcium Citrates: Monocalcium Dihydrogen Citrate, Dicalcium Citrate and Tricalcium Citrate

Type These are used as buffering agents and firming agents and also as sequestrants.

Foods added to They can be found in flour, confections, jellies and jams, carbonated drinks, wines and cheese products. Calcium Citrates may also be added to commercial supplies of the artificial sweetener Saccharin (see p. 186).

Toxicological evaluation and possible health hazards JECFA has twice evaluated the Calcium Citrates along with Citric Acid (see E330) and with its Sodium and Potassium Salts (see E331 and E332). There has been a handful of experiments feeding these chemicals to animals, but the information they provide is seen as supplementing what is known about their metabolism in humans. Calcium Citrates are considered sufficiently safe for their use to be approved without quantitative restrictions, or an ADI. No adverse effects have been reported, nor are they suspected. They are generally assumed to be safe.

Regulatory status They are permitted and widely used in the UK, the EEC and many other countries, listed as GRAS in the USA.

E334: Tartaric Acid

Type It is an antioxidant synergist and an acidifier. It has a strong tart taste, and it is sometimes used to supplement the flavour of those fruits such as grapes in which it occurs naturally. Tartaric Acid is extracted commercially from waste products of the wine industry.

Foods added to It is added sometimes to baking powder, canned fruit and vegetables, jams, dried egg whites, wine and confectionery.

Toxicological evaluation and possible health hazards JECFA has evaluated this on several occasions, and most recently in 1977, alongside the Sodium and Potassium Salts (see

E335–E337). By the standards of many additives Tartaric Acid and the Tartrates have not been particularly well tested. Some tests have been conducted with as few as three rabbits and four dogs. A group of that size is so small that it is not much use, because the sample is too slight. They have been approved because they are normal constituents of foods, and are used as additives at levels marginally higher than those which occur naturally. There is clear evidence that they can be toxic in concentrated doses, but they are presumed safe as food additives. In 1970 the FACC report listed Tartaric Acid in Group A, and in 1973, JECFA set an ADI of 30mg/kg bw for this group of chemicals.

Regulatory status Permitted and widely used in the UK, the EEC and the USA where it is listed as GRAS.

E335: Sodium Tartrates:
Monosodium Tartrate and Disodium Tartrate

Type These are used for their antioxidant, emulsifier and acidifier effects.

Foods added to They are added to some cheese products, jellies, confections and soft drinks.

Toxicological evaluation and possible health hazards JECFA has evaluated these on several occasions, and most recently in 1977, alongside Tartaric Acid and its Potassium Salts (see E334–E337). By the standards of many additives Tartaric Acid and the Tartrates have not been particularly well tested. Some tests have been conducted with as few as three rabbits and four dogs. A group of that size is so small that it is not much use, because the sample is too slight. They have been approved because they are normal constituents of foods, and are used as additives at levels marginally

higher then those which occur naturally. They are sometimes used as laxatives and at effective doses they can provoke vomiting, nausea and abdominal cramps. There is clear evidence that they can be toxic in concentrated doses, but they are presumed safe as food additives. In 1970 the FACC report listed Tartaric Acid and the Tartrates in Group A, and in 1973, JECFA set an ADI of 30mg/kg bw for this group of chemicals.

Regulatory status Permitted and widely used in the UK, the EEC and in the USA where they are listed as GRAS.

E336: Potassium Tartrates:
Monopotassium Tartrate and
Dipotassium Tartrate
also known as Cream of Tartar:

Type They are used for their synergistic support to antioxidants and for their acidifying and emulsifying effects.

Foods added to They can be found in some baking powders, jams, jellies and soft drinks.

Toxicological evaluation and possible health hazards JECFA has evaluated these on several occasions, and most recently in 1977. By the standards of many additives Tartaric Acid and the Tartrates have not been particularly well tested. Some tests have been conducted with as few as three rabbits and four dogs. A group of that size is so small that it is not much use, because the sample is too slight. They have been approved because they are normal constituents of foods, and are used as additives at levels marginally higher than those which occur naturally. There is clear evidence that they can be toxic in concentrated doses, but they are presumed safe as food additives. In 1970 the FACC report listed Tartaric Acid and the Tartrates in Group A, and in 1973, JECFA set an ADI of 30mg/kg bw for this group of chemicals. There is, none the less, a report that Potassium Tartrates may cause difficulties to people with weakened kidneys or liver.

Regulatory status Permitted and used in the UK, the EEC and in the USA where they are listed as GRAS.

E337: Potassium Sodium Tartrate
also known as Rochelle salt

Type This is extracted from the waste products of the wine industry, and is used as an antioxidant synergist and as a buffer.

Foods added to It is sometimes added to confections, fruit jelly, jams, cheese and meat products and is sometimes an additive to commercial supplies of Saccharin (see p. 186).

Toxicological evaluation and possible health hazards JECFA evaluated this compound in 1963 and 1973, alongside Tartaric Acid and its Sodium and Potassium Salts (see E334–E336). By the standards of many additives Tartaric Acid and the Tartrates have not been particularly well tested. Some tests have been conducted with as few as three rabbits and four dogs. A group of that size is so small that it is not much use, because the sample is too slight. They have been approved because they are normal constituents of foods, and are used as additives at levels marginally higher than those which occur naturally. There is clear evidence that they can be toxic in concentrated doses, but they are presumed safe as food additives. In 1970 the FACC report listed Tartaric Acid and the Tartrates in Group A, and in 1973, JECFA set an ADI of 30mg/kg bw for this group of

chemicals. No adverse effects have been reported and it is presumed safe.

Regulatory status It is permitted and used in the UK, the EEC and in the USA where it is listed as GRAS.

E338: Orthophosphoric Acid
also known as Phosphoric Acid

Type It is used primarily as an acidifier, but it can also be used as an antioxidant synergist. It is one of the cheapest and strongest of the food-grade acidifiers, and it is the only inorganic acid used in this way. It is usually manufactured using the action of sulphuric acid on phosphate rock.

Foods added to It is used quite widely, and particularly in soft drinks such as the cola products, but also in animal and vegetable fats, cheese products, jams, evaporated milk, meats and sausages.

Toxicological evaluation and possible health hazards JECFA evaluated this acid five times between 1961 and 1982. They treat it in the context of an evaluation of the Orthophosphates as a group (see E339–E341). Orthophosphoric Acid is a natural and essential constituent of the human body and some foods. It is vital, for example, to the ways in which we metabolize carbohydrates, fats and proteins. As JECFA explain, our skeleton acts as a mineral depot, and a hormonal system controls the active levels in our blood. Orthophosphoric Acid is expelled with the faeces as Calcium Phosphate, which suggests that excessive levels of Phosphoric Acid and Sodium Phosphate (see E339) might cause a loss of essential calcium. An estimate of a safe level for this substance as an additive would have to take into account the levels at which it occurs in foods. At low doses it appears to be safe for humans and animals, but at moderately high doses it does damage the kidneys of rats. At high doses it can be an irritant, but that is what one has to expect with a strong acid. The FACC report listed Phosphoric Acid in Group A. JECFA's ADI for Orthophosphoric Acid has grown over the years: it currently stands at a total of 70mg/kg bw, where this figure covers Orthophosphoric Acid and all other Phosphates both natural and added. No adverse effects have been reported from ordinary use, and it is presumed to be safe.

Regulatory status Permitted and widely used in the UK, the EEC and the USA where it is listed as GRAS.

E339: Sodium Hydrogen Orthophosphates: Sodium Dihydrogen Orthophosphate, Disodium Hydrogen Orthophosphate and Trisodium Orthophosphate

Type These are used as buffering agents and sequestrants.

Foods added to These can be found in some processed meat products, in fizzy drinks, pudding mixes and cheese products.

Toxicological evaluation and possible health hazards JECFA has evaluated this substance three times, most recently in 1982. They treat it in the context of an evaluation of the Orthophosphates as a group (see E338–E341). Orthophosphoric Acid is a natural and essential constituent of the human body and some foods. It is expelled with the faeces as Calcium Phosphate, which suggests that excessive levels of Phosphoric Acid and Sodium Phosphate might cause a loss of essential calcium. An estimate of a safe level for this substance as an additive would have to take into account the levels at which it occurs in

foods. At low doses it appears to be safe for humans and animals, but at moderately high doses it does damage the kidneys of rats. The FACC report listed Phosphoric Acid in Group A. JECFA's ADI for the Orthophosphates has grown over the years: it currently stands at a total of 70mg/kg bw, where this figure covers Orthophosphoric Acid and all other Phosphates both natural and added. No adverse effects have been reported from ordinary use, and it is presumed to be safe.

Regulatory status Permitted and used in the UK, and the EEC. In the USA it is permitted but not listed as GRAS. This chemical is permitted in many more types of food product in Britain than are allowed in many other countries.

E340: Potassium Orthophosphates: Potassium Dihydrogen Orthophosphate, Dipotassium Hydrogen Orthophosphate and Tripotassium Orthophosphate

Type These are used as buffering agents and sequestrants, which are synthesized from Orthophosphoric Acid (see E338). They are colourless white powders, and are used widely in the wine and brewing industries as a yeast food.

Foods added to They are added to some wines, meat products and coffee-whitening products.

Toxicological evaluation and possible health hazards JECFA evaluated the Potassium Orthophosphates most recently in 1982. They treated them in the context of an evaluation of the Orthophosphates as a group (see E338–E341). Orthophosphoric Acid is a natural and essential constituent of the human body and some foods. An estimate of a safe level for this substance as an additive would have to take into account the levels at which it occurs in foods. At low doses it appears to be safe for humans and animals, but at moderately high doses it does damage the kidneys of rats. JECFA's ADI for Orthophosphoric Acid currently stands at a total of 70mg/kg bw, but this figure covers Orthophosphoric Acid and all other Phosphates both natural and added. No adverse effects have been reported from ordinary use, and it is presumed to be safe.

Regulatory status Permitted and used in the UK and the EEC.

E341(a): Acid Calcium Phosphate (ACP)

Type It is a multipurpose additive and used as a buffer, yeast food, sequestrant and texturizer.

Foods added to It may be found in baking powder, potato snacks, bread, rolls, tinned tomatoes, tinned sweet peppers, and jelly ingredients.

Toxicological evaluation and possible health hazards JECFA evaluated the Calcium Orthophosphates most recently in 1982. They treat them in the context of an evaluation of the Orthophosphates as a group (see E338–E341). Orthophosphoric Acid is a natural and essential constituent of the human body and some foods. An estimate of a safe level for this substance as an additive would have to take into account the levels at which it occurs in foods. At low doses it appears to be safe for humans and animals, but there is one report that at high doses it could be a gastric irritant. JECFA's ADI for Orthophosphoric Acid currently stands at a total of 70mg/kg bw, but this figure covers Orthophosphoric

Acid and all other Phosphates, both natural and added. No adverse effects have been reported from ordinary use, and it is presumed to be safe.

Regulatory status Permitted and used in the UK and the EEC, and in the USA, where it is listed as GRAS.

E341(b): Calcium Hydrogen Orthophosphate

Type It is a multipurpose additive, and used as a yeast food, dough conditioner, emulsifier and sequestrant.

Foods added to It can be found in some pastry mixes, baking powder, cereals, bread, buns, rolls and pie fillings.

Toxicological evaluation and possible health hazards See E341(a).

Regulatory status Permitted and used in the UK, the EEC, and the USA where it is listed as GRAS.

E341(c): Tricalcium Phosphate

Type It is used as an anti-caking agent, a yeast food, a firming agent and a buffer.

Foods added to It can be found in some table salt, powdered sugar, puddings, meat products, cereal flours, and cake mixes.

Toxicological evaluation and possible health hazards See E341(a).

Regulatory status Permitted and used in the UK, the EEC and the USA where it is listed as GRAS.

350: Sodium Hydrogen Malate

Type It is a buffer and humectant. It is produced from Malic Acid (see 296).

Foods added to It can be found in some canned tomatoes and apples, frozen vegetables, soups, fried potato snack products, soft drinks, jam, marmalade, grape juice and wine.

Toxicological evaluation and possible health hazards As early as 1968, an FACC report listed this substance in Group A, and in 1982 JECFA approved it for use without specific quantitative restrictions. The SCF, however, has not published an opinion on this substance, and it is not approved for general use in the EEC.

Regulatory status Approved and used in the UK, and a few other countries.

351: Potassium Malate

Type It is a buffering and seasoning agent.

Foods added to It can be found in some fruit preserves.

Toxicological evaluation and possible health hazards JECFA has twice considered the identity and purity of this substance, but has yet to issue an evaluation of it. The FACC report of 1968 listed it in Group A, but the SCF has offered no opinion, and it has no 'E' number. There are no reports of adverse effects and it is presumed to be safe.

Regulatory status Approved in the UK, and a few other countries.

352: Calcium Malate and Calcium Hydrogen Malate

Type They are buffering and seasoning agents.

Foods added to They can be found in some fruit preserves.

Toxicological evaluation and possible health hazards JECFA evaluated these chemicals in 1979 in the context of its consideration of Malic Acid (see 296), and they counted it within the ADI of Malic Acid. Neither the SCF nor the FACC have commented on

these, but no adverse effects have been reported and they are presumed to be safe.

Regulatory status They are approved in the UK, and a few other countries.

353: Metatartaric Acid

Type It is an acidifier, antioxidant synergist and sequestrant.

Foods added to It is used mainly in wine.

Toxicological evaluation and possible health hazards JECFA has considered this chemical in the context of its treatment of Tartaric Acid and its salts (see E334–E337). No adverse effects have been reported, and it is presumed to be safe.

Regulatory status Permitted in the UK, and a few other countries.

355: Adipic Acid

Type It is used as a buffer, and it occurs naturally in beets.

Foods added to It is in some beverages, gelatin desserts, confections and baking powder.

Toxicological evaluation and possible health hazards JECFA reviewed it in 1965 and 1977, and on the latter occasion set an ADI of 5mg/kg bw. No adverse effects have been reported and it is presumed to be safe.

Regulatory status It is permitted and used in the UK, and in many EEC countries, but it does not have an 'E' number. In the USA it is listed as GRAS.

363: Succinic Acid

Type It is used as an acidic buffer. It can be found naturally occurring in broccoli, rhubarb, beets and some meats. It is odourless with a very acid taste.

Foods added to It can be found in some baked goods and breakfast cereals.

Toxicological evaluation and possible health hazards JECFA has not evaluated this substance, nor has the FACC or the SCF. It is however listed as GRAS in the USA. No adverse effects have been reported and it is presumed to be safe, but we do not know enough about it to be sure.

Regulatory status Approved for use in the UK and the USA, but it has no 'E' number.

370: 1–4–Heptonolactone

Type It is a sequestrant and acid.

Foods added to It can be found in dried soups and instant desserts.

Toxicological evaluation and possible health hazards It has not been reviewed by JECFA or the SCF, and no ADI has been set. No adverse effects have been reported and it is presumed to be safe, but we do not know enough about it to be sure.

Regulatory status It is permitted and used in the UK without any specific limits having been set.

375: Nicotinic Acid
also known as Niacin or Nicotinamide

Type It is an essential nutrient and a form of Vitamin B. It is commercially available as a white or yellow crystalline powder. It is used as a vitamin supplement and colour preservative.

Foods added to It can be found in some breakfast cereals, peanut butter, enriched flours, bread, rolls and cornmeal. It occurs naturally in liver, yeast, meat, peanuts and pulses.

Toxicological evaluation and possible health hazards JECFA has not evaluated it as an additive, and neither has the SCF. But it is known to be an essential nutrient. The illness called pellagra is caused by a lack of B vitamins. There is some clinical evidence that in large doses it can provoke unpleasant symptoms, but at food additive doses it is presumed to be safe.

Regulatory status It is permitted and used in the UK, in EEC countries, and in the USA where it is listed as GRAS. It does not yet have an 'E' number.

380: Triammonium Citrate

Type It is a buffering agent and emulsifying salt.

Foods added to No specific uses have been reported.

Toxicological evaluation and possible health hazards JECFA considered this chemical in 1979, but they did not specify an ADI. The SCF has not evaluated this substance. It has not been sufficiently tested or discussed. It is officially presumed to be safe.

Regulatory status It is permitted and used in the UK, but it is not approved for general use in the EEC, and has no 'E' number. It is not permitted in the USA.

381: Ammonium Ferric Citrate

Type It can be used as a dietary iron supplement.

Foods added to It can be found in flour and milk-formula infant foods.

Toxicological evaluation and possible health hazards It has not been evaluated by JECFA or the SCF. It has not been sufficiently tested or discussed. It is officially presumed to be safe.

Regulatory status It is permitted and used in the UK, but it is not approved for general use in the EEC, and has no 'E' number. It is not permitted in the USA.

385: Calcium Disodium Ethylene Diamine Tetra-Acetate

also known as Calcium Disodium EDTA

Type It can be used as an anti-oxidant synergist, sequestrant and preservative. It has medical applications in the treatment of poisoning with heavy metals such as lead. When used for this purpose it is called a chelating agent.

Foods added to It can be found in some salad dressings, mayonnaise, cooked tinned mushrooms, soft drinks and alcoholic beverages.

Toxicological evaluation and possible health hazards JECFA has evaluated this substance in 1965 and 1973. The animal studies which they report do show toxic effects at high doses, but appear to indicate that it is safe at lower doses, and they set an ADI of 2.5mg/kg bw. In 1977, the SCF endorsed JECFA's evaluation, but added that it should not be used in products intended for consumption by children up to two years. This recommendation has not been adopted in the UK. There are, moreover, several reports that when fed to young rats in tests it induced liver lesions, kidney disorder, plus degenerative lesions in the kidney tubes. From clinical experience we know that if ingested in large quantities it can lead to mineral imbalance. While it has a therapeutic use in medicine, side effects indicate a capacity to damage the human kidney.

Regulatory status It is permitted and used in the UK and the USA, but it does not have an 'E' number.

E400: Alginic Acid

Type This is a thickening agent and stabilizer which is obtained from brown seaweeds, and was first produced in 1881.

Foods added to It can be found in some ice cream, cheese products, custard, salad dressing, instant desserts, puddings and beverages.

Toxicological evaluation and possible health hazards JECFA has considered this acid along with its Sodium, Potassium, Ammonium and Calcium salts (see E401–E404), in 1963 and again in 1973. Its effects have been reasonably well studied in humans, rats, dogs and guinea-pigs. JECFA set a full ADI of 25mg/kg bw, on the basis of an NEL in tests on rats. (In fact, two JECFA publications give different figures, but 25mg/kg bw is the correct figure.) In 1970 the FACC report listed this substance in Group A. No adverse effects have been reported and it is presumed to be safe.

Regulatory status It is permitted and used in the UK and the EEC, and is listed as GRAS in the USA.

E401: Sodium Alginate

Type It is a thickening agent and stabilizer, which is produced from Alginic Acid (see E400).

Foods added to It can be found in some beverages, ice cream, custard, instant desserts, baked goods, confectionery, cheese products, salad dressings and in comminuted meat and fish products.

Toxicological evaluation and possible health hazards JECFA has considered this salt along with its Alginic Acid (see E400) and its salts (see E401–E404), in 1963 and again in 1973. Its effects have been reasonably well studied in humans, rats, dogs and guinea-pigs. JECFA set a full ADI of 25mg/kg bw. (In fact, two JECFA publications give different figures, but 25mg/kg bw is the correct figure.) In 1970 the FACC report listed this substance in Group A. No adverse effects have been reported and it is presumed to be safe.

Regulatory status It is permitted and used in the UK, the EEC and the USA where it is listed as GRAS.

E402: Potassium Alginate

Type It is a thickening agent and stabilizer, which is produced from Alginic Acid (see E400).

Foods added to It can be found in some beverages, ice cream, custard, instant desserts, baked goods, confectionery, cheese products and salad dressings.

Toxicological evaluation and possible health hazards See E401.

Regulatory status It is permitted in the UK and the EEC, and in the USA where it is listed as GRAS.

E403: Ammonium Alginate

Type It is a thickening agent and stabilizer, which is produced from Alginic Acid (see E400).

Foods added to It can be found in some beverages, ice cream, custard, instant desserts, baked goods, confectionery, cheese products and salad dressings.

Toxicological evaluation and possible health hazards See E401.

Regulatory status It is permitted and used in the UK, the EEC and the USA where it is listed as GRAS.

E404: Calcium Alginate

Type It is a thickening agent and stabilizer, and it is manufactured from Alginic Acid (see E400).

Foods added to It can be found in

some beverages, ice cream, custard, instant desserts, baked goods, confectionery, cheese products and salad dressings.

Toxicological evaluation and possible health hazards See E401.

Regulatory status It is permitted and used in the UK, the EEC and the USA where it is listed as GRAS.

E405: Propane–1,2–diol Alginate

also known as Propylene Glycol Alginate

Type This substance is produced by reacting moist Alginic Acid (see E400) with propylene oxide. It is used as a thickening agent, emulsifier and defoaming agent. It was first isolated from brown algae in 1881.

Foods added to It can be found in some beverages, ice cream, custard, instant desserts, baked goods, sauces, confectionery, cheese products and salad dressings.

Toxicological evaluation and possible health hazards In the 1970 FACC report this was listed in Group B, pending the identification of an NEL in mice and rats. JECFA considered this chemical in 1969, 1971 and 1973. The information available on this substance is relatively extensive. It has been tested in rats, cats, guinea-pigs, dogs and chicks for short-term toxicity, and mice and rats for the long term, although no tests for carcinogenicity or mutagenicity have been reported. An NEL has been identified in rats and this has provided a basis for JECFA's ADI of 25mg/kg bw. This is in spite of the fact that JECFA reports some evidence provided as early as 1949 showing that it can provoke allergic and intolerant symptoms in a modest percentage of a very small sample of humans. JECFA has not considered it since. More recently there is some evidence that it can act to bind water in the digestive tract and therefore might inhibit the absorption of some nutrients. The SCF simply lists it as permissible, but has not published a review of its toxicology.

Regulatory status It is permitted and used in the UK, the EEC and the USA.

E406: Agar
also known as Agar Agar, and as Japanese Isinglass

Type It is a thickening agent and stabilizer extracted from seaweed. It is reputed to have been discovered in Japan in 1658. It is a tasteless, odourless carbohydrate which is produced mainly in Japan.

Foods added to It can be found in some beverages, ice cream, meat products, glazes, sweetened jellies and frozen custard.

Toxicological evaluation and possible health hazards JECFA has reviewed this substance twice, in 1963 and again in 1973. The amount of toxicological information was very slight. They could report only five studies, all of which had been completed by 1957. They had no data on its metabolism, acute oral toxicity, long-term toxicity, carcinogenicity or mutagenicity. Agar has, however, been used since the 1920s as a mild human laxative. In Japan, Agar in seaweed has been consumed as part of human diets for many years, and on this basis JECFA accepted it for use as an additive without any specific restrictions, although they did suggest that further toxicological work is desirable. They have not considered it since then. In 1970 the FACC report listed it in Group A. The SCF lists it as acceptable for

use in food, but they have not published an evaluation or review of it. At high doses it may cause allergic reactions and intestinal disorders, but otherwise it is considered to be safe.

Regulatory status It is permitted and used in the UK, the EEC and the USA where it is listed as GRAS.

E407: Carrageenan
also known as Irish Moss

Type It is a thickening, gelling and stabilizing agent. It is a complex polysaccharide which is found in some red seaweeds. There has been a long tradition of using Irish Moss in foods in Ireland, and its use began in the USA in 1835, but it became increasingly common in World War II as a replacement for Agar (see E406). Its name is derived from the town of Carragheen in Ireland. It is very useful for stabilizing processed dairy products. In 1986 the specifications of its identity were modified to incorporate Furcellaran (see E408).

Foods added to It is used in some ice cream, gassed cream, confections, chocolate milk, cheese products, chocolate products, custard, jams and jellies.

Toxicological evaluation and possible health hazards JECFA has evaluated this substance, in 1969, 1970, 1973 and most recently in 1984, alongside Furcellaran (see E408). On the first occasion they set a full ADI at 500mg/kg bw, but a year later they reduced it by a factor of 10, and in 1973 they set the ADI at 75mg/kg bw, and revised the specification of identity and purity and characterized these new specifications as temporary. In 1984 they tightened the specifications and approved its use without quantitative restrictions. There are two types of

Carrageenan: Native and Degraded Carrageenan. The former is used in food and toiletries, while the latter is not. The latter is used on the Continent to treat some forms of indigestion and has been used extensively as a toxicological model for the former, because while it produces similar problems it is thought to produce them more rapidly and consistently. Native Carrageenan, moreover, degrades in the digestive tract.

There is a vast amount of data on Carrageenan. Studies have been conducted on mice, rats, guinea-pigs, hamsters, gerbils, ferrets, rabbits, dogs, pigs, monkeys, squirrel monkeys and humans. The main reason why it has been the focus of so many studies is because from time to time using different species at different laboratories problems keep cropping up. One of the main problems concerns its ability to provoke ulcers in the digestive tract of at least three of the species in which it has been tested. Another problem concerns evidence of possible toxic effects on embryos, while the most recent concerns relate to the possibility that Carrageenan might be carcinogenic.

The 1970 FACC report stated, quite accurately, that there was little information available on Carrageenan, and listed it as Group A on the grounds that it had been in use for many years. In 1973 JECFA concluded that, despite evident problems at higher doses, they could identify an NEL in a long-term rat feeding study on which they could base an ADI of 75mg/kg bw (as Carrageenan or Furcellaran or the sum of both). Since that crucial study was completed before 1959, and used only ten rats at each dose level, it can hardly be considered an adequate basis for such a judgement. It is remarkable that in 1969 JECFA set an ADI of 500mg/kg bw, then they reduced it to 50mg/kg bw, and raised it to 75mg/kg bw in 1973. They had received new data on each occasion when they changed the ADI, but not all has been published.

The SCF considered the position in 1978 and explained that during the 1970s the algae from which Carrageenan had traditionally been extracted had become rather scarce, and that the industry had turned to other varieties from which they were extracting and marketing a complex mixture of Carrageenan and Furcellaran (E408) with increasing fractions of the latter. They had been asked to approve a combined purity standard and toxicological evaluation. The SCF did approve this change. They relied on some more recent evidence that high molecular weight components are safer than those with a lower molecular weight, and recommended that the use of the degraded product with the lower molecular weights should be minimized. They did not, however, show that commercial products contain the safer varieties, nor did they provide any evidence that Furcellaran and Carrageenan are toxicologically similar.

A toxicological review of Carrageenan published in 1981 identified twelve different toxic hazards which have been identified in laboratory and clinical tests. These have included damage to the foetus and the colon, and evidence of carcinogenicity. As a result we cannot be confident that Carrageenan and/or Furcellaran are safe, and we are entitled to expect the official agencies to review their current evaluations.

Regulatory status It is permitted and used in the UK and the EEC.

In the USA the use of Degraded Carrageenan has been restricted, but they continue to permit its use undegraded.

E408: Furcellaran

Type It is a thickening, gelling and stabilizing agent, and is extracted from seaweeds alongside Carrageenan (see E407). It is extracted primarily from Danish seaweed. In 1986 the specifications of the identity of Carrageenan (see E407) were modified to incorporate this substance.

Foods added to It is used in some ice cream, gassed cream, confections, chocolate milk, cheese products, chocolate products, custard, jams and jellies.

Toxicological evaluation and possible health hazards JECFA has evaluated this substance in 1969, 1970, and most recently in 1973, alongside Carrageenan (see E407). On the first occasion they set a full ADI at 500mg/kg bw, but a year later they reduced it by a factor of 10, and in 1973 they set the ADI at 75mg/kg bw and revised the specification of identity and purity and characterized these new specifications as temporary. In 1984 they removed all quantitative restrictions for sufficiently pure materials. Almost all the available data relate to Carrageenan rather than to Furcellaran. In 1972 the FACC considered this material, and listed it in Group A on the grounds that it is structurally similar to Carrageenan (see E407) and Agar (see E406). We cannot be certain that Carrageenan is safe, and since we know far less about Furcellaran, we can be even less certain of its safety.

Regulatory status It is permitted and used in the EEC and the USA.

E410: Locust Bean Gum
also known as Carob Gum

Type It is a thickening agent and stabilizer which is extracted from the seeds of the Carob tree. There is a report that ancient Egyptians used this substance in mummy-binding. The fruit of the Carob tree also provides a dark pod which is similar in colour and flavour to cacao. It is sometimes preferred to cacao because it does not contain Caffeine (see p. 192).

Foods added to It can be found in some butterscotch, caramel, chocolate, wine, root beer, ice cream, soups, non-caffeine-containing substitutes for cocoa and chocolate, confectionery and baked products.

Toxicological evaluation and possible health hazards In 1970 the FACC listed it in Group A, mainly on the grounds that it has been in use for many years, and despite the fact that little is known about its biological effects. JECFA has published five evaluations of this substance, the first in 1969, and most recently in 1981. JECFA has not set any ADI for this substance because too little is known about it, and too little data are available. In a clinical study, however, fifty-six human patients were given Carob Gum as a laxative and showed no adverse effects. Much of the information on which JECFA has relied has not been published, which makes it harder for others to rely on JECFA's judgement. This substance has yet to be fully tested, and although it is often presumed to be safe, this presumption may be premature.

Regulatory status It is permitted and used in the UK, the EEC and the USA where it is listed as GRAS.

E412: Guar Gum

also known as Jaguar Gum or Guar Flour

Type It is a thickening agent and stabilizer, and is found naturally occurring in the seeds of a plant which has been cultivated on the Indian subcontinent for hundreds of years. It was first introduced commercially into the USA in 1903, but has only been in large-scale commercial production in America since the 1950s.

Foods added to It can be found in some fruit drinks, ice cream, ices, baked goods, bottled sauces, salad dressings, soups, toppings, syrups and frozen desserts.

Toxicological evaluation and possible health hazards JECFA considered it in 1969, 1973 and 1975. In 1970 the FACC listed Guar Gum in Group B because the available data were judged to be unsatisfactory. In the meantime, it continued to be permitted, and further studies were requested. The most recent JECFA review lists seventeen sources, ten of which were unpublished. JECFA recognized that currently available studies were inadequate, and that at least some adverse effects had been noted. They were none the less sufficiently satisfied to approve Guar Gum for general use without specific restrictions, because it is part of traditional diets in some parts of the world. The SCF considered Guar Gum in 1978, and despite the fact that they reported additional evidence that some components of Guar Gum can be toxic to some laboratory animals, they endorsed JECFA's evaluation. When Guar Gum was fed to rats at high doses it caused both growth depression and inflammation of the intestines. We do not have sufficient information to be certain that it is safe when consumed at low doses, in part because it has been insufficiently tested.

Regulatory status It is permitted and used in the UK, the EEC and the USA where it is listed as GRAS.

E413: Tragacanth Gum

Type It is a thickening agent, stabilizer and emulsifier. It is obtained from small thorny bushes which grow in the dry and mountainous parts of the Middle East. It has been used in foods since antiquity.

Foods added to It can be found in some fruit jelly, salad dressing, confections, fruit sherbets, sauces and some cheese products.

Toxicological evaluation and possible health hazards JECFA evaluated this substance six times between 1969 and 1985. They have never set an ADI, but approve it for use without restrictions. There have been reports since the 1940s that it can provoke severe symptoms of intolerance in a small proportion of the population. In 1970 the FACC listed it in Group A on account of its long history of use. In 1978 the SCF reported that more toxicological information was available, but that its chronic toxicity remained to be investigated in animals. They gave temporary approval pending further data. In 1983 JECFA noted that there was a distinct possibility that this substance might cause liver damage, since it had been shown to do so in rats. JECFA were unable to set an ADI, and requested further data. In the same year the SCF reported that further data had been received, although more were still required, and that it should be considered temporarily acceptable until

1985 when they approved its use without restrictions.

It is often presumed to be safe for most people because it has been in use for so many years.

Regulatory status It is permitted and used in the UK, the EEC and the USA where it is listed as GRAS.

E414: Gum Arabic
also known as Gum Acacia

Type It is a thickening agent and stabilizer, but as it can also be used to inhibit the crystallization of sugar it can be used as a glazing agent. It is extracted from a type of tree which is grown in North and Central Africa, and it is a secretion with which the tree responds to a particular but poorly understood infection. It has been extracted and used for a wide variety of purposes since antiquity.

Foods added to It can be found in some jellies, chewing gum, soft drinks, glazes, sugar confectionery and cake mixes.

Toxicological evaluation and possible health hazards JECFA evaluated it three times between 1969 and 1982. In 1970 the FACC listed it in Group A because of the long history of its use. JECFA does not specify any ADI, but accepts it for use in foods without specific restrictions. They cite several reports that it can provoke symptoms of intolerance in those exposed to it at high doses in the course of their occupation. It is accepted by JECFA for general use primarily because it has been used in food products for so many years.

Regulatory status It is permitted and used in the UK, the EEC and the USA where it is listed as GRAS.

E415: Xanthan Gum
also known as Corn Sugar Gum

Type It is a thickening agent and stabilizer. Unlike several other gums, this substance was not discovered in antiquity, but created in the laboratories of the United States Department of Agriculture in Peoria, Illinois, as part of a project to create new uses for surplus corn production. It is a biotechnology product made by fermenting corn syrup. It was developed in the 1960s and has been accepted for use in foods in the USA since the end of that decade. It is said to have good 'freeze-thaw stability', which makes it very useful to the manufacturers of processed foods intended for freezing. It can be used as a substitute for gluten in products intended for those who cannot metabolize those proteins.

Foods added to It can be found in some dairy products, salad dressings, ice cream, instant puddings, bottled sauces and toppings.

Toxicological evaluation and possible health hazards In 1972 the FACC listed it in Group A, and recommended that approval should be given for its use. JECFA evaluated it in 1974 and 1977. By the standards of a modern food chemical, it has been tested fairly thoroughly, mostly in rats, but also with dogs and mice. In 1974 JECFA set an ADI of 10mg/kg bw, based on an NEL in the rat, but in 1977 JECFA approved it for general use without any specific restriction. In 1978 the SCF endorsed an ADI of 10mg/kg bw, but proposed tightened purity specifications. No adverse effects have been reported and it is presumed to be safe.

Regulatory status It is permitted and used in the UK, the EEC, and the USA.

416: Karaya Gum

Type It is a thickening agent and stabilizer. It is secreted by a large bushy tree which is grown in India.

Foods added to It can be found in some ice cream, ice lollies, baked goods, meat products, toppings, sauces and pickles.

Toxicological evaluation and possible health hazards JECFA evaluated this substance six times between 1969 and 1985. On the first two occasions no ADI was set, on the third a decision was postponed, but more recently it was awarded a temporary ADI of 20mg/kg bw. In 1970 the FACC listed it in Group A on the grounds that it had been in use for many years. By 1974, however, JECFA reported that there were insufficient data to enable them to provide any evaluation, and also that at high doses this gum is known to provoke symptoms of acute intolerance in some people. In 1978 the SCF reported that they were still unable to evaluate this substance because too little was known about it, and they then considered it unacceptable for use in foods, although they did demand further data which they wanted quickly. In Britain the FACC did not revise its judgement, and this substance has remained in continuous use. In 1983, the SCF was satisfied to the extent that they awarded a temporary ADI at 12.5mg/kg bw, but they still demanded yet further information, and a new report is awaited. In the same year, JECFA reviewed similar data and set a temporary ADI of 20mg/kg bw, which was reiterated in 1985.

While a few adverse effects have been reported, it is not yet possible to be certain about its general safety, and it would be premature to presume that it is safe.

Regulatory status It is permitted and used in the UK and in other EEC countries, but the Council of Ministers have not yet awarded it an 'E' number. In the USA it is approved and listed as GRAS.

E420(i): Sorbitol

Type It is a sweetening agent, and also a humectant, sequestrant, and texturizer. In its pure form it is a white, crystalline, water-soluble powder with a sweet taste. It can be found naturally occurring in some berries, cherries, plums, pears and apples, but it is manufactured synthetically.

Foods added to It can be found in some confectionery, ice cream, desserts, chewing gums and soft drinks.

Toxicological evaluation and possible health hazards JECFA evaluated this substance six times between 1963 and 1982. By the standards of many food additives, there was relatively little information on the effects which this substance has on animals, but this was compensated for by the fact that there is quite a lot of information on its effects on humans. JECFA approved it for general use without any specific quantitative restrictions. Sorbitol was considered as part of the 1982 FACC report on sweeteners, and it was listed then in Group B. They reported that there is some evidence that when fed to rodents at high doses it contributed to the formation of bladder tumours, and there were several other toxic effects. The CoT therefore recommended that its effects be studied in far greater detail, and that they should be provided with far more information about the patterns of its consumption. The SCF considered Sorbitol in 1984 but they did not mention the evidence of possible carcinogenicity to which the CoT had referred. They said, but did not explain, that they 'did not consider it appropriate to establish an ADI for Sorbitol', but they did not object to its continued use. It has been used for many years in foods, especially for diabetics.

When consumed in large doses it is known to produce diarrhoea. It was formerly presumed to be safe, but that presumption can no longer be maintained.

Regulatory status It is permitted and used in the UK, the EEC and the USA where it is listed as GRAS. Because of its laxative effect, this substance is not permitted in foods intended for babies and young children in Britain.

E420(ii): Sorbitol Syrup

Type It is a sweetening agent, humectant, texturizer and sequestrant.

Foods added to It can be found in diabetic confectionery, biscuits, cakes, soft drinks, and ice cream.

Toxicological evaluation and possible health hazards See E420(i).

Regulatory status It is permitted and used in the UK, the EEC and the USA. Because of its laxative effect, this substance is not permitted in foods intended for babies and young children in Britain.

E421: Mannitol

also known as Manna Sugar and as Mannite

Type It is a sweetening agent and humectant. It occurs naturally in many plants including pine wood, but is produced commercially both by extraction from seaweed known as manna and by synthesis from sugar. It is a white, crystalline, odourless solid and is sweet to taste, but less so than sucrose.

Foods added to It is used as a sweetener in some 'sugar-free' products. It can also be found in some chewing gum, candy, ice cream, confectionery and desserts. It is used less often than Sorbitol (see E420(i) and E420(ii)).

Toxicological evaluation and possible health hazards From 1966 to 1985 JECFA evaluated it on four occasions. On the most recent occasion they set a temporary ADI of 50mg/kg bw. Mannitol was discussed in the 1982 FACC report on sweeteners, and it was listed by the CoT in Group B. They reported that there was some evidence that it had produced marked toxic effects in several strains of female rats, and the effects which they reported indicate that it might contribute to provoking cancer in rats at high doses. The CoT therefore called for further studies and more information about patterns of its consumption.

The SCF reviewed this substance in 1984 along with sixteen other sweeteners. They reported that they had sufficient data from mice, rats and humans to satisfy them as to its safety. Studies have been conducted on possible mutagenicity and carcinogenicity, but no hazard was reported. The SCF commented that there was no multigeneration reproductive toxicity study, but they did not request that such a study should be conducted. Clinical evidence indicates that it can have a marked laxative effect. The effective dose varies greatly from person to person and with age. Babies and young children are especially susceptible, and for this reason they recommend that neither Mannitol nor any of the other bulk sweeteners should be used in food intended for babies and young children up to three years. For reasons which they did not explain, the SCF 'considered it inappropriate' to set an ADI, but approved it for continued use.

Since the CoT has listed Mannitol in Group B it cannot be presumed to be safe.

Regulatory status Permitted and used in the UK, the EEC and the USA where it is listed as GRAS. Because of its laxative effect, this substance is not permitted in foods intended for babies and young children in Britain.

E422: Glycerol
also known as Glycerin

Type It is used as a humectant and also as a solvent for colouring and flavouring additives. This is a clear liquid which is about half as sweet as sucrose sugar. It occurs in the cells of many plants, and is obtained from oils and fats as a by-product of soap production.

Foods added to It can be found in some marshmallows, pastilles, edible gums, meat products, cheese products, beverages, baked goods, gelatin desserts and cake icings. It is also used in commercial preparations of some colouring, flavouring and emulsion-stabilizing additives.

Toxicological evaluation and possible health hazards JECFA considered Glycerol only once in 1976. They did not specify an ADI, but approved it for use without quantitative restrictions. There are several reports that at high doses this substance can provoke a range of unpleasant, but not severe,

symptoms. These include irritation to the mouth and throat, headaches and nausea; but at the levels at which it is used as an additive it is presumed to be safe.

Special restrictions Since it is manufactured from animal sources it is not acceptable to vegetarians or vegans, and it is not kosher or halal.

Regulatory status It is permitted and used in the UK, the EEC and the USA where it is listed as GRAS.

430: Polyoxyethylene (8) Stearate
Type It is a synthetic emulsifer.

Foods added to It can be found in some baked goods including cakes, cake mixes and dessert toppings, and it is added to extend the shelf life of the products and to make them appear fresh.

Toxicological evaluation and possible health hazards JECFA evaluated this substance in 1963 and again in 1973 alongside Polyoxyethylene (40) Stearate (see 431). In 1970 the FACC report listed it in Group A despite the fact that it provoked bladder stones and tumours in rats when fed to them as 20 per cent of their diet. They argued that there was a threshold below which this effect would not occur because the cancers were contingent on the bladder stones, and so it could safely be used in bread and cakes at levels up to 0.5 per cent. The report of the 1973 JECFA meeting reviewed essentially similar data and came to a very similar conclusion, setting an ADI of 25mg/kg bw (to apply to Polyoxyethylene (8) Stearate and Polyoxyethylene (40) Stearate singly or in combination). The SCF reviewed this substance in 1978 and again in 1983. On the former occasion they concluded that their information accentuated some of JECFA's doubts to the extent that they would not award any ADI, but give only temporary approval for its use, pending the receipt within four years of tests on the mechanism causing the formation of the bladder stones, and of a further conventional long-term feeding study. In July 1983 the SCF announced that they had not received the new data which they had previously requested on Polyoxyethylene (8) Stearate and Polyoxyethylene (40) Stearate and so they listed them as substances which are not toxicologically acceptable for use in foods. Despite this fact, these emulsifiers continue to be permitted and used in the UK, but not in most other EEC countries. It is time that JEFCA and the CoT looked at this again.

There are reports that this substance may provoke a variety of adverse symptoms including skin and intestinal inflammations and cancer, and so it cannot be assumed to be safe.

Special restrictions According to the office of the Chief Rabbi this additive may not be kosher; it may not be halal either.

Regulatory status Permitted and used in the UK, but it is banned in most other EEC countries and it does not have an 'E' number, nor is it permitted in the USA.

431: Polyoxyethylene (40) Stearate

Type It is a synthetic emulsifier.

Foods added to It can be found in some baked goods including cakes, cake mixes and dessert toppings, and it is added to extend the shelf life of the products and to make them appear fresh.

Toxicological evaluation and possible health hazards JECFA evaluated this substance in 1963 and again in 1973 alongside Polyoxyethylene (8) Stearate (see 430). In 1970 the FACC report listed it in Group B on the grounds that it had not been sufficiently tested. They requested a long-term feeding study in at least one further animal species. The report of the 1973 JECFA meeting reviewed essentially similar data and set an ADI of 25mg/kg bw (to apply to Polyoxyethylene (40) Stearate and Polyoxyethylene (8) Stearate singly or in combination). The SCF reviewed this substance in 1978 and again in 1983. On the former occasion they concluded that they would endorse a temporary ADI of 25mg/kg bw, but they also requested further information within two years. In July 1983, the SCF announced that they had not received the new data which they had previously requested on Polyoxyethylene (8) Stearate and Polyoxyethylene (40) Stearate and so they listed them as substances which are not toxicologically acceptable for use in foods. Despite this fact, these emulsifiers continue to be permitted and used in the UK, but not in most other EEC countries. It is time that JECFA and the CoT looked at this again. There is a report that this substance, when fed to malnourished rats, enhanced their vulnerability to stomach cancer, yet this document is not referred to by the official committees.

We cannot assume that this substance is safe.

Special restrictions According to the office of the Chief Rabbi this additive may not be kosher; it may not be halal either.

Regulatory status Permitted and used in the UK, but it is banned in most other EEC countries, and it does not have an 'E' number, nor is it permitted in the USA.

432: Polyoxyethylene (20) Sorbitan Monolaurate

also known as Polysorbate 20 and as Tween 20

Type It is a synthetic emulsifier, surface active agent and dispersing agent which is manufactured from Sorbitol (see E420i).

Foods added to It can be found in some breads and cakes, packet cake mixes, fillings and toppings.

Toxicological evaluation and possible health hazards This substance has been reviewed twice by JECFA in 1963 and 1973. Because of the supposed toxicological similarities, it has been considered alongside Polyoxyethylene (20) Sorbitan Monooleate (see 433), Polyoxyethylene (20) Sorbitan Monopalmitate (see 434), Polyoxyethylene (20) Sorbitan Monostearate (see 435) and Polyoxyethylene (20) Sorbitan Tristearate (see 436).

In 1970, the FACC listed this substance in Group A, and in 1973 JECFA's review reported that this group of compounds had a low acute oral toxicity to mice, rats and hamsters. In short-term feeding studies, however, Polyoxyethylene (20) Sorbitan Monolaurate caused chronic diarrhoea in hamsters, along with other significant damage when fed at (and above) a level of 5 per cent in the diet. They reported that both this substance and Polysorbate 80 (see 433) increased the rate at which some drugs could be absorbed through the wall of the digestive tract. Observations of humans who had eaten these sub-stances did not reveal any adverse effects. JECFA commented that some earlier studies on these compounds using rats and hamsters had indicated that they might be more toxic than they had come to appear, but this was blamed on the conduct of the experiments, and disregarded. JECFA also reported that localized tumours had been produced by injecting these substances into mice, but these reports were also disregarded because feeding studies did not indicate any carcinogenicity. JECFA identified an NEL in rats and consequently set an ADI of 25mg/kg bw to apply to the entire group of compounds collectively.

The SCF reviewed this group of compounds in 1978 and stated that they had no data other than that which JECFA had previously reviewed. They set a temporary ADI at the same level as JECFA's, but made it temporary pending the receipt of the results of further studies within two years. They noted that there is evidence that these compounds can act to enhance some skin carcinogens, but they argued that this is irrelevant to their use as food additives. In their most recent review in 1983, the SCF reported that they had received sufficient data and that they were setting a combined ADI of 10mg/kg bw for this entire group of compounds; they presumed that it was safe if used at or below that level.

Special restrictions According to the office of the Chief Rabbi this additive may not be kosher; it may not be halal either.

Regulatory status This group of compounds is permitted and used in the UK and the USA, but they are not permitted in some other EEC countries, and they do not have an 'E' number.

433: Polyoxyethylene (20) Sorbitan Mono-oleate
also known as Polysorbate 80, and as Tween 80

Type It is a synthetic emulsifier and dispersing agent, which is manufactured from Sorbitol (see E420i).

Foods added to It can be found in some breads, cake and cake mixes, dietary products, custard and icing.

Toxicological evaluation and possible health hazards This substance has been reviewed twice by JECFA in 1963 and 1973. Because of the supposed toxicological similarities, this has been considered alongside Polyoxyethylene (20) Sorbitan Monolaurate (see 432), Polyoxyethylene (20) Sorbitan Monopalmitate (see 434), Polyoxyethylene (20) Sorbitan Monostearate (see 435) and Polyoxyethylene (20) Sorbitan Tristearate (see 436).

In 1970 the FACC listed this substance in Group B, because there was some evidence that when it was applied directly to the skin of mice it contributed to the formation of skin cancers. They asked for the results of a further long-term feeding study to check on its possible carcinogenicity. In the meantime, they continued to permit its use. In 1972 the FACC reported that on the basis of a 1964 report from JECFA and one new study on mice they were prepared to reclassify it in Group A.

In 1973 JECFA's review reported that this group of compounds had a low acute oral toxicity to mice, rats and hamsters. In short-term feeding studies, however, Polyoxyethylene (20) Sorbitan Monolaurate caused chronic diarrhoea in hamsters, along with other significant damage when fed at (and above) a level of 5 per cent in the diet. They reported that both this substance and Polysorbate 20 (see 432) increased the rate at which some drugs could be absorbed through the wall of the digestive tract. Observations of humans who had eaten these substances did not reveal any adverse effects. JECFA commented that some earlier studies on these compounds using rats and hamsters had indicated that they might be more toxic than they had come to appear, but this was blamed on the conduct of the experiments, and disregarded. JECFA also reported that localized tumours had been produced by injecting these substances into mice, but these reports were also disregarded because feeding studies did not indicate any carcinogenicity. JECFA identified an NEL in rats and consequently set an ADI of 25mg/kg bw to apply to the entire group of compounds collectively.

The SCF reviewed this group of compounds in 1978 and stated that they had no data other than that which JECFA had previously reviewed. They set a temporary ADI at the same level as JECFA's, but made it temporary pending the receipt of the results of further studies within two years. They noted that there was evidence that these compounds could act to enhance some skin carcinogens, but they argued that this was irrelevant to their use as food additives. In their most recent review in 1983, the SCF reported that they had received sufficient data and that they were setting a combined ADI of 10mg/kg bw for this entire group of compounds; they presumed that it was safe if used at or below this level.

Special restrictions According to the office of the Chief Rabbi this additive may not be kosher; it may not be halal either.

Regulatory status Permitted and used in the UK and the USA, but they are not permitted in some other EEC countries, and they do not have an 'E' number.

434: Polyoxyethylene (20) Sorbitan Monopalmitate

also known as Polysorbate 40 and Tween 40

Type It is an emulsifier and dispersing agent, which is manufactured from Sorbitol (see E420i).

Foods added to It can be found in some breads, cakes, cake mixes, custard, fruit sherbet, fillings and toppings.

Toxicological evaluation and possible health hazards This substance has been reviewed twice by JECFA in 1963 and 1973. Because of the supposed toxicological similarities, it has been considered alongside Polyoxyethylene (20) Sorbitan Monolaurate (see 432), Polyoxyethylene (20) Sorbitan Mono-oleate (see 433), Polyoxyethylene (20) Sorbitan Monostearate (see 435) and Polyoxyethylene (20) Sorbitan Tristearate (see 436).

In 1970 the FACC listed this substance in Group A, in spite of some evidence that it acted as a co-carcinogen when applied to the skin of mice. In 1973, JECFA's review reported that this group of compounds had a low acute oral toxicity to mice, rats and hamsters. The only data that they reported referring specifically to this compound concerned its acute toxicity and the level of feeding at which it killed 50 per cent of a small population of rats. JECFA's evaluation of this substance was otherwise based entirely on analogies with other compounds in this group. JECFA identified an NEL in rats in feeding studies with these other compounds, and consequently set an ADI of 25 mg/kg bw to apply to the entire group collectively.

The SCF reviewed this group of compounds in 1978 and stated that they had no data other than that which JECFA had previously reviewed. They set a temporary ADI at the same level as JECFA's, but made it temporary pending the receipt of the results of further studies within two years. They noted that there was evidence that these compounds could act to enhance some skin carcinogens, but they argued that this was irrelevant to their use as food additives. In their most recent review in 1983, the SCF reported that they had received sufficient data, and that they were setting a combined ADI of 10mg/kg bw for this entire group of compounds; they presumed that it was safe if used at or below this level.

Special restrictions According to the office of the Chief Rabbi this additive may not be kosher; it may not be halal either.

Regulatory status This group of compounds is permitted and used in the UK and the USA, but they are not permitted in some other EEC countries, and they do not have an 'E' number.

435: Polyoxyethylene (20) Sorbitan Monostearate

also known as Polysorbate 60, and as Tween 60

Type It is an emulsifier and

dispersing agent, which is manufactured from Sorbitol (see E420).

Foods added to It can be found in some edible oils, whipped vegetable oil toppings, mayonnaise, cake, cake mixes, cake icing or filling, confectionery, gelatin desserts and non-alcoholic beverages.

Toxicological evaluation and possible health hazards This substance has been reviewed twice by JECFA in 1963 and 1973. Because of the supposed toxicological similarities, this has been considered alongside Polyoxyethylene (20) Sorbitan Monolaurate (see 432), Polyoxyethylene (20) Sorbitan Mono-oleate (see 433), Polyoxyethylene (20) Sorbitan Monopalmitate (see 434), and Polyoxyethylene (20) Sorbitan Tristearate (see 436).

In 1970 the FACC listed this substance in Group A, in spite of some evidence (which they discounted) suggesting that it could act as a co-carcinogen when applied to the skin of mice. In 1973 JECFA's review reported that this group of compounds had a low acute oral toxicity to mice, rats and hamsters. From a long-term feeding study, JECFA identified an NEL in rats and consequently set an ADI of 25mg/kg bw to apply to the entire group of compounds collectively.

A report was published in 1976 which suggested that when used in isolation this compound might be relatively safe, but when used in combination with several other additives could produce severe and even fatal toxicity to young male rats. The experiment involved feeding Polyoxyethylene (20) Sorbitan Monostearate in combination with Amaranth (see E123) and Sodium Cyclamate to rats.

(Cyclamates are artificial sweeteners which are not currently permitted in the UK, but the manufacturers are seeking permission to reintroduce them and to rescind their ban imposed in 1969.) This combination was extremely dangerous to the rats, but its effects could be mitigated by increasing the fibre content of the rats' diet. This suggested that, if humans were like rats, the dietary use of this compound could be a hazard to a significant but undetermined portion of the population.

The SCF reviewed this group of compounds in 1978 and stated that they had no data other than that which JECFA had previously reviewed. They set a temporary ADI at the same level as JECFA's, but made it temporary pending the receipt of the results of further studies within two years. They noted that there was evidence that these compounds could act to enhance some skin carcinogens, but they argued that this was irrelevant to their use as food additives. In their most recent review in 1983, the SCF reported that they had received sufficient data, and that they were setting a combined ADI of 10mg/kg bw for this entire group of compounds; they presumed that it was safe if used at or below that level.

Special restrictions According to the office of the Chief Rabbi this additive may not be kosher; it may not be halal either.

Regulatory status This group of compounds is permitted and used in the UK and the USA, but they are not permitted in some other EEC countries, and they do not have an 'E' number.

436: Polyoxyethylene (20) Sorbitan Tristearate

also known as Polysorbate 65, and as Tween 65

Type It is an emulsifier and dispersing agent, which is manufactured from Sorbitol (see E420i).

Foods added to It can be found in some cakes, cake mixes, doughnuts, vegetable oil based toppings, mayonnaise and cream substitutes for coffee.

Toxicological evaluation and possible health hazards This substance has been reviewed twice by JECFA in 1963 and 1973. Because of the supposed toxicological similarities, this has been considered alongside Polyoxyethylene (20) Sorbitan Monolaurate (see 432), Polyoxyethylene (20) Sorbitan Mono-oleate (see 433), Polyoxyethylene (20) Sorbitan Monopalmitate (see 434) and Polyoxyethylene (20) Sorbitan Monostearate (see 435).

In 1970 the FACC listed this substance in Group B, and called for both long- and short-term feeding studies in a species other than the rat. In 1972 the FACC reported that they had promoted this substance to Group A on the basis of the results from tests on Polyoxyethylene (20) Sorbitan Mono-oleate (see 433). They judged that these two substances were sufficiently similar for them to be evaluated together, and announced that further testing of these compounds should be given a low priority.

In 1973 JECFA's review reported that this group of compounds had a low acute oral toxicity to mice, rats and hamsters. This particular compound had been subjected to both short- and long-term feeding studies

in rats, but it had not been thoroughly tested. JECFA's judgement was based on analogies with other compounds in the group, and they were evaluated collectively. JECFA identified an NEL for this substance in rats and consequently set an ADI of 25mg/kg bw to apply to the entire group of compounds collectively.

The SCF reviewed this group of compounds in 1978 and stated that they had no data other than that which JECFA had previously reviewed. They set a temporary ADI at the same level as JECFA's, but made it temporary pending the receipt of the results of further studies within two years. They noted that there was evidence that these compounds could act to enhance some skin carcinogens, but they argued that this was irrelevant to their use as food additives. In their most recent review in 1983, the SCF reported that they had received sufficient data, and that they were setting a combined ADI of 10mg/kg bw for this entire group of compounds; they presumed that it was safe if used at or below this level.

Special restrictions According to the office of the Chief Rabbi this additive may not be kosher; it may not be halal either.

Regulatory status This group of compounds is permitted and used in the UK and the USA, but they are not permitted in some other EEC countries, and they do not have an 'E' number.

E440(a): Pectin, Ammonium Pectate, Sodium Pectate and Potassium Pectate

Type Pectin is an emulsifying, gelling and thickening agent which occurs naturally in the roots, fruits and stems of plants, especially in apples and citrus fruits. Orange and lemon rind contain about 30 per cent Pectin.

Foods added to It can be found in some beverages, syrups, ice creams, confections, jams and jellies.

Toxicological evaluation and possible health hazards JECFA considered this substance and its salts in 1961, 1973 and most recently in 1981. In 1970 the FACC listed Pectin (along with Calcium and Sodium Pectates) in Group A, saying that they were satisfied as to their safety provided that manufacturers obtained their materials from citrus fruits and apples. In 1973 JECFA commented that little formal animal testing had been conducted, but since it was a normal constituent of human diets they did not consider it necessary. When used at high levels as a component in intravenous drip solutions it resulted in some degenerative damage, but at the levels at which it was eaten or used as an additive it was presumed to be safe. JECFA approved it for general use without any specific quantitative restrictions, or any ADI. This judgement was endorsed by the SCF in 1978 and 1983, and reaffirmed by JECFA in 1981. No adverse effects have been reported and it is presumed to be safe.

Regulatory status It is permitted and used in the UK, the EEC and in the USA where it is listed as GRAS.

E440(b): Amidated Pectin

Type It is a gelling and thickening agent produced by chemical modification of Pectin (see E440(a)). Amidated Pectin has been in commercial use since approximately 1945.

Foods added to It can be found in many jellies and preserves.

Toxicological evaluation and possible health hazards JECFA has evaluated this compound on five occasions between 1969 and 1981 inclusive. On the first occasion they did not set an ADI but said rather that its use would be limited by 'good manufacturing practice', without specifying the latter in detail. In 1973 they reported some evidence that Amidated Pectin appeared to be significantly more toxic than un-amidated Pectin, and set a temporary ADI at the level of 25mg/kg bw on the basis of a short-term feeding study in rats. They also requested detailed specifications of the identity of the material. It is unusual and perhaps unsatisfactory, but not unique, for JECFA to rely on the results of a short-term feeding study to set an ADI. Their normal practice is to require long-term feeding studies in at least two species. In 1974 they reported again having received the results of two (incomplete and unpublished) sets of long-term feeding tests on small groups of rats. The information which had been provided was inadequate and so JECFA was not able to rely on it, and merely reiterated the temporary ADI of 25mg/kg bw. The following year they reported again, citing two long-term feeding studies the results of which were not published. JECFA would not accept these tests as adequate, and repeated its temporary ADI, and called for a proper long-term feeding study in a rodent species, plus proper reproduction and embryotoxicity studies by 1980. The SCF adopted a similar position on the basis of the same information in 1978, and endorsed this view again in 1983. JECFA reported again in 1981, and then felt able to accept this material as sufficiently safe for it to be generally accepted without any quantitative restrictions. The SCF echoed this judgement in 1983, but they failed to cite the sources on which they based their conclusions. The history of this substance indicates that chemicals can be, and have been, permitted and used even though insufficient information is available, both to officials and even more to the general public, to permit a proper evaluation.

No adverse effects have been reported and it is now presumed to be safe.

Regulatory status It is permitted and used in the UK and the EEC.

442: Ammonium Phosphatides
also known as the Ammonium Salts of Phosphatidic Acid and as Emulsifier YN

Type These are synthetic emulsifiers, which are produced from partially hardened rapeseed oil. The identity of these compounds has not yet been fully established, and the commercial products contain up to 40 per cent of unreacted triglycerides. They are often used in cacao and chocolate products as a substitute for Lecithin (see E322).

Foods added to They can be found in many chocolate and cocoa products at levels of approximately 0.5 per cent.

Toxicological evaluation and possible health hazards JECFA has evaluated these compounds on three occasions: in 1969, 1973 and in 1974. On the first two occasions they set a temporary ADI at 15mg/kg bw, but in 1974 they established a full ADI at the higher figure of 30mg/kg bw. In 1970 the FACC listed them in Group B. The CoT reported that while they received reports of metabolic and short-term studies, they had not been provided with the results of any long-term feeding studies. Since these compounds are frequently included in chocolate products, people will be eating them over the long term, and so they asked for a long-term animal study and for metabolic studies in humans. In the meantime, they were prepared to accept their continued usage. By 1973, JECFA was able only to repeat the views of the British authorities, but they did set a temporary ADI. In 1974, however, JECFA was able to report the results of a long-term feeding study and a reproductive study, and these enabled them to set a full ADI at 30mg/kg bw (with the qualification that the consumption of these compounds should be included in the ADI for Phosphates as a whole). They had not, however, received any evidence on how this material was metabolized by humans. In 1978 the SCF reviewed the toxicology of this group of compounds and endorsed JECFA's ADI, but they too had not received evidence of their metabolism by humans, and some of the evidence on which both organizations relied remains unpublished.

No adverse effects have been reported and they are presumed to be safe.

Regulatory status Permitted and used in the UK and the EEC, but not in the USA.

E450(a): Sodium and Potassium Diphosphates: Disodium Dihydrogen Diphosphate, Trisodium Diphosphate, Tetrasodium Diphosphate and Tetrapotassium Diphosphate
Type These are synthetically manufactured and used as buffers,

emulsifiers, stabilizers and seques-trants.

Foods added to They can be found in some cereals, breakfast foods, frozen poultry and other meat pro-ducts, bread, sausages, cheese spread and cheese products, cream and con-densed milk.

Toxicological evaluation and possible health hazards JECFA evaluated these substances, individually and collectively, on several occasions between 1963 and 1981. The evalua-tions have covered Phosphoric Acid, the Polyphosphates and their various salts. Phosphoric Acid is an essential constituent of the human body, where it is found in bones and teeth, playing a vital role in many enzyme systems. We excrete the Phosphates as Calcium Phosphate, and therefore there is a risk that high levels of consumption of Phosphates might lead to a loss of essential calcium. Large doses of these substances are also reported to have a marked laxative effect. We have some knowledge of their meta-bolism, and at moderate doses they have been shown to cause kidney damage to rats in short-term feeding studies. A level has been found at which no adverse effects can be observed in rats in long-term feeding studies and this has provided a basis for an over-all ADI of 70mg/kg bw to apply to all the Phosphates and Polyphosphates. No adverse effects have been reported and they are presumed to be safe.

Regulatory status These are permitted and used in the UK, the EEC and the USA.

E450(b): Sodium and Potassium Triphosphates: there are two substances listed under this heading: **Pentasodium Triphosphate and Pentapotassium Triphosphate**

Type These are synthetic chem-icals used as emulsifiers and textur-izers.

Foods added to They can be found in some meat products, processed cheeses, cheese spreads, bread and sausages.

Toxicological evaluation and possible health hazards JECFA evaluated these substances, individually and collectively, on several occasions between 1963 and 1981. The evalua-tions have covered Phosphoric Acid, the Polyphosphates and their various salts. Phosphoric Acid is an essential constituent of the human body, where it is found in bones and teeth, playing a vital role in many enzyme systems. We excrete the Phosphates as Calcium Phosphate, and therefore there is a risk that high levels of consumption of Phosphates might lead to a loss of essen-tial calcium. Large doses of these sub-stances are also reported to have a marked laxative effect. We have some knowledge of their metabolism, and at moderate doses they have been shown to cause kidney damage to rats in short-term feeding studies. A level has been found at which no adverse effects can be observed in rats in long-term feeding studies and this has provided a basis for an over-all ADI of 70mg/kg bw to apply to all the Phosphates and Polyphosphates. No adverse effects have been reported and they are presumed to be safe.

Regulatory status They are per-mitted in the UK, the EEC and the USA.

E450(c): Sodium and Potassium Polyphosphates

Type These are used as emulsifiers, texturizers and sequestrants. The 1979 SCF report says that 'They are claimed to contribute to colour, tenderness, juiciness and flavour, and to decrease cooking shrinkage.' These substances have, however, attracted a great deal of critical comment because they affect the character of many products so as to increase the amount of water which they hold, and this accounts for the 'tenderness' which they are supposed to provide. Their use enables manufacturers to increase the effective weight of their products at extremely low cost. The use of these chemicals occasioned the publication of an advertisement in the *Meat Trades Journal* in April 1975 saying 'Why Sell Meat When You Can Sell Water?'

Foods added to They can be found in some bread, sausages, meat products, poultry, fish products, coffee whiteners, ice creams and cheese products.

Toxicological evaluation and possible health hazards JECFA evaluated these substances, individually and collectively, on several occasions between 1963 and 1981. The evaluations have covered Phosphoric Acid, the Polyphosphates and their various salts. Phosphoric Acid is an essential constituent of the human body, where it is found in bones and teeth, playing a vital role in many enzyme systems. We excrete the Phosphates as Calcium Phosphate, and therefore there is a risk that high levels of consumption of Phosphates might lead to a loss of essential calcium. Large doses of these substances are also reported to have a marked laxative effect. We have some knowledge of their metabolism, and at

moderate doses they have been shown to cause kidney damage to rats in short-term feeding studies. A level has been found at which no adverse effects can be observed in rats in long-term feeding studies and this has provided a basis for an over-all ADI of 70mg/kg bw to apply to all the Phosphates and Polyphosphates. This evaluation was also endorsed by the SCF in 1978. No adverse effects have been reported and they are presumed to be safe.

Regulatory status Permitted and widely used in the UK, the EEC and the USA.

E460(a): Microcrystalline Cellulose

Type It is used as an emulsifier, anti-caking and dispersing agent. It is obtained by treating cellulose from the walls of plant fibres chemically. It can be used to absorb liquid foods and convert them into a dry granular form.

Foods added to It can be found in some low-calorie products and high-fibre breads, salad dressings, whipped toppings, synthetic cream and in some ice creams.

Toxicological evaluation and possible health hazards JECFA considered this substance in 1971, 1973 and 1975. The first report indicated that, by the standards of many additives, this substance had not been particularly thoroughly tested on animals. There had been short- and long-term feeding studies and a reproductive study in rats, although seven of the nine studies reviewed by JECFA had not been published, and one of the two which had dated from 1928. They pointed out, however, that this material was used as dietary fibre as part of clinical treatment for constipation, and that experience indicated that it passed straight through undigested. On that basis they approved it for general use without any quantitative restrictions, and subject only to what they called 'good manufacturing practice'. JECFA's 1973 report claimed to present a revised account, but they had merely changed the order of the paragraphs: no more of the data had been published. By 1975, they could cite six further published reports. Their review is unremarkable, except for two points. A study to investigate its effects on offspring had been conducted. They reported that there was some evidence that the test material had increased the rate at which pregnant rats reabsorbed their embryonic foetuses back into the tissue of their wombs, as well as changing the sex ratio of the rats' offspring. JECFA says, rather enigmatically, that the scientists who conducted the experiment had concluded that Microcrystalline Cellulose did not cause birth defects. This uniquely coy way of putting it implies that JECFA was not prepared to endorse that opinion. Finally, JECFA admitted that, even if they wanted to, they were not able to set an ADI, because an NEL had not been found in the long-term feeding study. They then concluded that no ADI was required, and that it could be used as an additive without any specific restrictions.

The SCF reviewed this material in 1978. They were willing to endorse JECFA's evaluation, but said that they wished to be informed of the results of any further work, which would then be reviewed. This could be interpreted as providing industry with an incentive for ensuring that no further work would be conducted. Most of the basic information remains unpublished, and neither has industry any incentive to alter this situation.

No adverse effects have been reported, and it is generally presumed to be entirely safe.

Regulatory status It is permitted and used in the UK, but it may not be added to foods intended for babies and young children. It is also permitted and used in the EEC.

E460(b): Alphacellulose
also known as Powdered Cellulose

Type It is used as a bulking, anti-caking and gelling agent, and a texturizer. It is obtained by mechanical treatment of cellulose from plants.

Foods added to It can be found in some low-calorie products and high-fibre breads, salad dressings, whipped toppings, synthetic cream and in some ice creams.

Toxicological evaluation and possible health hazards JECFA treats this material as toxicologically indistinguishable from Microcrystalline Cellulose (see E460(a)).

Regulatory status It is permitted and used in the UK, but it may not be added to foods intended for babies and young children. It is also permitted and used in the EEC and the USA.

E461: Methyl Cellulose

Type It is a thickening agent, emulsifier and stabilizer, which is extracted from wood pulp or cotton. It was first produced by the Dow Chemical Company in 1938.

Foods added to It can be found in some slimming foods, food products for diabetics, baked goods, beverages and in some jelly and jams.

Toxicological evaluation and possible health hazards JECFA evaluated this material three times between 1963 and 1973. JECFA considered it as just one member of the class of modified celluloses, and these include Methyl Cellulose, Hydroxypropyl Cellulose (see E463), Hydroxypropyl Methyl Cellulose (see E464), Ethylmethyl Cellulose (see E465) and Sodium Carboxymethyl Cellulose (see E466). In 1970 the FACC listed this substance in Group A. These substances have been tested to an average extent in animals, but we have direct clinical evidence as a result of their use in the treatment of human constipation. They all appear to be indigestible, and to pass through unchanged. Methyl Cellulose has not been subjected to a long-term animal feeding study, but three of the five have been so tested, and JECFA treats them as toxicologically equivalent. They set an ADI of 25mg/kg bw, and added that this figure could be exceeded in the context of low-calorie diets. There are clinical reports, however, that at high doses it can cause swelling in the digestive tract. There are probably better ways of losing weight than eating large amounts of inert filler. No other adverse effects have been reported and it is presumed to be safe.

Regulatory status It is permitted and used in the UK, the EEC and the USA where it is listed as GRAS.

E463: Hydroxypropyl Cellulose

Type It is an emulsifier, thickening agent and stabilizer, which is synthesized from Cellulose.

Foods added to It can be found in some pie fillings and in some cake batter.

Toxicological evaluation and possible health hazards JECFA evaluated this material three times between 1963 and 1973 and considered it as just one member of the class of modified cel-

luloses, and these include Methyl Cellulose (see E463), Hydroxypropyl Cellulose, Hydroxypropyl Methyl Cellulose (see E464), Ethylmethyl Cellulose (see E465) and Sodium Carboxymethyl Cellulose (see E466). In 1970 the FACC listed this substance in Group A. These substances have been tested to an average extent in animals, but we have direct clinical evidence as a result of their use in the treatment of human constipation. They all appear to be indigestible, and to pass through unchanged. Hydroxypropyl Cellulose has not been subjected to a long-term animal feeding study, but three of the five have been so tested, and JECFA treats them as toxicologically equivalent. They set an ADI of 25mg/kg bw, and added that this figure could be exceeded in the context of low-calorie diets. There are clinical reports, however, that at high doses it can cause swelling in the digestive tract. There are probably better ways of losing weight than eating large amounts of inert filler. Otherwise, no adverse effects have been reported and it is presumed to be safe.

Regulatory status Permitted and used in the UK, the EEC and the USA.

E464: Hydroxypropyl Methyl Cellulose

Type It is a thickening agent, emulsifier and stabilizer.

Foods added to It can be found in some pie fillings, ices, cake batter, low-calorie dressings and in some baked products. It is also the active ingredient of some eye drops which are also known as artificial tears.

Toxicological evaluation and possible health hazards JECFA evaluated this material three times between 1963 and 1973. JECFA considered it as just one member of the class of modified celluloses, and these include Methyl Cellulose (see E464), Hydroxypropyl Cellulose (see E463), Hydroxypropyl Methyl Cellulose, Ethylmethyl Cellulose (see E465) and Sodium Carboxymethyl Cellulose (see E466). In 1970 the FACC listed this substance in Group A. These substances have been tested to an average extent in animals, but we have direct clinical evidence as a result of their use in the treatment of human constipation. They all appear to be indigestible, and to pass through unchanged. Hydroxypropyl Methyl Cellulose has been subjected to a long-term animal feeding study as one of the three of five which have been so tested, though JECFA treats them as toxicologically equivalent. They set an ADI of 25mg/kg bw, and added that this figure could be exceeded in the context of low-calorie diets. There are clinical reports, however, that at high doses it can cause swelling in the digestive tract. There are probably better ways of losing weight than eating large amounts of inert filler. No other adverse effects have been reported and it is presumed to be safe.

Regulatory status Permitted and used in the UK, the EEC and the USA.

E465: Ethylmethyl Cellulose

Type It is used as a thickening agent, emulsifier, foaming agent and stabilizer. It is synthesized from wood pulp or chemical cotton.

Foods added to It can be found in some vegetable fat whipped toppings, fruit cake and bottled sauces.

Toxicological evaluation and possible

health hazards JECFA evaluated this material three times between 1963 and 1973. JECFA considered it as just one member of the class of modified celluloses, and these include Methyl Cellulose (see E461) Hydroxypropyl Cellulose (see E463), Hydroxypropyl Methyl Cellulose (see E464), Ethylmethyl Cellulose and Sodium Carboxymethyl Cellulose (see E466). In 1970 the FACC listed this substance in Group A. These substances have been tested to an average extent in animals, but we have direct clinical evidence as a result of their use in the treatment of human constipation. They all appear to be indigestible, and to pass through unchanged. Ethylmethyl Cellulose has been subjected to a long-term animal feeding study as one of the three of five which have been so tested, though JECFA treats them as toxicologically equivalent. They set an ADI of 25mg/kg bw, and added that this figure could be exceeded in the context of low-calorie diets. There are clinical reports, however, that at high doses it can cause swelling in the digestive tract. There are probably better ways of losing weight than eating large amounts of inert filler. No other adverse effects have been reported and it is presumed to be safe.

Regulatory status It is permitted and used in the UK, the EEC and the USA.

E466: Sodium Carboxymethyl Cellulose
also known as CMC

Type It is a thickening agent which is made from a cotton by-product. It was first used as a food additive around 1924, but only became widely used during the early years of the

Second World War in the USA.

Foods added to It can be found in some ice creams, sorbets, beverages, confections, baked goods, icings, toppings, chocolate milk, gassed cream, cheese spreads and certain cheeses, and in some cheesecake mixes.

Toxicological evaluation and possible health hazards JECFA evaluated this material three times between 1963 and 1973. JECFA considered it as just one member of the class of modified celluloses, and these include Methyl Cellulose (see E461), Hydroxy-propyl Cellulose (see E463), Hydroxy-propyl Methyl Cellulose (see E464), Ethylmethyl Cellulose (see E465) and Sodium Carboxymethyl Cellulose. In 1970 the FACC listed this substance in Group A. These substances have been tested to an average extent in animals, but we have direct clinical evidence as a result of their use in the treatment of human constipation. They all appear to be indigestible, and to pass through unchanged. Sodium Carboxymethyl Cellulose has been subjected to long-term animal feeding studies in mice and rats as one of the three of five which have been so tested, though JECFA treats them as toxicologically equivalent. There were reports in 1957 and 1961 that when injected under the skin of rats this material caused cancers at the injection sites. Feeding studies have not indicated that it can cause cancer when consumed orally. JECFA set an ADI of 25mg/kg bw, and added that this figure could be exceeded in the context of low-calorie diets. There are clinical reports, however, that at high doses it can cause swelling in the digestive tract. There are probably better ways of losing weight than eating large amounts of inert filler. No other adverse effects have been reported and it is often presumed to be safe, except by those people who worry about the cancers at the injection sites.

Regulatory status Permitted and used in the UK, the EEC and the USA where it is listed as GRAS.

E470: Sodium, Potassium and Calcium Salts of Fatty Acids

Type This is a group of emulsifiers and anti-caking agents and they are types of soap. They are white and have a soapy texture with a slight odour of tallow.

Foods added to They can be found in some icing sugar, soup mixes, potato snacks and cake mixes.

Toxicological evaluation and possible health hazards JECFA evaluated a group of these compounds in 1969 and 1973. On those occasions they considered specifically the Salts of Myristic, Palmitic and Stearic Acids. These three acids are naturally occurring fatty acid components of animal fats and tallow, as well as of some vegetable oils. These Fatty Acids and their Salts are also natural metabolites of fats, and their metabolism is well understood. JECFA concluded that these substances could be used as additives without any specific quantitative restrictions. No adverse effects have been reported and they are presumed to be safe.

Special restrictions Since the production of these chemicals can depend upon animal sources, they are not acceptable to vegetarians or vegans, and are not kosher, or halal.

Regulatory status Permitted and used in the UK, the EEC and the USA.

E471: Mono- and Di-Glycerides of Fatty Acids (MDGs) including Glyceryl Mono- and Di-Stearates, Mono- and Di-Palmitates, Mono- and Di-Oleate

Type These are emulsifiers and stabilizers, which are synthesized from Glycerine and tallow or vegetable fatty acids. Mixtures with varying proportions of Mono- and Di- Glycerides are used to provide emulsifiers for a wide range of different uses.

Foods added to These compounds are very widely used and can be found in crisps, potato snacks, aerosol cream products, margarine and baked products.

Toxicological evaluation and possible health hazards JECFA has evaluated these compounds twice, in 1966 and 1973. In 1970 the FACC report listed the MDGs in Group A on the grounds that they are normal products of fat metabolism. In 1973 JECFA considered six reports, five of which had been published before 1963, and only one dated from 1969. JECFA explained that the fats which are found in foods are mainly Triglycerides, but that Mono- and Di-Glycerides can be found naturally occurring in small amounts, and in the digestive process the Triglycerides are broken down into Mono- and Di-glycerides. There had been a short-term test with hamsters, and a long-term study in rats. They do not appear to have been tested for carcinogenicity or mutagenicity. On the basis of the rather slight amount of available data, JECFA decided that they would approve the use of these compounds without any specific restrictions (except that both the CoT and JECFA expressed some reservations about the chemical identity of the commercial ingredients).

No health hazards have been reported, and they are presumed to be safe.

Special restrictions Since the production of these chemicals can depend upon animal sources, they are not acceptable to vegetarians or vegans, and are not kosher, or halal.

Regulatory status Permitted and used in the UK, the EEC and the USA where they are listed as GRAS.

E472(a): Acetic Acid Esters of Mono- and Di-Glycerides of Fatty Acids

Type These are synthetic emulsifiers and stabilizers, which are derived from the MDGs that are obtained from edible fats and oils (see E471). They are also used as lubricants and defoaming agents in sugar beet and yeast processing.

Foods added to They can be found in some margarines, ices, cheesecake mixes, soups, bread and baked products.

Toxicological evaluation and possible health hazards JECFA evaluated these compounds in 1966 and again in 1973. Of the eight studies on which they relied, only one had been conducted in the 1960s, and the other dated from the 1950s. They were able to report the results of metabolic studies, as well as short- and long-term tests, but the number of animals used was so small that no reliance would be placed on them if the data were presented for the first time in the 1980s. In one of the long-term studies there was evidence that the substances under test adversely affected the testicles of rats and reduced their production of sperm. JECFA discounted this evidence arguing that the dose levels did not model possible levels of human consumption. They argued that these compounds break down in the digestive tract into normal dietary constituents, and for this reason they were prepared to accept their use without any specific restrictions (except that the total consumption of Tartaric Acid (see E334) should not exceed 30mg/kg bw). No adverse effects have been reported, and they are presumed to be safe.

Special restrictions Since the production of these chemicals can depend upon animal sources, they are not acceptable to vegetarians or vegans, and are not kosher or halal.

Regulatory status Permitted and used in the UK and the EEC, and the USA.

E472(b): Lactic Acid Esters of Mono- and Di-Glycerides of Fatty Acids
also known as Lactoglycerides

Type These are emulsifiers and stabilizers which are synthesized from Lactic Acid (see E270).

Foods added to They can be found in some margarines, ices, cheesecake mixes, soups, cakes, breads and baked products, and at levels of about 8 per cent in cooking fats.

Toxicological evaluation and possible health hazards JECFA evaluated these compounds in 1966 and again in 1973. The 1970 FACC report listed them in Group B on the grounds that they just did not believe that they had sufficient information. In 1973 JECFA explained that there are many esters in commercial use, but the main ones are Glycerol Lactopalmitate (abbreviated to GLP) and Glycerol Lactostearate. Almost all the toxicological work which they report was conducted with GLP. Three of the five studies on which they relied in

1973 were unpublished, and they had all been completed by 1962. They reported a handful of studies on acute, short- and long-term toxicity, but they had all been conducted on such small groups of animals that little reliance could have been placed on them then, and even less so today. JECFA decided that these substances could be used without any specific restrictions (except that the total consumption of Tartaric Acid (see E334) should not exceed 30mg/kg bw). They reached this conclusion on the basis of two metabolic studies, one on hogs and the other on dogs. No evidence was presented to indicate whether human metabolism mirrors those of hogs or dogs.

No adverse effects have been reported and they are presumed to be safe, but on a very thin evidential basis.

Special restrictions Since the production of these chemicals can depend on animal sources, they are not acceptable to vegetarians or vegans, and are not kosher or halal.

Regulatory status Permitted and used in the UK, the EEC and the USA.

E472(c): Citric Acid Esters of Mono- and Di-Glycerides of Fatty Acids
also known as Citroglycerides

Type These are emulsifiers, stabilizers and sequestrants, and are synthesized from Citric Acid (see E330).

Foods added to These can be found in some cheesecake mixes, ices, margarines, soups, breads and baked products.

Toxicological evaluation and possible health hazards JECFA evaluated these compounds in 1966 and again in

1973. On the first occasion, and on the basis of a minute amount of data, JECFA set an ADI at the very high level of 100mg/kg bw, believing that these compounds are fully metabolized by humans into chemicals which are normal constituents of the human diet. When the FACC considered these compounds in 1970, however, they consigned them to Group E, because on the available evidence they could not say how humans metabolize them, and the FACC were especially anxious that they might be metabolized into ethyl citrate which is toxic. They were not prepared to accept JECFA's initial judgement of 1966. In 1972 the FACC considered them again and reported that they had promoted Citroglycerides to Group B on the grounds that they had received some evidence that they might be metabolized safely. This evidence was only partially satisfactory, and the FACC called for more evidence confirming that Citroglycerides can be safely metabolized, while at the same time recommending that provisional permission should be granted for their use.

When JECFA last evaluated these compounds, as long ago as 1973, they relied on only four reports, none of which had been published, and all of which had been completed by 1966. They had access to the results of one short-term study and three metabolic studies, but no long-term data whatsoever. They concluded, however, that since they are metabolized in a harmless fashion by rats, they are safe for humans too. They argued that these compounds break down in the digestive tract into normal dietary constituents, and for this reason they were prepared to accept their use with-

out any specific restrictions (except that the total consumption of Tartaric Acid (see E334) should not exceed 30mg/kg bw).

No adverse effects have been reported, and they are presumed to be safe – on the basis of flimsy evidence.

Special restrictions Since the production of these chemicals can depend upon animal sources, they are not acceptable to vegetarians or vegans, and are not kosher or halal.

Regulatory status Permitted and used in the UK and the EEC.

E472(d): Tartaric Acid Esters of Mono- and Di-Glycerides of Fatty Acids

Type These are synthetic emulsifiers prepared from Tartaric Acid (see E334).

Foods added to They can be found in some margarines, edible ices and ice mixes, and they are used as defoamers in yeast production.

Toxicological evaluation and possible health hazards JECFA evaluated these compounds in 1966 and again in 1973. They relied on only two reports, both unpublished, and both completed by 1966. One study on a small group of rats at only one dose level showed no toxic effects in a two-year feeding study, but JECFA had biochemical evidence that these substances are readily metabolized in the intestinal tract to normal dietary constituents, and for this reason they were prepared to accept their use without any specific restrictions (except that the total consumption of Tartaric Acid (see E334) should not exceed 30mg/kg bw).

No adverse effects have been reported, and they are presumed to be safe.

Special restrictions Since the production of these chemicals can depend on animal sources, they are not acceptable to vegetarians or vegans, and are not kosher or halal.

Regulatory status Permitted and used in the UK and the EEC.

E472(e): Mono- and Di-Acetyl Tartaric Acid Esters of Mono- and Di-Glycerides of Fatty Acids

Type These are emulsifiers and stabilizers.

Foods added to They can be found in some cheesecake mixes, crisps, margarines, soups, gravy granules and in bakery fats used in bread, rolls, biscuits and cakes.

Toxicological evaluation and possible health hazards When the FACC reviewed these compounds in 1970 they listed them in Group B because of the lack of proper data. JECFA evaluated Di-Acetyl Tartaric and Fatty Acid Esters of Glycerol in 1966 and again in 1973. JECFA relied on four reports, two of which were un-published. Unlike E472(a–d), Di-Acetyl Tartaric Acid is not a natural constituent of human diets. Its acute toxicity had been studied in rats and rabbits, and its short-term toxicity had been studied using thirteen dogs. A long-term feeding study had been conducted using groups of only eight rats. No adverse effects were revealed by these studies, but they could hardly be considered adequate by modern standards. JECFA set a full ADI at 50mg/kg bw. Mono-Acetyl Tartaric Acid Esters are not discussed in the literature.

In spite of these limitations these compounds are presumed to be safe.

Special restrictions Since the production of these chemicals can depend upon animal sources, they are not acceptable to vegetarians or vegans, and are not kosher or halal.

Regulatory status Permitted and used in the UK and the EEC, and Di-Acetyl Tartaric Acid Esters of Mono- and Di-Glycerides of Fatty Acids are GRAS in the USA.

E473: Sucrose Esters of Fatty Acids

Type These are emulsifiers and stabilizers which are synthesized from fatty acids.

Foods added to They can be found in some dessert mixes, soft margarines and cakes.

Toxicological evaluation and possible health hazards In 1970 the FACC listed this group of compounds in Group E, meaning that in their opin-ion there was not enough information available for them to make a judge-ment. They did however express par-ticular concern about two residual contaminants both of which are known to be toxic: one was methyl alcohol and the other, called dimethylformamide, comes from the solvents used in manufacture. The further information which they re-quested had to include evidence about the levels and toxicity of these con-taminants. The FACC reviewed these substances again in 1972 and reported that they had been informed that the levels at which the contaminants occurred was rather low, and on those grounds they promoted these materials to Group B. They reaffirmed their worries about the toxicity of dimethylformamide, and called for long-term feeding studies on two species of animals, while recom-mending provisional approval for these materials in the interim.

JECFA has evaluated these

compounds four times between 1969 and 1980. They deal with these substances under six separate headings: Sucrose Monopalmitate, Sucrose Monostearate, Sucrose Monoleate, Sucrose Monolinoleate, Palm Oil Sucrose Esters, and Lard and Tallow Sucrose Esters. By 1973 the available evidence on these six compounds was patchy and incomplete. Five had been tested for short-term toxicity in rats, and there were long-term toxicity data available on only three of them. Half of the twenty-two reports on which JECFA was relying had not been published. JECFA decided on that occasion to set a collective temporary ADI for this group at 2.5mg/kg bw, and called for further studies. By 1976 they had received sufficient data to persuade them to make this ADI full rather than temporary, and in 1980 they raised the ADI to 10mg/kg bw.

No adverse effects have been reported, and these compounds are presumed to be safe.

Special restrictions Since the production of these chemicals can depend on animal sources, they are not acceptable to vegetarians or vegans, and they are not kosher or halal.

Regulatory status Permitted and used in the UK and the EEC, but not in the USA.

E474: Sucroglycerides

Type These are emulsifiers and stabilizers.

Foods added to These can be found in some crisps and soft margarines, cakes and pudding mixes.

Toxicological evaluation and possible health hazards In 1970 the FACC listed this group of compounds in Group E, meaning that in their opinion there was not enough information available for them to make a judgement. They did however express particular concern about two residual contaminants both of which are known to be toxic: one was methyl alcohol and the other, called dimethylformamide, comes from the solvents used in manufacture. The further information which they requested had to include evidence about the levels and toxicity of these contaminants. The FACC reviewed these substances again in 1972 and reported that they had been informed that the levels at which these contaminants occurred were rather low, and on those grounds they promoted these materials to Group B. They reaffirmed their worries about the toxicity of dimethylformamide, and called for long-term feeding studies on two species of animals, while recommending provisional approval for these materials in the interim.

JECFA has evaluated them alongside the Sucrose Esters of Fatty Acids (see E473), and the overall ADI of 10mg/kg bw should cover E473 and E474 together.

No adverse effects have been reported, and these compounds are presumed to be safe.

Special restrictions Since the production of these chemicals can depend on animal sources, they are not acceptable to vegetarians or vegans, and are not kosher or halal.

Regulatory status Permitted and used in the UK and the EEC but not in the USA.

E475: Polyglycerol Esters of Fatty Acids

Type These are emulsifiers and stabilizers, and they are derived from lard, tallow and vegetable oils. This is quite a large and diverse group of compounds.

Foods added to They can be found in some oils, fats, margarines, pudding mixes, baked products, chocolate and chocolate coatings and crisps.

Toxicological evaluation and possible health hazards JECFA has evaluated this group of compounds three times and most recently in 1973. They commented then that their assessment of this diverse group depended on tests of only one member of the group, but they were sufficiently satisfied to set an ADI of 25mg/kg bw. They did, however, say that the results of further tests on other members of the group were 'desirable', but they did not actually request such studies, and they have not reconsidered their opinion since then. The SCF commented on this group of compounds in 1978. They decided that when JECFA had evaluated these compounds five years earlier they had not known precisely the materials with which they had been dealing. The SCF are confident that they have got it sorted out, and concur with JECFA's ADI for the materials which are actually being used. No adverse effects have been reported and they are presumed to be safe.

Special restrictions Since the production of these chemicals can depend on animal sources, they are not acceptable to vegetarians or vegans, and are not kosher or halal.

Regulatory status Permitted and used in the UK, the EEC and the USA.

476: Polyglycerol Esters of Polycondensed Fatty Acids of Castor Oil

also known as Polyglycerol Polyricinoleate

Type These are a group of emulsifiers which are sold commercially as highly viscous liquids.

Foods added to They can be found in chocolate and dessert mixes, and they are used to grease pans in the baking industry.

Toxicological evaluation and possible health hazards JECFA evaluated these compounds in 1969 and in 1973. On the first occasion they set a temporary ADI of 3.75mg/kg bw and requested further tests. When the FACC reviewed them in 1970 they listed them in Group B, voicing some concern and recommending restrictions on the use of these substances. Evidence provided revealed that at a wide range of doses these materials caused enlargement of livers and kidneys in mice and rats. They asked for two further sets of experiments, first on the metabolic fate of the materials, and second a short-term study in a species other than the rat in which an NEL could be established. They did not specify the source of any of their data. In 1972 the FACC promoted these materials into Group A on the basis of some new, but again unspecified, evidence.

In 1973 JECFA reviewed them again, on the basis of fifteen documents, only one of which had been published (and that was in 1962), while the other fourteen were provided by Unilever Ltd and unpublished. Unilever had carried out a fairly extensive set of tests, especially to study the persistent problem of liver enlargement in mice and rats, though their studies did not reveal any carcinogenic potential in these rodents. The odd thing about JECFA's judgement is that they stated that Unilever scientists could find an NEL only in rats, not in mice. Their response was to base an ADI of 7.5mg/kg bw on the short-term rat study. This is problematic because they had failed to find the NEL in mice which the FACC had required and expected. If they were being cautious one might have expected them to have drawn their inferences from the more sensitive species, namely the mouse, but they relied on the rat. It is usual, moreover, to establish an NEL in long-term tests, and not to rely on short-term studies to set an ADI. In 1978 the SCF reviewed these compounds and cited even more unpublished data from the same source, but they mentioned only the liver enlargement problem and endorsed the ADI which JECFA had set five years earlier. Neither JECFA nor the FACC have commented publicly since then.

No adverse effects on humans have been reported and they are presumed to be safe.

Regulatory status Permitted and used in the UK, but they have not been approved for general use by the EEC Council of Ministers, and so do not have an 'E' number. They are also not permitted in the USA.

E477: Propane-1,2-diol Esters of Fatty Acids

also known as Polypropylene Glycol Esters of Fatty Acids

Type This is a group of emulsifiers. The commercial product is a complex mixture which is viscous and slightly bitter-tasting.

Foods added to They can be found in some confectionery, ice cream, toppings, beverages and meat products.

Toxicological evaluation and possible health hazards In 1970 the FACC listed these mixtures in Group B, because although they thought that they were probably safe, they wanted several further studies to reassure themselves. They reviewed them again in 1972, and on that occasion promoted them into Group A, stating that they were satisfied that these additives could be safely metabolized into chemical components which are already approved as safe for use in foods.

JECFA evaluated these substances three times, in 1966, 1969 and in 1973. On the most recent occasion they reported that they were satisfied that these substances are metabolized into unproblematic fatty acids and Propylene Glycol (see p. 207), for which they had established an ADI (but which has never been assigned a Euro-number). When the SCF reported on these compounds in 1978 they formulated some fresh doubts. They voiced some concern that the identity of the material which JECFA had approved was not the same as the material currently being marketed. In so far as the materials were identical, the SCF endorsed JECFA's view, but they asked for more information about the further components which JECFA had not specifically considered. In 1983 the SCF reported that the levels at which the dubious materials were being used were being reduced to 0.5 per cent of the mixtures, and at that level the SCF were content not to pursue the matter further.

No adverse effects have been reported and they are presumed to be safe.

Special restrictions Since the production of these chemicals can depend on animal sources, they are not acceptable to vegetarians or vegans, and are not kosher or halal.

Regulatory status Permitted and used in the UK, the EEC and the USA.

478: Lactylated Fatty Acid Esters of Glycerol and Propane-1,2-diol

Type This is a group of emulsifiers and stabilizers.

Foods added to They can be found in some dessert mixes, cakes and other baked goods to 'improve volume', i.e. to fill them with air.

Toxicological evaluation and possible health hazards We can find no discussion of this group of substances in the publications of JECFA or the FACC and CoT. In 1978, however, the SCF reviewed three unpublished studies on these compounds. One of these studies had been sent to JECFA in 1973, but they had not been prepared to pronounce on it. The other two unpublished reports came in the late 1960s from a company called Industrial Bio-Test (IBT). In the late 1970s IBT was at the centre of a scandal concerning the fabrication and misrepresentation of data, and none of their work can be considered entirely reliable. None the less, the SCF gave temporary permission for the use of these compounds, conditional upon limitations on the composition of the mixtures used, and the provision of further data within two years. In 1983 the SCF reported that the requisite data were not then available, and so they reclassified this group into category 4, meaning that no ADI could be established and that they are not toxicologically acceptable for use in food. They continue to be per-

mitted and used in the UK and in the USA.

No adverse effects have been reported, and in the absence of adequate information they are presumed by some people to be safe.

Special restrictions Since the production of these chemicals can depend on animal sources, they are not acceptable to vegetarians or vegans, and are not kosher or halal.

Regulatory status Permitted and used in the UK and the USA, but they are not approved for use in the EEC and they have no 'E' number.

E481: Sodium Stearoyl-2-Lactylate

Type This is an emulsifier, dough conditioner and stabilizer, which first entered commercial use in the 1960s.

Foods added to It can be found in some crisps, potato snacks, baked goods especially high protein and gluten breads, cake icings, both dairy and non-dairy whipped toppings, shortening, non-dairy whiteners, edible fats and oils.

Toxicological evaluation and possible health hazards JECFA evaluated this substance in 1969, 1971 and 1973 alongside Calcium Stearoyl-2-Lactylate (see E482). In 1973 JECFA based their evaluation on four reports which had been published in the 1950s and fourteen unpublished reports. They had not received any long-term test results, but only tests on how these substances are metabolized in animals. They were satisfied that the animals metabolize them in an innocuous fashion, and they were ready to presume that humans metabolize them in a similar way, but they requested evidence in support of this assumption. They set an ADI at 20mg/kg bw on the basis of a short-term test on rats. A curious feature of this judgement is that it was based on an NEL of 1000mg/kg bw, which suggests that JECFA employed a safety factor of 50 rather than 100. No explanation was provided for this deviation from standard practice.

In 1972 the FACC reviewed this compound. They were not prepared to recommend its use in bread in general, but they did believe that there was a need for it in high protein and high gluten breads. The FACC listed it in Group B on the basis of a long-term feeding study on dogs, and called for further studies on two other animal species, and investigations of the route by which humans metabolize this additive. In 1978 the SCF simply endorsed the JECFA ADI, on the basis of the same data.

No adverse effects have been reported and it is presumed to be safe.

Special restrictions Since the production of this chemical can depend on animal sources, it is not acceptable to vegetarians or vegans, and is not kosher or halal.

Regulatory status It is permitted and used in the UK and the EEC, but not in the USA.

E482: Calcium Stearoyl-2-Lactylate

Type This is an emulsifier and stabilizer.

Foods added to It can be found in gravy granules and in some bread, buns and cakes. It can also be used as an egg-white whipping aid.

Toxicological evaluation and possible health hazards JECFA evaluated this substance in 1969, 1971 and 1973 alongside Sodium Stearoyl-2-Lactylate (see E481). In 1973 JECFA based their evaluation on four reports

which had been published in the 1950s and fourteen unpublished reports. They had not received any long-term test results, but only tests on how these substances are metabolized in animals. They were satisfied that the animals metabolize them in an innocuous fashion, and they were ready to presume that humans metabolize them in a similar way, but they requested evidence in support of this assumption. They set an ADI at 20mg/kg bw on the basis of a short-term test on rats, in spite of the fact that they had noted that short-term tests with rats had given variable and inconsistent results.

In 1972 the FACC reviewed this compound. They were not prepared to recommend its use in bread in general, but they did believe that there is a need for it in high protein and high gluten breads. The FACC listed it in Group B on the basis of a long-term feeding study on dogs, and called for further studies on two other animal species, and investigations of the route by which humans metabolize this additive. In 1978 the SCF simply endorsed the JECFA ADI, on the basis of the same data.

No adverse effects have been reported and it is presumed to be safe.

Special restrictions Since the production of this chemical can depend upon animal sources, it is not acceptable to vegetarians or vegans, and is not kosher or halal.

Regulatory status It is permitted and used in the UK and the EEC, but not in the USA.

E483: Stearyl Tartrate

Type This is a flour treatment agent which is prepared from Tartaric Acid (see E334).

Foods added to It can be found in some cakes and packet cake mixes.

Toxicological evaluation and possible health hazards This has been evaluated only once by JECFA in 1965, when they set a full ADI at 500 ppm. No adverse effects have been reported and it is presumed to be safe.

Special restrictions Since the production of this chemical can depend on animal sources, it is not acceptable to vegetarians or vegans, and is not kosher or halal.

Regulatory status It is permitted and used in the UK and the EEC, but not in the USA.

491: Sorbitan Monostearate

Type It is an emulsifier and defoaming agent and is synthetized from Stearic Acid (see 570).

Foods added to It can be found in some chocolate, margarine, cakes, cake mixes, whipped vegetable oil toppings, milk and cream substitutes for use in coffee and beverages.

Toxicological evaluation and possible health hazards JECFA reviewed this compound in 1963 and 1973 alongside Sorbitan Tristearate (see 492) and Sorbitan Monopalmitate (see 495). When the FACC reviewed this compound in 1970 they had received results from short-term tests with rats, dogs and monkeys and long-term tests with rats, as well as some tests on humans. They listed it in Group B and permitted it temporarily, but asked for long-term tests in a second species. By 1973 JECFA had received no further results but set a full ADI of 25mg/kg bw without waiting for further long-term data (this ADI was intended to cover all three compounds). This judgement was based on the results of a long-term feeding study on rats. When

the SCF considered it in 1978 they reviewed two reports from JECFA and seven unpublished reports, then merely endorsed JECFA's evaluation.

No adverse effects have been reported and it is presumed to be safe.

Special restrictions Since the production of this chemical can depend upon animal sources, it is not acceptable to vegetarians or vegans, and is not kosher or halal.

Regulatory status It is permitted and used in the UK and the USA, but the Council of EEC Ministers have not given it an 'E' number.

492: Sorbitan Tristearate

also known as Span 65

Type It is an emulsifier.

Foods added to It can be found in some chocolate and packet cake mixes, but it is also used to stabilize flavour emulsions which are used in soft drinks.

Toxicological evaluation and possible health hazards JECFA reviewed this compound in 1963 and 1973 alongside Sorbitan Monostearate (see 491) and Sorbitan Monopalmitate (see 495). When the FACC reviewed this compound in 1970 they had received results from short-term tests on twenty rats, ten of which received the test substance through a stomach tube, while the other ten had it administered by injection. They also had the results of one long-term test on thirty male rats which was conducted as long ago as 1947, but no data on humans. They listed it as Group B and permitted it temporarily, but asked for a long-term test in a second species. By 1973 JECFA had received no further results but set a full ADI of 25mg/kg bw without waiting for further long-term data (this ADI was intended to cover all three compounds). This judgement was based on the results of a long-term feeding study on rats. When the SCF considered it in 1978 they reviewed two reports from JECFA and three unpublished reports, then merely endorsed JECFA's evaluation.

No adverse effects have been reported and it is presumed to be safe.

Special restrictions Since the production of this chemical can depend on animal sources, it is not acceptable to vegetarians or vegans, and is not kosher or halal.

Regulatory status Permitted in the UK, but it is not generally approved in the EEC (and so has no 'E' number) or in the USA.

493: Sorbitan Monolaurate
also known as Span 20

Type It is an emulsifier and anti-foaming agent.

Foods added to It is used to prevent foaming in some cooked sugar mixes and so can be found in some jams, preserves and boiled sweets.

Toxicological evaluation and possible health hazards The FACC listed this substance as Group B in 1970 because they considered the data available to them to be inadequate. They called for data from short-term studies and a long-term test in a second species other than a rat. In 1978 the SCF reported that on the basis of seven unpublished studies, five of which were undated, they were prepared to set an ADI of 5mg/kg bw for this substance and Sorbitan Mono-oleate (see 494) together. The SCF report fails to reveal whether or not they had received the data for which the FACC had been asking eight years before. It

was not until 1982 that JECFA evaluated this compound, and then set a full ADI of 25mg/kg bw in respect of the group of Sorbitan compounds (see 491–495).

No adverse effects have been reported and it is presumed to be safe.

Special restrictions Since the production of this chemical can depend on animal sources, it is not acceptable to vegetarians or vegans, and is not kosher or halal.

Regulatory status Permitted in the UK, but it is not generally approved in the EEC (and so has no 'E' number) or in the USA.

494: Sorbitan Mono-oleate
also known as Span 80

Type It is an emulsifier and defoamer.

Foods added to It can be found in some dietary products, chewing gum and packet cake mixes.

Toxicological evaluation and possible health hazards The FACC listed this substance in Group B in 1970 because they considered the data available to them to be inadequate. They called for data from short-term studies and a long-term test in a second species other than the rat. In 1978 the SCF reported that they were prepared to set an ADI of 5mg/kg bw for this substance and Sodium Monolaurate (see 493) together. The SCF report fails to reveal whether or not they had received the data for which the FACC had been asking eight years before. It was not until 1982 that JECFA evaluated this compound, and then set a full ADI of 25mg/kg bw in respect of the group of Sorbitan compounds (see 491–495).

No adverse effects have been reported and it is presumed to be safe.

Special restrictions Since the production of this chemical can depend on animal sources, it is not acceptable to vegetarians or vegans, and is not kosher or halal.

Regulatory status Permitted in the UK, but it is not generally approved in the EEC (and so has no 'E' number) or in the USA.

495: Sorbitan Monopalmitate
also known as Span 40

Type This is an emulsifier and flavour dispersing agent.

Foods added to It can be found in some chocolate and cake mixes.

Toxicological evaluation and possible health hazards JECFA reviewed this compound in 1963 and 1973 alongside Sorbitan Monostearate and Sorbitan Tristearate (see 491 and 492). When the FACC reviewed this compound in 1970 they had received results from short-term tests in ten male rats and a long-term test on rats, but no data on humans. They listed it in Group B and permitted it temporarily, but asked for a long-term test in a second species. By 1973 JECFA had received no further results, but set a full ADI of 25mg/kg bw without waiting for further long-term data (this ADI was intended to cover all three compounds). When the SCF considered it in 1978 they reviewed two reports from JECFA and five unpublished reports (three of which were undated), and then merely endorsed JECFA's evaluation.

No adverse effects have been reported and it is presumed to be safe.

Special restrictions Since the production of this chemical can depend upon animal sources, it is not acceptable to vegetarians or vegans, and is not kosher or halal.

Regulatory status Permitted in the UK, but it is not generally approved in the EEC (and so has no 'E' number) or in the USA.

500: Sodium Carbonate, Sodium Hydrogen Carbonate, (also known as Bicarbonate of Soda) **and Sodium Sesquicarbonate**

Type This group of common salts is used because they can act as buffers, foaming agents, release and raising agents. They occur naturally as saline residues in the form of white or colourless crystals. They are, however, generally manufactured synthetically because it is often cheaper.

Foods added to They can be found in some tinned custard, bread products, cheesy potato snacks, sweetened condensed milks and ice cream.

Toxicological evaluation and possible health hazards This is a group of salts with which chemists have been familiar for hundreds of years. There is also a long medical tradition of using these substances as an antacid to relieve some symptoms of indigestion.

JECFA evaluated them only once, and that was in 1965. On that occasion they approved the general use of these compounds without any specific restrictions. We know that if we consume them in large quantities they can produce corrosion of the gastrointestinal tract, mineral imbalances, vomiting or diarrhoea; but when they are used at additive doses they are presumed to be safe.

Regulatory status Permitted and used in the UK and the USA where they are listed as GRAS, but they do not have an 'E' number.

501: Potassium Carbonates
also known as Salt of Tartar, and Potassium Hydrogen Carbonate

Type These are used as alkaline buffers.

Foods added to They can be found in some confections, cocoa products, and custard powders. They are also used in combination with Potassium Hydroxide to extract the colour from Annatto seeds (see E160(b)).

Toxicological evaluation and possible health hazards JECFA evaluated them only once, and that was in 1965. On that occasion they approved the general use of these compounds without any specific restrictions. In large quantities they are irritants with caustic action, but they are presumed to be safe at realistic additive doses.

Regulatory status Permitted and used in the UK, the EEC and the USA where they are listed as GRAS, but they do not have an 'E' number.

503: Ammonium Carbonate Ammonium Hydrogen Carbonate

Type These are used as bleaching and leavening agents, buffers and neutralizers. In their commercial form they come as shiny, hard crystals with a slight odour of ammonia.

Foods added to They can be found in some baked goods, confections and ice creams.

Toxicological evaluation and possible health hazards JECFA evaluated these salts three times between 1965 and 1982. On each occasion they were satisfied that they can be used without any specific restrictions needing to be set. In large quantities they may irritate the mucous membranes of the stomach or cause mineral imbalance in the circulatory system, but they are presumed to be safe at realistic additive doses.

Regulatory status Permitted and used in the UK and the USA where they are listed as GRAS, but they do not have an 'E' number.

504: Magnesium Carbonate

Type This is a naturally occurring mineral which is used as an anti-caking and antibleaching agent.

Foods added to It can be found in some ice cream, sour cream, icing sugar and some canned peas.

Toxicological evaluation and possible health hazards JECFA evaluated it only once, and that was in 1965. On that occasion they approved the general use of this compound without any specific restrictions.

No adverse effects have been reported, and it is presumed to be safe.

Regulatory status Permitted and used in the UK and in the USA where it is listed as GRAS, but it does not have an 'E' number.

507: Hydrochloric Acid

Type This is used as an acidifier.

Foods added to It is used to process food starch and in the brewing industry.

Toxicological evaluation and possible health hazards. The human stomach produces Hydrochloric Acid as one of the main constituents of our gastric juices. The acid in our stomach is so strong that if we were to put some on our lips or in our mouths it would sting. When concentrated it is severely corrosive, but when used as an additive it is invariably presumed to be safe, although it is hazardous to workers in industry if they have to handle it in bulk quantities. JECFA evaluated it only once, and that was in 1965. On that occasion they approved the general use of this material without any specific restrictions.

When used as an additive it is assumed to be safe.

Regulatory status It is permitted and used in the UK and in the USA where it is listed as GRAS, but it does not have an 'E' number.

508: Potassium Chloride

Type It is used as a seasoning (as an alternative to common salt), a gelling agent and as a yeast food.

Foods added to It can be found in some canned red kidney beans, salt substitutes, dietary supplements and is used in the brewing process.

Toxicological evaluation and possible health hazards Between 1974 and 1978 JECFA considered specifications on the levels of impurities in commercially available sources of this compound. Only when they were satisfied on this matter did they evaluate it for safety in 1979. On that occasion they did not set an ADI.

There is evidence that when used in large doses this material may be toxic, but at the doses at which it is used as an additive it is presumed to be safe.

Regulatory status It is permitted and used in the UK and in the USA where it is listed as GRAS, but it does not have an 'E' number.

509: Calcium Chloride

Type It is used as a sequestrant and as a firming agent. It does occur naturally, particularly in sea water over chalky rocks, but it is a commercial product of the Solvay process.

Foods added to It can be found in some processed cheese products, tinned fruit, vegetables and beans and some dried and condensed milk products.

Toxicological evaluation and possible health hazards JECFA evaluated this compound in 1963 and 1973. They stated that this material enters into the natural metabolism of the body and can therefore be disregarded toxicologically when used as an additive. They concluded that it is sufficiently safe to be permitted without any specific restrictions. There is some evidence, however, that at high doses this material may be slightly hazardous, and so some quantitative restrictions may be in order, but it is generally presumed to be safe.

Regulatory status It is permitted and used in the UK and in the USA where it is listed as GRAS, but it does not yet have an 'E' number.

510: Ammonium Chloride
also known as Sal Ammoniac

Type It is used as a dough conditioner and yeast food.

Foods added to It can be found in some bread, rolls and buns.

Toxicological evaluation and possible health hazards JECFA evaluated this material just once in 1979. They judged it to be sufficiently safe that they could approve its use as a food additive without any specific restrictions. There is some evidence, however, that at high doses this material may be a potential hazard and so some quantitative restrictions may be in order, but it is presumed to be safe.

Regulatory status It is permitted and used in the UK and in the USA, but it does not have an 'E' number.

513: Sulphuric Acid

Type It is a common acid.

Foods added to It is used to regulate acidity in the brewing industry and to modify starch.

Toxicological evaluation and possible health hazards. This fluid is notoriously corrosive when in a concentrated form; indeed, if it is ingested undiluted it can be fatal. JECFA and the SCF have provided no toxicological evaluation of Sulphuric Acid, but JECFA has set purity standards for use in foods. Likely additive usage is presumed to be safe.

Regulatory status Permitted and used in the UK and the USA where it is listed as GRAS, but it does not have an 'E' number.

514: Sodium Sulphate

Type It occurs naturally in the minerals mirabilite and thenardite.

Foods added to It is used to dilute mixtures containing other additives and in some chewing gum bases. It is also used in the dye industry and as a disinfectant.

Toxicological evaluation and possible health hazards Neither JECFA nor the SCF have ever had occasion to evaluate this compound, and presumably this is because they consider it to be safe. There is a report that it has the effect of stimulating the production of stomach juices. Those people who have been advised to eat a diet low in Sodium would wish to avoid this substance.

Regulatory status It is permitted and used in the UK and the USA, but it does not yet have an 'E' number.

515: Potassium Sulphate

Type It is a salt substitute, which is available as a colourless or white crystalline powder with a bitter taste.

Foods added to It is sometimes used as a substitute for common salt in dietetic products for those who should have a low-Sodium diet, and it is also used in beer production. It is also incorporated in some fertilizers and medicines.

Toxicological evaluation and possible health hazards Neither JECFA nor the SCF have ever had occasion to evaluate this compound, and presumably this is because they consider it to be safe. There is a report that in large doses it can cause gastro-intestinal bleeding, but when used as an additive it is presumed to be safe.

Regulatory status It is permitted and used in the UK and the USA, but it does not yet have an 'E' number.

516: Calcium Sulphate
also known as Plaster of Paris

Type It is a firming agent, sequestrant, dough conditioner and yeast food. It occurs naturally as a mineral.

Foods added to It can be found in some cereal flours, bread, rolls, buns and cheese products.

Toxicological evaluation and possible health hazards JECFA evaluated this salt in 1969 and 1973. They noted that Calcium is an essential nutrient which is present in large quantities and so it is unlikely that a slight addition to our intake would be toxicologically significant. They reported that another FAO/WHO expert group had stated that our Calcium intake could safely range between 400mg and 2–3 g a day.

No adverse effects have been reported and it is presumed to be safe.

Regulatory status It is permitted and used in the UK and the USA, but it does not yet have an 'E' number.

518: Magnesium Sulphate
also known as Gypsum and as Epsom Salts

Type It is a firming agent and dietary supplement. It occurs naturally in sea water and some rocks.

Foods added to It is used in brewing, and is a traditional ingredient in indigestion treatments.

Toxicological evaluation and possible health hazards Neither JECFA nor the SCF have ever had occasion to evaluate this compound, and presumably this is because they consider it to be safe when used as a food additive, even though it may cause diarrhoea at medicinal doses.

Regulatory status It is permitted and used in the UK and the USA, but it does not yet have an 'E' number.

524: Sodium Hydroxide
also known as Lye and as Caustic Soda

Type It is an alkali.

Foods added to It can be found in some edible oils and fats, sour cream, cocoa products, tinned vegetables and jams.

Toxicological evaluation and possible health hazards JECFA evaluated this material once in 1965 and then approved it for use as an additive without any quantitative restrictions. When in a concentrated form this material is notoriously corrosive. In the USA household drain cleaning liquids may contain no more than 10 per cent Sodium Hydroxide, and this provision is intended to protect both the users and the drains. Given that it is so unpleasant it poses a hazard to industrial workers who handle it in bulk and concentrated forms.

Regulatory status It is permitted and used in the UK and the USA where it is listed as GRAS, but it does not yet have an 'E' number.

525: Potassium Hydroxide
also known as Caustic Potash

Type It is an alkali.

Foods added to It can be found in some cocoa products, jams, and cheese products. It is also used to extract Annatto colouring from the seeds (see E160(b)).

Toxicological evaluation and possible health hazards JECFA evaluated this material once in 1965 and then approved it for use as an additive without any quantitative restrictions. When in a concentrated form this material is notoriously corrosive. In the USA household drain cleaning liquids may contain no more than 10 per cent Potassium Hydroxide, and this provision is intended to protect both the users and the drains. Given that it is so unpleasant it poses a hazard to industrial workers who handle it in bulk and concentrated forms.

Regulatory status It is permitted and used in the UK and the USA where it is listed as GRAS, but it does not yet have an 'E' number.

526: Calcium Hydroxide
also known as Slaked Lime

Type It is used as a firming agent and alkaline buffer.

Foods added to It can be found in some fruit, cheese and cocoa products, and jams.

Toxicological evaluation and possible health hazards JEFCA evaluated this material once in 1965 and then approved it for use as an additive without any quantitative restrictions.

When used as an additive no adverse effects have been reported, and it is presumed to be safe.

Regulatory status It is permitted and used in the UK and the USA where it is listed as GRAS, but it does not yet have an 'E' number.

527: Ammonium Hydroxide

Type It is an alkali.

Foods added to It can be found in some baked goods, confections and cocoa products. It is also used to dilute some solutions of food colours.

Toxicological evaluation and possible health hazards JECFA evaluated this material once in 1965 and then approved it for use as an additive without any quantitative restrictions. In large quantities it would be caustic and it may adversely affect people with a faulty kidney or liver.

Regulatory status It is permitted and used in the UK and the USA where it is listed as GRAS, but it does not yet have an 'E' number.

528: Magnesium Hydroxide

Type It is used as an alkali and to dilute some solutions of food colours. It is also used in the manufacture of some Caramels (see E150).

Foods added to It can be found in some tinned vegetables, cheese and cocoa products.

Toxicological evaluation and possible health hazards JECFA evaluated this material once in 1965 and then approved it for use as an additive without any quantitative restrictions.

No adverse effects have been reported and it is presumed to be safe.

Regulatory status It is permitted and used in the UK and the USA where it is listed as GRAS, but it does not yet have an 'E' number.

529: Calcium Oxide

also known as Lime and as Quicklime

Type It is an alkali, dough conditioner and yeast food.

Foods added to It can be found in some dairy products, sour cream, confections and tripe.

Toxicological evaluation and possible health hazards JECFA evaluated this material once in 1965 and then approved it for use as an additive without any quantitative restrictions. In concentrated solutions it is very caustic and can severely damage skin and mucous membranes, but at realistic additive doses it is presumed to be safe.

Regulatory status It is permitted and used in the UK and the USA where it is listed as GRAS, but it does not yet have an 'E' number.

530: Magnesium Oxide
also known as Magnesia

Type It is an alkaline anti-caking agent.

Foods added to It can be found in some dairy products, tinned peas and some cocoa products. It is also a major active ingredient in Milk of Magnesia products for the relief of indigestion.

Toxicological evaluation and possible health hazards JECFA evaluated this material once in 1965 and then approved it for use as an additive without any quantitative restrictions.

No adverse effects have been reported from its use as an additive and it is presumed to be safe.

Regulatory status It is permitted and used in the UK and the USA where it is listed as GRAS, but it does not yet have an 'E' number.

535: Sodium Ferrocyanide
also known as Sodium Hexacyano-
ferrate (II)

Type This is used as an anti-caking agent and in the manufacture of some wines.

Foods added to It is added to some table salt and wines.

Toxicological evaluation and possible health hazards JECFA evaluated this compound three times between 1969 and 1974 alongside Potassium Ferrocyanide (see 536). In 1973 they commented that the bond between the iron and the cyanide in this compound was so strong that the potentially toxic cyanide part of the molecule was effectively inactivated. They had data from short-term tests in dogs and rats, and biochemical evidence from dogs, rabbits, rats and humans. They did not, however, have any long-term data in any species. They pointed out that the material became unstable in acid solutions. They set a temporary ADI at 0.025mg/kg bw, and requested a metabolic study in humans within a year, and said that if any untoward effects were noticed they would require a long-term study in one animal species. This judgement was based on an NEL in a short-term rat study, and they rather cautiously used a safety factor of 1,000 rather than the standard figure of 100.

One year later their report was introduced with the statement that they had received further data and extended their review. A careful reading of both documents reveals that the second one does not list any data or sources other than those which are in the first. What they did, however, was simply to change the summary and declare in effect that the information which had been considered inadequate the previous year had suddenly become sufficient. No further tests were required but the ADI was changed from being 'temporary' to 'full'.

Despite the relative poverty of our knowledge of this substance it is officially presumed to be safe.

Regulatory status This substance was not permitted in the UK under 1974 regulations, but it would appear that at some time in the early 1980s it was added to the British permitted list

It is not permitted in the USA and it does not have an 'E' number.

536: Potassium Ferrocyanide

Type It is an anti-caking agent.

Foods added to It can be found in table salt and wines.

Toxicological evaluation and possible health hazards JECFA evaluated this compound three times between 1969 and 1974 alongside Sodium Ferrocyanide (see 535). In 1973 they commented that the bond between the iron and the cyanide in this compound is so strong that the potentially toxic cyanide part of the molecule is effectively inactivated. They had data from short-term tests in dogs and rats, and biochemical evidence from dogs, rabbits, rats and humans. They did not, however, have any long-term data in any species. They pointed out that the material becomes unstable in acid solutions. They set a temporary ADI at 0.025mg/kg bw, and requested a metabolic study in humans within a year, stating that if any untoward effects were noticed they would require a long-term study in one animal species. This judgement was based on an NEL in a short-term rat study, and they rather cautiously used a safety factor of 1,000 rather than the standard figure of 100.

One year later their report was introduced with the statement that they had received further data and extended their review. A careful reading of both documents reveals that the second one does not list any data or sources other than those which are in the first. What they did, however, was simply to change the summary and declare in effect that the information which had been considered inadequate the previous year had suddenly become sufficient. No further tests were required

but the ADI was changed from being 'temporary' to 'full'.

Regulatory status This substance was not permitted in the UK under 1974 regulations, but it would appear that at some time in the early 1980s it was added to the British permitted list. It is not permitted in the USA, and it does not have an 'E' number.

540: Di-Calcium Di-Phosphate and Calcium Hydrogen Phosphate

Type These are used as yeast foods, dough conditioners and in mineral supplements.

Foods added to They can be found in some bread, rolls, cereal flours, and cheese products.

Toxicological evaluation and possible health hazards JECFA evaluated these compounds alongside Phosphoric Acid (see E338), the Polyphosphates and their Calcium (see E450 and 544), Potassium (see E450) and Sodium Salts (see E450) in 1973, 1976 and 1983. JECFA say that the Calcium Phosphates provide sources of Calcium and Phosphate ions, and these are both essential nutrients. For this reason they are presumed to be safe when used as food additives. JECFA have set an ADI of 70mg/kg bw, where this figure applies to the sum of added Phosphates and food Phosphates.

Regulatory status Permitted and used in the UK and in the USA where they are listed as GRAS, but they do not yet have an 'E' number.

541: Sodium Aluminium Phosphate

also known as Salp when in an acid solution and as Kasal when in alkaline solution

Type Salp is used as a leavening agent, and Kasal as an emulsifier.

Foods added to Salp can be found

in some packet mixes, while Kasal can be found in some processed cheeses and some self-raising flour.

Toxicological evaluation and possible health hazards JECFA evaluated both Salp and Kasal in 1982 and set a temporary ADI of 6mg/kg bw to cover them both. People who have been advised to eat a low-Sodium diet might wish to avoid these compounds even though they are used in very small quantities as an additive. They are otherwise presumed to be safe.

Regulatory status Permitted and used in the UK and the USA where they are listed as GRAS. but they do not yet have an 'E' number.

542: Edible Bone Phosphate

Type This is essentially similar to Tricalcium Phosphate (see E341(c)) and it is used as a mineral supplement and anti-caking agent. It is obtained by steaming animal bones which have first been degreased.

Foods added to No specific food uses have been reported, but it is commonly used in pharmaceutical tablets and mineral supplements.

Toxicological evaluation and possible health hazards JECFA evaluated this substance in 1969 and in 1982 and on the latter occasion set a full ADI of 70mg/kg bw.

No adverse effects have been reported and it is presumed to be safe.

Special restrictions Since the production of this chemical depends on animal sources, it is not acceptable to vegetarians or vegans, and is not kosher or halal.

Regulatory status Permitted and used in the UK, but it does not yet have an 'E' number.

544: Calcium Polyphosphates

Type These are used as texturizers, emulsifiers, moisture retaining agents and sequestrants.

Foods added to They can be found in some cheeses and processed meat products.

Toxicological evaluation and possible health hazards JECFA evaluated these compounds most recently in 1982 when they set a full ADI of 70mg/kg bw.

No adverse effects have been reported and they are presumed to be safe.

Regulatory status These are permitted and used in the UK, but do not yet have an 'E' number.

545: Ammonium Polyphosphates

Type In 1984 JECFA stated that the function of these chemicals was not yet clear to them.

Foods added to They can be found in some processed cheese and meat products.

Toxicological evaluation and possible health hazards JECFA evaluated these compounds most recently in 1982 when they set a full ADI of 70mg/kg bw.

No adverse effects have been reported and they are presumed to be safe.

Regulatory status These are permitted and used in the UK, but do not yet have an 'E' number.

551: Silicon Dioxide
also known as Silica

Type It is used as an anti-caking agent, is derived from sand or rocks, and is available in the form of a tasteless powder or transparent crystals. For use in the food industry it is often processed into a fine powder and mixed with water to form a gel.

Foods added to It can be found for example in some milk products, cocoa products, edible oils and fats, and shaped crisps. In particular it is often added to milk and cream powders when they are used in vending machines. Silica can also be found in potatoes, milk and tap water. Silica is often used in combination with Dimethyl Polysiloxane (see 900).

Toxicological evaluation and possible health hazards JECFA evaluated it three times between 1969 and 1978 alongside several Silicates including those of Calcium (see 552), Magnesium (see 553a) and Aluminium (see 554, 556 and 559). JECFA observed that Silica can be found in very small amounts in all human body tissue, but no evidence has yet been found that it plays any physiological role. It has been the subject of several short-term tests on rats, rabbits, dogs and chickens, which revealed high doses at which it could do harm. Forty rats were fed moderate doses daily for two years, but no adverse effects were noted. There is some evidence from a few tests with humans that the material is almost indigestible. JECFA concluded therefore that Silica can safely be used as a food additive without any quantitative restrictions.

No adverse effects have been reported from its use as an additive, and it is presumed to be safe.

Regulatory status It is permitted and used in the UK and in the USA where it is listed as GRAS, but it does not have an 'E' number.

552: Calcium Silicate

Type It is an anti-caking agent, glazing agent and acidity regulator.

Foods added to It can be found in some chewing gum coatings, meat pies, table salt, confectionery and crisps, but it is also used in vending machines (in combination with other anti-caking agents) in milk, cream and sugar.

Toxicological evaluation and possible health hazards JECFA evaluated it in 1969 and 1973 alongside Silicon Dioxide (see 551) and several Silicates, including those of Magnesium (see 553a) and Aluminium (see 554, 556 and 559). JECFA observed that Silica can be found in very small amounts in all human body tissue, but no evidence has yet been found that it plays any physiological role. Almost all of the tests to which they referred had been conducted on Silicon Dioxide rather than on Calcium Silicate, but JECFA concluded that they could readily extrapolate from Silica to Calcium Silicate, and that the latter can safely be used as a food additive without any quantitative restrictions.

No adverse effects have been reported from its use as an additive, and it is presumed to be safe.

Regulatory status Permitted and used in the UK and in the USA where it is listed as GRAS, but it does not yet have an 'E' number.

553(a): Magnesium Silicate and Magnesium Trisilicate

Type These are synthetic anti-caking agents, which are available as fine, white, odourless and tasteless powders.

Foods added to They can be found in some table salt, vanilla powder, packet noodles and crisps. Magnesium Trisilicate is a common active ingredient in tablets and powders intended to treat acid indigestion.

Toxicological evaluation and possible health hazards JECFA evaluated these compounds five times between 1969 and 1982 in the context of their discussion of Silica and the Silicates (see 551–559). In 1973 they reported that they had two reservations about the safety of Magnesium Silicate. One concerned the fact that in short-term feeding tests on beagle dogs using quite low doses conspicuous lesions were noticeable in their kidneys, and second they were worried about levels of contamination from asbestos-like particles. They temporarily permitted the use of these compounds without any specific restrictions, but called for further studies on the kidney lesions and the contamination problem to be completed by the summer of 1976. When they reported in 1976 they were still not completely satisfied and while they renewed their approval it remained temporary. It was not until 1980 that they eventually concluded that the unlimited ADI could be made permanent. Through the time of uncertainty and doubt these additives continued to be used.

No adverse effects to human consumers have been reported and they are presumed to be safe at additive doses.

Regulatory status Permitted and used in the UK and the USA, but they do not yet have an 'E' number.

553(b): Talc
also known as Magnesium Hydrogen Metasilicate

Type It is used as an anti-caking agent, dusting powder and a filtering aid. It is a naturally occurring mineral.

Foods added to It can be found in some packet noodles, icing sugar, chewing gum base and vitamin supplements. It is also sometimes used to coat rice grains.

Toxicological evaluation and possible health hazards JECFA evaluated this substance in 1980. Before that time there were persistent worries about the

levels of asbestos contamination in commercial supplies of Talc. In 1980 JECFA approved this substance without any specific restrictions. It is known from occupational studies that prolonged inhalation of this powder can cause lung damage. The high incidence of stomach cancer among the Japanese is suspected to be due to a diet high in rice which has been treated with talc.

At additive doses it is usually presumed to be safe.

Regulatory status Permitted and used in the UK and in the USA where it is listed as GRAS, but it does not yet have an 'E' number.

554: Aluminium Sodium Silicate
also known as Sodium Aluminosilicate

Type This naturally occurring mineral is used as an anti-caking agent.

Foods added to It can be found in some packet noodles and in vending machines in cream, milk, sugar and cocoa powders. It is also used in the manufacture of some food colouring preparations.

Toxicological evaluation and possible health hazards JECFA evaluated this material in 1969, 1973 and 1978 in the context of their discussion of Silica and the Silicates (see 551–559). Despite the fact that there are very little data available on this particular substance, JECFA have approved it for use without any specific restrictions. In 1978 the US Food and Drug Administration pointed out that it had still not been tested for mutagenic, teratogenic and reproductive effects.

No adverse effects have been reported and it is officially presumed to be safe.

Regulatory status Permitted and used in the UK and in the USA where it is listed as GRAS, but it does not yet have an 'E' number.

556: Aluminium Calcium Silicate
also known as Calcium Aluminium Silicate

Type It is a naturally occurring mineral which is used as an anti-caking agent.

Foods added to It can be found in some table salt, icing sugar and vanilla powder.

Toxicological evaluation and possible health hazards JECFA evaluated this compound in 1973 and again in 1974. They did so in the context of their evaluation of Silica and the Silicates (see 551–559). They approved it for use without restriction, except that it should not be used in conjunction with starch.

No adverse effects have been reported and it is officially presumed to be safe.

Regulatory status Permitted and used in the UK and in the USA where it is listed as GRAS, but it does not yet have an 'E' number.

558: Bentonite
Type This is used as an anti-caking agent, a clarifying agent and an emulsifier. It is extracted from clays in the mid-West of the USA and Canada.

Foods added to It can be found as a residue in some wine when it has been used as a clarifying agent.

Toxicological evaluation and possible health hazards Neither JECFA nor the SCF have evaluated this compound, and there is practically no published information about its toxicology. There was a report in 1978 that the US Food and Drug Administra-

tion intends to study it further.

No adverse effects have been reported and it is officially presumed to be safe.

Regulatory status Permitted and used in the UK and in the USA where it is listed as GRAS, but it does not yet have an 'E' number.

559: Kaolin
also known as Aluminium Silicate

Type This is an anti-caking agent which occurs naturally in rocks in Britain, Europe, North America and Asia.

Foods added to It can be found in vending machines in milk and cream powders.

Toxicological evaluation and possible health hazards. JECFA evaluated this substance in 1969 and 1973 in the context of their discussion of Silica and the Silicates (see 551–559). They were sufficiently satisfied as to its safety to approve it for use without any specific restrictions.

No adverse effects have been reported and it is officially presumed to be safe.

Regulatory status Permitted and used in the UK, but not in the USA, and it does not yet have an 'E' number.

570: Stearic Acid
also known as Octadecanoic Acid

Type It is an anti-caking agent which can be found naturally occurring in some vegetable oils, animal fats and bark extract.

Foods added to It can be found in some confectionery, chewing gum base and vanilla flavouring for beverages. It is also used in some ointments, suppositories and cosmetics.

Toxicological evaluation and possible

health hazards Neither JECFA nor the SCF have ever directly evaluated this compound. When evaluating the salt of Stearic Acid (see 572) however, they pointed out that Stearic Acid is a naturally occurring component of tallow and other animal and vegetable oils, and that it occurs as a natural metabolite. For that reason they considered it to be toxicologically unproblematic. There is one report that at moderate doses it might provoke symptoms of intolerance in some sensitive people, but otherwise it is presumed to be safe.

Special restrictions Since the production of this chemical can depend on animal sources, it is not acceptable to vegetarians or vegans, and is not kosher or halal.

Regulatory status It is permitted and used in the UK and the USA, but it does not have an 'E' number.

572: Magnesium Stearate
Type This is an anti-caking agent and emulsifier, which JECFA say should not be used in combination with starch.

Foods added to It can be found in some dehydrated products such as soup powder mixes, and in confectionery.

Toxicological evaluation and possible health hazards JECFA evaluated this compound in 1969 and 1973 alongside the several salts of Myristic, Palmitic and Stearic Acids. In 1973 they stated that they had received some new data, but they then failed to provide any details or any references to that new material. JECFA were satisfied that this compound is toxicologically innocuous.

No adverse effects have been reported and it is presumed to be safe.

Special restrictions Since the production of this chemical can depend on animal sources, it is not acceptable to vegetarians or vegans, and is not kosher or halal.

Regulatory status Permitted and used in the UK, but not in the USA, it also does not yet have an 'E' number.

575: Glucono Delta-Lactone
also known as D-Glucono-1,5-Lactone

Type It is a leavening agent and acidifier. It is commercially available as a sweet-tasting, fine, white, odourless powder.

Foods added to It can be found in some baking powders, jelly powders, soft drinks powders, beer, milk and packet cake mixes.

Toxicological evaluation and possible health hazards JECFA evaluated this material in 1966 and 1974. In 1974 they explained that when dissolved in water it decays into two familiar chemicals which are known to be human metabolites of glucose, and so it is toxicologically innocuous. They did report some new information that this substance did no damage to pregnant and foetal animals, but the source of the information is concealed. They just said: 'Anonymous (1974) Unpublished report submitted by the United States Food and Drug Administration'. They set an ADI of 50mg/kg bw.

No adverse effects have been reported, and it is presumed to be safe.

Regulatory status It is permitted and used in the UK, but it does not have an 'E' number. In the USA the meat industry is allowed to add up to 8oz of Glucono Delta-Lactone to each

100lb of mechanically recovered meat so that it can be more readily coloured and so that it can be smoked more rapidly.

576: Sodium Gluconate

Type It is a sequestrant and yeast food.

Foods added to It can be found in some confections, apple slices, and nutritional supplements.

Toxicological evaluation and possible health hazards JECFA considered this substance in 1979 by reference to Gluconic Acid (which is not currently on any permitted list in the UK or the USA), but they gave their approval to the use of Sodium Gluconate on the basis of the ADI of 50mg/kg bw which was set for the Acid.

No adverse effects have been reported and it is presumed to be safe.

Regulatory status Permitted and used in the UK, where it does not have an 'E' number, and in the US where it is listed as GRAS.

577: Potassium Gluconate

Type It is a yeast food.

Foods added to It can be found in baked goods in which yeast has been used.

Toxicological evaluation and possible health hazards JECFA considered this substance in 1979 by reference to Gluconic Acid (which is not currently on any permitted list in the UK or the USA), but they gave their approval to the use of Potassium Gluconate on the basis of the ADI of 50mg/kg bw which was set for the Acid.

No adverse effects have been reported and it is presumed to be safe.

Regulatory status It is permitted and used in the UK, but not in the USA. It does not have an 'E' number.

578: Calcium Gluconate

Type It is a buffer and firming agent.

Foods added to It can be found in some canned fruit and vegetables, confections and apple slices.

Toxicological evaluation and possible health hazards JECFA considered this substance in 1973 and again in 1979: on the first occasion by reference to its contribution to our Calcium intake, but on the latter occasion by reference to Gluconic Acid (which is not currently on any permitted list in the UK or the USA). They gave their approval to the use of Calcium Gluconate on the basis of the ADI of 50mg/kg bw which was set for the Acid.

No adverse effects have been reported and it is presumed to be safe.

Regulatory status It is permitted and used in the UK and in the USA where it is listed as GRAS, but it does not yet have an 'E' number.

620: L-Glutamic Acid

Type It is a flavour enhancer and salt substitute. It is commercially available as a white crystalline powder that is almost odourless. Although it is a naturally occurring, non-essential amino acid, it is usually manufactured from vegetable protein.

Foods added to It can be found in some savoury snacks, soup mixes, packet sauces, sausages and meat pies.

Toxicological evaluation and possible health hazards JECFA evaluated this compound in 1970 and again in 1973, alongside its Ammonium, Calcium, Monosodium and Potassium Salts (see 621–623). Given the extensive arguments which have raged around this class of compound since then, it is remarkable that they have not returned to it. They might argue that they had dealt with it thoroughly and comprehensively at the time. After all, on that occasion they reviewed almost 150 reports (of which 20 per cent were unpublished) and their treatment was longer and more detailed than any in their entire catalogue. Most of the controversy has related to the possible effects of MSG or Monosodium Glutamate (see 621), but this is mainly because it is the most heavily used of all the Glutamates, rather than because it has been shown to be intrinsically more toxic.

During the late 1940s and early 1950s Glutamic Acid and the Glutamates were used by a few doctors to treat people who had been diagnosed as 'mentally retarded'. In some cases they claimed to have produced an improvement because of their effect on the chemistry of the brain. At that stage, little effort was expended to identify their possible effects on the remainder of the population who were not mentally retarded.

The controversy intensified during the early 1960s when some evidence was provided indicating not only that Glutamic Acid and the Glutamates could have profound effects on the chemistry of the brain, but also that high doses could provoke undesirable changes in the brains of mice. This was complicated by some evidence that Glutamic Acid concentrates in the placental fluid of pregnant women. Furthermore, in the late 1960s some evidence emerged that in some (but not all) tests Glutamic Acid and MSG damaged the reproductive processes of rabbits and chicks, although in previous tests in rats no problems had emerged. In the late 1960s some direct human evidence indicated that, on an empty stomach, Glutamates could provoke acute symptoms of discomfort.

JECFA concluded that since Glutamic Acid is a normal component of proteins it can be adequately metabolized, as long as the digestive system is not overloaded. They concluded that in so far as animal experiments had demonstrated that at high doses Glutamic Acid and the Glutamates may be harmful, their systems would have been overloaded, and that therefore it was entirely possible to establish an NEL, and an ADI at which these compounds could safely be used as food additives. They dismissed the results of crucial tests with rabbits because they had not been reproduced in subsequent tests. They recognized that there was some evidence that Glutamic Acid and the Glutamates had appeared to damage the central nervous systems of young mice, rats and monkeys, and so they recommended that these compounds should not be used in foods prepared specifically for babies and young children. In 1973 they set an ADI of 120mg/kg bw to apply to the group of chemicals as a whole. In 1978, however, a group of scientists in Japan announced that they had found circumstances in which L-Glutamic Acid produced mutations. This is *prima facie* evidence that this additive might cause birth defects and cancer in humans. The decision which has to be made in these circumstances is rather difficult. Glutamic Acid is naturally present in many foods, and it is also used as an additive. If Glutamic Acid is toxic it will be so whether it occurs naturally in the food, or if it is introduced as an additive. You could ban its use as an additive, but you can't ban the dietary use of proteins. What you could do would be to argue that the marginal increase in the possible hazard is not worth the supposed benefits of using the additive. Currently industry and government agree that benefits outweigh risks.

Regulatory status It is permitted and used in the UK and the USA, where it is listed as GRAS, and in many other countries, but it does not have an 'E' number.

621: Monosodium Glutamate
also known as MSG

Type It is called a flavour enhancer. It has only a slight flavour on its own, but when added to foods it stimulates our taste buds and so deceives us into thinking that the foods have more flavour than they really do. This is particularly useful (to the food companies) in those products where the processing has diminished or damaged the original flavour(s). MSG is also often used to enhance the flavour of artificial flavour additives. It can be extracted from some fermented protein foods, such as soya sauce, but commercially available MSG is a synthetic fermentation product.

Foods added to One report estimates that MSG is currently added to over 10,000 different processed food items in the USA. It is also added to some animal feeds to stimulate appetites. By the mid-1960s the Japanese were producing 140 million pounds of MSG a year, and Americans were consuming some 45 million pounds annually, equal to more than 2.6lb per person per year. Since then consumption has increased rapidly. Only some of the products containing MSG have labels, and it is listed on only some of those.

Toxicological evaluation and possible health hazards JECFA have evaluated this controversial compound on three occasions. In 1969 they considered it, but refused to set an ADI, postponed their decision and asked for further data. In 1970 they set an ADI of 120mg/kg bw and reconfirmed this evaluation in 1973. They have published no further reports on this chemical, and the silence is almost deafening. The fact that the SCF has never commented on this substance is also remarkable. The FACC and the CoT did comment briefly in 1978, but they added nothing new to the debate; they behaved rather as if there was no debate, and just listed this compound in Group A.

JECFA's evaluation of MSG is one part of their over-all treatment of L-Glutamic Acid (see 620) and the Glutamates (see 621–623). The vast majority of the 150 documents to which JECFA referred were reports on studies with MSG. They reported that during the late 1940s and early 1950s Glutamic Acid and the Glutamates were used by a few doctors to treat people who had been diagnosed as 'mentally retarded'. In some cases they claimed to have produced an improvement because of their effect on the chemistry of the brain. At that stage, little effort was expended to identify their possible effects on the remainder of the population not mentally retarded.

The controversy about MSG intensified during the early 1960s when some evidence was provided indicating not only that MSG and Glutamic Acid could have profound effects on the chemistry of the brain, but also that high doses of MSG could provoke undesirable changes in the brains of mice. This was complicated by some evidence that Glutamic Acid concentrates in the placental fluid of pregnant women. Furthermore, in the late 1960s some evidence emerged that in some (but not all) tests MSG and Glutamic Acid damaged the reproductive processes of rabbits and chicks, although in previous tests in rats no problems had emerged. In the late 1960s some direct human evidence indicated that, on an empty stomach, Glutamates could provoke acute symptoms of discomfort.

Both JECFA and the FACC admit that MSG has been shown to provoke symptoms of discomfort and intolerance, and not only on empty stomachs. MSG has been particularly popular with some Chinese restaurants, and customers and doctors came to recognize what is called Chinese Restaurant Syndrome, which is attributed to MSG and consists of headaches and respiratory and muscular tightness. One American commentator reported a small study in which approximately 20 per cent of a test sample of schoolchildren, and 30 per cent of an adult group, were intolerant of MSG; the CoT figures are in line with this estimate. JECFA did not comment on the frequency of these problems and just passed on to the next topic. The CoT follow the traditional strategy of 'blaming the victim'. They bluntly remark that: ' . . . the remedy lies essentially in the hands of the individual consumer' and they list it in Group A. The CoT's comment may have been callous, but it may have been correct in a sense which they did not intend. Some results were published in 1981, from tests on people suffering with Chinese Restaurant Syndrome, and they showed that those with the syndrome suffered from Vitamin B6 deficiency and that, with a dietary supplement, they ceased to respond. This in part explains why estimates of the incidence of the syndrome provide such inconsistent answers.

JECFA concluded that since Glutamic Acid is a normal component of proteins it (along with MSG) can be adequately metabolized as long as the digestive system is not overloaded. They concluded that in so far as animal experiments had demonstrated that at high doses MSG and Glutamic Acid may be harmful, their systems would have been overloaded, and therefore that it was entirely possible to establish an NEL, and from that an ADI at which these compounds could safely be used as food additives. They dismissed the results of crucial tests with rabbits because they had not been reproduced in subsequent tests. They recognized that there was some evidence that MSG and Glutamic Acid had appeared to damage the central nervous systems of young mice, rats and monkeys, and so they recommended that these compounds should not be used in foods prepared specifically for babies and young children. In 1973 they set an ADI of 120mg/kg bw to apply to the group of chemicals as a whole. It was not until 1978, however, that the CoT in Britain got round to recommending tht MSG should be excluded from infant foods.

In that same year a group of scientists in Japan announced that they had found circumstances in which L-Glutamic Acid produced mutations. This is *prima facie* evidence that this additive might cause birth defects and cancer in humans. Neither JECFA, the SCF nor the CoT have yet commented directly on this issue. Our decision on how to respond to the evidence of mutagenicity is more straightforward with MSG than it is with L-Glutamic Acid (see 620). Glutamic Acid is naturally present in many foods, but it is also used as an additive. If Glutamic Acid is toxic it will be so whether it occurs naturally in the food, or if it is introduced as an additive. You could ban its use as an additive, but you can't ban the dietary use of proteins. On the other hand, there is far more evidence that MSG might be toxic than there is against L-Glutamic Acid, and MSG does not occur naturally in any fresh food

(although it can be obtained from fermented food). MSG is also very widely used, and quite unnecessary. People who suffer from symptoms of intolerance may well choose to avoid this additive, and many others appear to be joining them.

Regulatory status It is permitted and used in the UK and the USA where it is listed as GRAS, and in many other countries, but it does not have an 'E' number. In the UK MSG should not be included in commercial baby foods, but it remains a risk to the rest of us.

622: Monopotassium Glutamate
also known as MPG

Type It is a flavour enhancer and salt substitute, and a close but less used relative of MSG (see 621).

Foods added to Except in a handful of circumstances, the food industry prefers to use MSG, but MPG can be found in some savoury snacks, dried convenience foods, and dietetic foods, especially those for losing weight or for those on a low-Sodium diet.

Toxicological evaluation and possible health hazards JECFA have evaluated this substance in parallel with Monosodium Glutamate (see 621). The vast majority of the evidence reported tests on Monosodium Glutamate (see 621) and L-Glutamic Acid (see 620), and the evaluation of MPG is subordinated to the more general review. In 1973 JECFA set an overall ADI of 120mg/kg bw to cover this group of chemicals. In so far as there are worries about the safety of MSG, they apply to MPG too. There is some direct human evidence that MPG is as likely to provoke symptoms of intolerance as MSG. It is similarly not acceptable in foods intended for babies.

Regulatory status It is permitted and used in the UK and the USA where it is listed as GRAS, and in many other countries, but it does not have an 'E' number.

623: Calcium Glutamate

also known as Calcium Di-Hydrogen Di-L-Glutamate

Type It is a flavour enhancer and salt substitute.

Foods added to It can be found in some dried convenience foods and in some dietetic foods.

Toxicological evaluation and possible health hazards JECFA have evaluated this substance in parallel with Monosodium and Monopotassium Glutamates (see 621 and 622). JECFA cited only one short-term feeding test conducted with this material, otherwise they relied entirely on reported tests on Monosodium Glutamate (see 621) and L-Glutamic Acid (see 620). In 1973 JECFA set an over-all ADI of 120mg/kg bw to cover this group of chemicals. Altogether too little is known about the toxicology of this substance, and too much about some of its close relatives, for us to be able to presume that it is safe.

Regulatory status It is permitted and used in the UK, but it does not have an 'E' number.

627: Sodium Guanylate

also known as Guanosine 5'-(Disodium Phosphate)

Type It is a flavour enhancer which can be found naturally occurring in several foods, including sardines, from which it can be extracted. It is often used in combinations with Sodium 5'-Inosinate (see 631).

Foods added to It can be found in some cured chopped meat products,

fried potato snacks, gravy granules, and pre-cooked dried rice.

Toxicological evaluation and possible health hazards JECFA considered this compound once in 1974, when they collectively evaluated Guanylic Acid and its Calcium and Disodium Salts. They stated that Guanylates are present in all known tissues, and while we know how they are metabolized in animals, we do not know how humans metabolize them, but they assumed it to be essentially similar. On this basis, plus several teratogenicity tests, they approved the entire class of compounds for use without any specific restrictions. In 1978 the CoT listed this substance in Group A, indicating that they were satisfied that it was safe. Since this substance is believed to be metabolized into Uric Acid, those who suffer from gout or from other kidney disorders might wish to avoid it.

Regulatory status Permitted and used in the UK, but not in foods intended for babies. It is not permitted in the USA, and does not have an 'E' number.

631: Sodium 5'-Inosinate

Type It is a flavour enhancer which occurs naturally in some meat and fish from which it can be extracted. It is often used in combination with Sodium Guanylate (see 627).

Foods added to It can be found in cured meat products, fried potato snacks and dried convenience foods.

Toxicological evaluation and possible health hazards JECFA considered this compound once in 1974 when they evaluated Inosinic Acid and its Calcium and Disodium Salts collectively. They stated that Inosinates are present in all known tissues, and while we knew how they were metabolized in animals, we did not know how humans metabolized them, but they assumed it to be essentially similar. On this basis, supplemented by animal tests data, they approved the entire class of compounds for use without any specific restrictions. In 1978 the CoT listed this substance in Group A, indicating that they were satisfied that it was safe. Since this substance is believed to be metabolized into Uric Acid, those who suffer from gout or from other kidney disorders might wish to avoid it.

Regulatory status Permitted and used in the UK and in the USA, but not in foods intended for babies. It does not have an 'E' number.

635: Sodium 5'-Ribonucleotides

Type This is a group of closely related compounds which are used as flavour enhancers, and which are produced from mixtures of Sodium Guanylate (see 627) and Sodium 5'-Inosinate (see 631).

Foods added to They can be found in some crisps, packet soups and potato products.

Toxicological evaluation and possible health hazards JECFA evaluated this material in 1974 and commented that Ribonucleotides were normally present in all tissue. They have been tested in rats, mice, monkeys and dogs, and in three human male volunteers. On the basis of this evidence JECFA approved it for use without any specific restrictions.

Regulatory status Permitted and used in the UK, but not in foods intended for babies, and it is also not permitted in the USA. It does not have an 'E' number.

636: Maltol

Type It is a flavouring agent and flavour enhancer. This material is very effective at making sweet foods give the impression that they taste sweeter. Small amounts of Maltol added to a food product can permit a reduction of up to 15 per cent of the sugar without its tasting markedly less sweet.

Foods added to It can be found in some bread, cakes, synthetic chocolate, soft drinks, vanilla flavouring, ice cream and jams, but it is banned from foods intended for babies and young children.

Toxicological evaluation and possible health hazards JECFA evaluated this material four times between 1967 and 1981. During that period the ADI fluctuated, but most recently was set at 1mg/kg bw. The amount of available data is not great and it is difficult to interpret.

No adverse effects on humans have been reported, and it is presumed to be safe.

Regulatory status Permitted and used in the UK and the USA, but it does not yet have an 'E' number.

637: Ethyl Maltol

Type It is a flavouring agent and flavour enhancer, and is a functional alternative for Maltol (see 636). Small amounts of Ethyl Maltol added to a food product can permit a useful reduction of sugar without its tasting markedly less sweet.

Foods added to It can be found in some bread, cakes, synthetic chocolate, soft drinks, vanilla flavouring, ice cream and jams, but it is banned from foods intended for babies and young children. It is also sometimes used in combination with Saccharin (p. 186) because it can be used to mask the bitter after-taste which is one of Saccharin's less useful characteristics.

Toxicological evaluation and possible health hazards JECFA evaluated this substance in 1970 and 1974. On the basis of some short-term tests with dogs and rats and a long-term study on rats, they approved it for use and set an ADI of 2mg/kg bw. No adverse effects have been reported and it is presumed to be safe.

Regulatory status Permitted and used in the UK and the USA, but it does not yet have an 'E' number.

GLAZING AGENTS
AND AUXILIARY ADDITIVES
900–907

900: Dimethylpolysiloxane
also known as Polydimethylsiloxane
and as Silicone

Type It is an anti-foaming anti-caking agent.

Foods added to It can be found in some vegetable oils, chewing gum, soft drinks, skimmed milk, jams, syrups and fruit juice.

Toxicological evaluation and possible health hazards JECFA considered this compound four times between 1969 and 1979. On the first occasion, and on the basis of a rather slight amount of information, they set a temporary ADI of 2.5mg/kg bw, while asking for more information. In 1971 they remarked that they had not yet received any further information and postponed any new decision until a further date. In 1974 they said that they had received some further data, supplied by the Dow Corning Corporation, anonymously authored and unpublished. This new information reported on how Polydimethylsiloxane is metabolized by mice and monkeys. It had also previously been tested in rats, rabbits, dogs and monkeys. In the course of some early tests on dogs, brown and black deposits were found in their livers in proportion to the administered doses of the test substance, but it is very difficult to know what toxicological significance these findings may have for humans. JECFA were sufficiently satisfied to set an ADI of 1.5mg/kg bw. In 1979 they again reviewed this

material, and set restrictions on the identity and purity of the material as a condition for the application of this ADI.

No adverse effects have been reported and it is officially presumed to be safe.

Regulatory status Permitted and used in the UK and the USA, but it does not have an 'E' number.

901: Beeswax
also known as Yellow Wax and when bleached sometimes known as White Wax

Type It is used as a glazing, polishing and release agent. It is found in bees' nests, and is systematically secreted and assembled in a honeycomb. Beeswax is yellow and has a honey flavour. When bleached it is white and has a milder flavour.

Foods added to It is used to glaze some confectionery products, and to add honey flavour to some soft drinks, ice cream and baked goods. It is also sometimes used in commercial preparations of food colourings.

Toxicological evaluation and possible health hazards This material has not been evaluated by JECFA or the SCF.

No adverse effects have been reported and it is presumed to be safe.

Regulatory status It is permitted and used in the UK and the USA, but it does not yet have an 'E' number.

903: Carnauba Wax

Type It is a glazing and polishing agent, extracted from the leaves and buds of a South American palm tree.

Foods added to It is used to shine the skins of some fresh oranges and to coat some chocolate products.

Toxicological evaluation and possible health hazards It has not been evaluated by JECFA or the SCF. In the late 1970s the US Food and Drug Administration had this substance listed as one for which there needed to be far more tests, especially regarding possible mutagenicity and teratogenicity.

No adverse effects have been reported and it is officially presumed to be safe.

Regulatory status Permitted and used in the UK and the USA where it is listed as GRAS, but it does not have an 'E' number.

904: Shellac

Type It is a glazing agent extracted from the resinous secretions of a group of insects which inhabit a particular type of tree in India. There are several commercial grades produced by slightly different methods of purification.

Foods added to It can be found on the skins of some oranges, on some confectionery and in some fizzy orange drinks.

Toxicological evaluation and possible health hazards JECFA and the SCF have not evaluated this compound, and very little is known about its toxicity. No adverse effects have been reported, and on the basis of very little reliable data, but a long history of use, it is officially presumed to be safe.

Special restrictions Since the production of this chemical depends on animal sources, it is not acceptable to vegetarians or vegans, and is not kosher.

Regulatory status It is permitted and used in the UK and the USA, but it does not yet have an 'E' number.

905: Mineral Hydrocarbons

also known as Food Grade Mineral Oils, and sometimes called Liquid Paraffin or Liquid Petroleum

Type These substances are distilled from petroleum and are used as polishing, sealing and release agents.

Foods added to They are used as coatings for some dried and fresh fruits, confectionery and cheese rinds. They are also used to coat baking tins, and so residues may be found on the surface of baked foods.

Toxicological evaluation and possible health hazards JECFA evaluated this group of compounds four times between 1970 and 1977. On each occasion these compounds were approved for general use without any specific restrictions, although possible grounds for concern can be discerned from JECFA's remarks. JECFA state that for the most part these oils are chemically inert and pass through the body unchanged, but approximately 2 per cent is absorbed. We do not know how they are absorbed, nor why the extent of their absorption varies substantially between the populations of North America and Western Europe. We know that many mineral oils contain carcinogenic compounds, and it is rather tame for JECFA merely to state that refined oils 'may be free from these carcinogenic compounds'. JECFA also report that mineral oils may impede the absorption of fat-soluble Vitamin A and essential fatty acids. Despite these factors, JECFA were sufficiently satisfied with the results of animal tests using mice, rats and rabbits that they approved it for use without any specific restrictions. They did not change their evaluation in 1976, even though they commented that there was a danger that changing production techniques might lead to the introduction in the food supply of oils containing small concentrations of severely carcinogenic compounds called aromatic polycyclic hydrocarbons. In an attempt to deal with this, in 1977 they tightened the specifications of identity and purity.

No adverse effects have been reported from their use as food additives, but when used at medicinal concentrations to treat constipation they have been known to cause anal soreness and seepage, but food additive usage implies low concentrations, and they are officially presumed to be safe.

Regulatory status Permitted and used in the UK and the USA, but they do not yet have an 'E' number.

907: Refined Microcrystalline Wax

Type It is a polishing and firming agent extracted and purified from petroleum.

Foods added to It can be found in some chewing gums.

Toxicological evaluation and possible health hazards JECFA and the SCF have not evaluated this compound, and there is very little toxicological information available. No adverse effects have been reported, and it is officially presumed to be safe.

Regulatory status Permitted in the UK, but not in the USA, and it does not have an 'E' number.

920: L-Cysteine Hydrochloride

Type It is used as an improving agent in flour. It is a non-essential amino acid, but is a natural constituent of some protein foods.

Foods added to It can be found in some flour and bakery products. In the UK until May 1986, the vast majority of the flour from which almost all white bread was made had been bleached. The government was warned about the safety of many bread additives as long ago as the 1920s. To this day they have continued to permit this compound. In May 1986, however, under pressure from the Food Additives Campaign Team, Britain's two leading bakery firms, Rank Hovis McDougall and Allied Bakeries, suddenly announced a change of policy and said that they were no longer going to use this chemical in their bread.

Toxicological evaluation and possible health hazards Neither JECFA nor the SCF have evaluated this compound, but since it is a natural constituent of protein foods it is generally presumed to be safe.

Regulatory status It is permitted in the UK and in the USA where it is listed as GRAS, but it does not yet have an 'E' number.

924: Potassium Bromate

Type It is a dough conditioner, oxidizing agent and bleaching agent.

Foods added to It can be found in some bread and baked products, where it helps to keep the dough full of air while it is baking.

Toxicological evaluation and possible health hazards In 1974 the Food Standards Committee considered Potassium Bromate to be provisionally acceptable, pending the results of future tests. JECFA evaluated this compound in 1963, 1975 and 1983. On the first occasion they accepted its use unconditionally up to levels of 20mg/kg bw in the flour i.e. up to 20ppm, with conditional acceptance up to 75ppm, and they asked for more information. In 1975 they considered it again and revised the specifications of identity and purity, but did not modify the levels of acceptability. In 1983, however, they reported new evidence that Potassium Bromate, dissolved in drinking water, caused cancer in rats. JECFA argued that in the baking process the additive is reduced to the bromide which is safely metabolized. For this reason they considered the use of Potassium Bromate in bread flour to be acceptable as long as residual levels in the baked bread were negligible. They temporarily accepted its use up to levels of 75ppm, and requested the results of further studies, which have yet to be received.

As a result of a serious accident in which moderately high concentrations of Potassium Bromate solution contaminated some sugar in New Zealand a few people died, apparently due to kidney failure. There is one report that even at the far lower levels at which it is used as an additive it may destroy Vitamin E and cause abdominal discomfort, but it is officially presumed to be safe when used as a food additive.

Regulatory status It is permitted and used in the UK and the USA, but it does not yet have an 'E' number.

925: Chlorine

Type It is used as a flour treatment agent to bleach it. When concentrated it is an unpleasant greeny-yellowish gas with a suffocating odour. It has even been used in chemical weapons.

Foods added to It can be found in some flour, cakes and puddings, and is also used in some water treatment plants because of its strong antibacterial action. In the UK until May 1986, the vast majority of the flour from which most white bread was made had been bleached. The government was warned about the safety of bleaches in bread flour as long ago as the 1920s. To this day they have continued to permit it. In May 1986, however, under pressure from the Food Additives Campaign Team, Britain's two leading bakery firms, Rank Hovis McDougall and Allied Bakeries, suddenly announced a change of policy and said that they were no longer going to use bleached flour in their white bread.

Toxicological evaluation and possible health hazards JECFA considered this only once in 1965, and the SCF have not commented on it at all. In 1965 JECFA approved its use as an additive without any specific restrictions. When in a concentrated form Chlorine is a powerful irritant and destroys Vitamin E in foods. The safety and desirability of bleaching flour have never been demonstrated.

Regulatory status It is permitted in

the UK and the USA, but it does not yet have an 'E' number.

926: Chlorine Dioxide

also known as Chlorine Peroxide

Type It is used as a flour treatment agent. It is a reddish yellow gas with an unpleasant odour.

Foods added to It can be found in some flour, and so in baked products including cakes and puddings. It was introduced as a substitute in 1955 when the material which was formerly used, called Agene, was banned because of its severe toxicity in dogs, a fact which had been established as long ago as 1946. In the UK until May 1986, the vast majority of the flour from which most white bread was made had been bleached. The government was warned about the safety of bleaches in bread flour as long ago as the 1920s. To this day they have continued to permit it. In May 1986, however, under pressure from the Food Additives Campaign Team, Britain's two leading bakery firms, Rank Hovis McDougall and Allied Bakeries, suddenly announced a change of policy and said that they were no longer going to use bleached flour in their white bread.

Toxicological evaluation and possible health hazards JECFA evaluated this compound once in 1963. On that occasion they set an unconditional ADI of 30mg/kg bw, and a conditional ADI up to 75mg/kg bw. At high concentrations this gas is severely irritating and corrosive to skin and mucous membranes and can even be lethal. There is a controversy about the effects of this chemical at the lower levels at which it is added to food. Several informed but unofficial sources have long argued that this material degrades the Vitamin E from the flour and produces toxic residues. Officially it is still presumed to be safe.

Regulatory status It is permitted and used in the UK and the USA, but it does not have an 'E' number, and is not permitted in most other EEC countries.

927: Azodicarbonamide

Type It is a maturing agent for flour. It is a very effective dough conditioning agent. By adding between 2 and 45ppm to dough, depending on the flour, bakers can get the flour to behave as if it had been resting in storage for many months, and bake a cheap loaf full of air and moisture.

Foods added to It is used in some flour, bread and baked products. In the UK until May 1986, the vast majority of the flour from which most white bread was made had been bleached. The government was warned about the safety of bleaches in bread flour as long ago as the 1920s. To this day they have continued to permit it. In May 1986, however, under pressure from the Food Additives Campaign Team, Britain's two leading bakery firms, Rank Hovis McDougall and Allied Bakeries, suddenly announced a change of policy and said that they were no longer going to use bleached flour in their white bread.

Toxicological evaluation and possible health hazards JECFA evaluated this material once in 1965, when they approved its use up to a level of 45mg/kg of dough, although they have modified the purity and identity specifications since then. It has been the subject of short- and long-term tests with rats and dogs, and appeared to be safe for them. No adverse human effects have been reported and it is officially presumed to be safe.

Regulatory status Permitted and used in the UK and the USA, but it does not yet have an 'E' number.

INTENSE SWEETENERS

Acesulfame Potassium
also known as Acesulfame-K

Type This is a synthetic sweetener, which is chemically related to Saccharin. Like Saccharin, it has a bitter after-taste and therefore is likely to be used in combination with sugar, Aspartame or some other sweetener. It is a white, odourless, crystalline powder which is approximately 200 times sweeter than sugar. Unlike Aspartame, however, it is relatively stable at high temperatures and so can be used in cooked and processed foods.

Foods added to Hoechst, the company which manufactures it, has sought permission for its use in table-top sweeteners, and for use in soft drinks, fruit preparations, desserts, cereals and chewing gums. It may be found in some reduced-sugar jams, jellies and marmalades, as well as soft drinks and dietetic products.

Toxicological evaluation and possible health hazards JECFA first reported on this compound in 1981. They said that they were not satisfied as to its safety because some studies had been inadequately reported, and because there was evidence that it might increase the rates of lung cancer in rats. They called for further data, and deferred a decision. The FACC evaluated it in 1982. They noted that the food industry was keen to use this substance as a partial replacement for Saccharin. The CoT cited thirty-four studies, all of which were unpublished. They also admitted that the studies were under-reported, but gave their approval none the less. They discounted the rat lung tumours because the rats had suffered from a respiratory infection, while a second strain of rats had neither infection nor tumours. The CoT listed Acesulfame-K in Group A and recommended that its use be approved in the UK. In 1983 JECFA reported that they too had, by then, received sufficient information to satisfy themselves that it did not cause either mutations or cancer in laboratory tests. On the basis of an NEL in a long-term feeding study on dogs, they set an ADI of 9mg/kg bw. On that occasion, however, they provided no information on how they had settled their doubts about rat lung cancers. All of the data which they were then reviewing were unpublished. The SCF reported on this substance in 1985, and merely endorsed JECFA's evaluation, by reference to (presumably the same) unpublished data. In the USA, however, the Freedom of Information Act will permit access to the data which in Europe is concealed.

As long as the information remains effectively concealed, and some doubts remain, we cannot be confident that it is safe.

Regulatory status It has been approved for use in the UK, Ireland and Switzerland, but not in Austria, Finland, France, Greece, Luxembourg, Norway, Portugal, Spain or the USA.

Aspartame

also marketed under the names Nutrasweet and Canderel

Type This is a synthetic sweetener which is made by combining two amino acids L-phenylalanine and L-aspartic acid. It is almost 200 times as sweet as sucrose, but a lot more expensive.

Foods added to It can be found in no fewer than 125 different products but these are mainly confined to soft drinks and soft drink mixes and low-calorie yoghurts.

Toxicological evaluation and possible health hazards Since 1973, the controversy which has raged around Aspartame has exceeded those which have afflicted all other additives. On the face of it, we might expect Aspartame to be one of the least problematic chemicals. It is synthesized from a combination of two common, vital and naturally occurring amino acids. Amino acids are the fundamental constituents of proteins, and Aspartame is thought to be digested as a protein. There are, however, two central questions in the Aspartame controversy: first, has it been tested properly (even by the indifferent standards which currently prevail), and second, is Aspartame safe?

The production and sale of Aspartame are dominated by G. D. Searle & Co, which owns most of the crucial patents. Searle first petitioned the American government for permission to market Aspartame in 1973, but it was not until 1981 that the FDA permitted its commercial use, limiting it initially to dry food products. It was only in 1983 that the FDA finally approved its use in carbonated soft drinks, which is the major market. In October 1985 it emerged that G. D. Searle & Co had been acquired by the large chemical company Monsanto which, historically, had been one of the major manufacturers of Saccharin. Following their acquisition Monsanto detached the Aspartame business from the remainder of Searle and established the Nutrasweet Company.

In 1982 the FACC recommended that the use of Aspartame should be permitted in Britain, and Aspartame came on to the British market in September 1983. The major controversy over Aspartame has taken place in the USA, starting in 1973 and continuing for at least twelve years, but until 1983 the British press remained ignorant of, or indifferent to, the American debates. It has been only since 1983 that the significance of these important arguments has been appreciated by a handful of British commentators.

Searle first filed a petition with the FDA for permission to market Aspartame in 1973, and the FDA proposed to grant permission in 1974. Before the consequences of that decision could be implemented, objections were raised by independent scientists alleging that Aspartame causes mental retardation, brain lesions and neuro-endocrine disorders. Before those issues could be resolved, a further complex set of objections was raised, the major of which concerned the fact that some scientists claimed that Searle had failed to conduct their safety tests properly, and their work had apparently been negligent.

The scandal was first uncovered by scientists from the FDA's drug control division. Dr Adrian Gross and his colleagues discovered, by examining carefully the laboratory records, that a large proportion of Searle's experimental work was profoundly unreliable. In response to these revelations the FDA established two Special Task Forces: one, under the auspices of the Bureau of Drugs, reviewed Searle's safety evaluations of their pharmaceutical products, while the second, under the Bureau of Foods, examined Aspartame.

The Aspartame Task Force had to institute careful reviews of as many as fifteen studies which were judged to be 'pivotal' in the sense of being integral to the approval of Aspartame. Their own internal review dealt with just three of these tests. Two concerned the potential embryotoxicity and teratogenicity in both rats and mice, while the third studied the carcinogenic potential to rats of a substance known as DKP (short for diketopiperazine), which is a breakdown product of Aspartame. The FDA decided not to rely entirely on their own resources to conduct all the reviews, and put pressure on Searle to oblige them to contract with the US Universities Association for Research and Evalution in Pathology (UAREP) to review and audit the validity of the remaining twelve sets of tests. Some commentators have argued that the members of the UAREP were not appropriately qualified to conduct the kind of investigation which was required, and consequently that their eventual conclusions cannot be considered to be reliable.

The results of the research by the Bureau of Foods Task Force make difficult but interesting reading. One of the central charges against Searle was that the conclusions of their tests, as described in the documents submitted to the FDA, failed to reflect accurately the raw data generated in the laboratories. The summaries, it was suggested, underestimated the possible toxicity of the chemical, and overestimated its safety when compared to the raw data. There were, moreover, ' . . . significant deviations from acceptable procedures for conducting non-clinical laboratory studies'. It is especially ironic, therefore, that the Task Force Report seems to reproduce the mistake which it criticizes Searle for making. The conclusions of the Task Force Report fail accurately to reflect the information contained in the body of that report. It states that while these three tests were not properly conducted, and although there were marked differences between raw data and the summaries submitted in the petition to the FDA, these differences: ' . . . were not of such a magnitude that they would significantly alter the conclusions of the studies'. The details of the Task Force Report, however, suggest precisely the opposite conclusion.

The Task Force had difficulty in evaluating the studies, in part because in some cases there just were no raw data with which to compare the supposed results. In other cases, it was impossible to determine which were the real raw results, and which were subsequent revisions or summaries. In some contexts, the Task Force had to rely on information and assumptions provided by Searle employees who had not been involved in the original work. At worst, it was impossible to identify the occasion on which a particular animal had died, for example, as the Report says: 'Observation records indicated that animal A23LM was alive at week 88, dead from week 92 through week 104, alive at week 108, and dead at week 112.' Most scientists do not believe in reincarnation, and we should not expect that the FDA or the FACC do so either.

When reviewing the test on DKP,

the Report lists no fewer than fifty-two major discrepancies in the Searle submission. One of the central problems concerned the quantities of DKP supposedly consumed by the rats. The FDA investigators found no fewer than three separate documents with different specifications for the content and the purity of the test substance, and they were unable to establish precisely which specification, if any, was correct. It was impossible to reconcile the quantity of the chemical requisitioned from stores with the quantities supposedly fed to the animals. There were questions raised as to the extent to which the DKP was uniformly incorporated into the animals' food. There is clear evidence to show that the test substance was not properly ground, and inadequately mixed, so that it might have been possible for the animals to avoid the DKP while eating their food.

The disparity between the substance and the conclusion of the FDA Task Force Report is hard to understand. The investigators found so many mistakes which were of such a magnitude, and of such importance, that it would seem that no reliance can be placed on the results of these tests. The authors of the Report's conclusion, however, appear to have decided, perhaps for political reasons, to interpret the evidence 'generously', while the evidence invites or even demands a stricter assessment.

In 1978, the UAREP submitted its 1,062-page report, which concluded that the twelve studies they had audited were authentic. Despite the fact that these two reviews had concluded that Aspartame had been properly tested, and that the substance was safe, the objectors were still not satisfied, and furthermore a new

complex set of objections to the safety of Aspartame were introduced. In an attempt to resolve the controversy once and for all, the FDA proposed the establishment of a so-called Public Board Of Inquiry (or PBOI). This was a unique institution; the procedure had never previously been used, and in all probability will not be used again.

The PBOI, which consisted of three academic scientists who were independent of both the FDA and Searle, were used as an alternative to the more usual formal evidential hearings, and were thought by some people to be better suited to dealing with the numerous scientific and technical complexities. The establishment of the Board was announced in June 1979, and they met early in 1980, publishing their conclusions in October 1980. They had two sets of issues on their agenda. On one of the crucial questions their view was that Aspartame consumption would not pose an increased risk of brain damage resulting in mental retardation, but on the other vital issue they concluded that the evidence available to them did not rule out the possibility that Aspartame could induce brain tumours. Consequently the Board recommended that Aspartame should not be permitted for use, pending the results of further testing.

In response, all the parties, namely G. D. Searle & Co, the Bureau of Foods, and the objectors, filed detailed exceptions to those parts of the Board's conclusions with which they disagreed. None the less, it was the responsibility of the Commissioner of the FDA to make a decision, for the Board's role was merely advisory and not decisive. In July 1981, the Commissioner, Arthur Hayes Jr, announced his decision to approve the use of Aspartame in food products other than soft drinks. In doing so he made it clear that he disagreed with the PBOI's interpretation of the issue concerning brain tumours. Hayes took the view that the available data were sufficient to persuade him that Aspartame does not cause brain tumours in laboratory animals. Subsequently, two of the three members of the Board have revised their own judgement and decided that they now agree with Hayes.

The issue is a rather subtle one; it concerns the way in which the experimental results are interpreted. The results of at least one experiment are very difficult to interpret. The reason for this is because the level of cancers in the concurrent control group of animals was unusually high. As a result, if one compares the results of the test group with concurrent controls then there is no statistically significant increase in cancer rates; whereas if one compares the test group with average historical control groups of the same types of animal, in similar tests, then one could conclude that there was a statistically significant increase in cancers.

This touches on a problem which affects large areas of toxicology, and is not confined either to tests for cancer or tests on Aspartame. The degree of variability in the background incidence of pathological symptoms in laboratory animals is vast, and poorly understood. In the toxicological literature there is extensive debate on whether the significant comparisons should be with concurrent controls or with historical averages, and the issue is unresolved, and probably unresolvable. In practice, we can find examples of firms and governments choosing comparisons with whichever

groups yield the result which they wish to establish. In this case, Hayes and the FDA chose to accept the comparison between test animals and concurrent control, and in doing so were able to cite other examples of relatively high levels of cancer in animals not receiving test substances. I don't think that we can say who is right or wrong; what we can conclude, however, is that regulatory toxicology is too unreliable and too uncertain to enable us to be confident that the safety of Aspartame can be established.

JECFA first reviewed Aspartame in 1975. At that time their main doubts focused on the effects which DKP has produced in rats. Scientists had reported that in long-term feeding studies DKP had produced lesions in the uteruses of the rats. Despite detailed assistance from experts of the International Agency for Research on Cancer (IARC), JECFA were unable to decide on the character and significance of these lesions. They therefore postponed any decision until these matters had been clarified. They considered the subject again in 1978 by which time they had been reassured about the uterine lesions, but had become aware of (at least some of) the serious doubts about the validity of the toxicology data. JECFA therefore deferred any decision until they could be reassured about the validity of the data.

In 1980 they reported first that they had accepted the reassurances of the UAREP as to the validity of the tests, and second they produced a substantial and detailed report which reviewed eighty-one documents on Aspartame, seventy-nine of which were unpublished. JECFA established an ADI of 40mg/kg bw for Aspartame, but an ADI of 7.5mg/kg bw for

Aspartame's decay product DKP.

In 1982, Searle petitioned the FDA for permission to use Aspartame in carbonated soft drinks. The FDA again reviewed the controversial issues, but reconfirmed their interpretation of the evidence, and accordingly granted permission for this new use. In 1983 James Turner (a lawyer acting for the Community Nutrition Institute) and Dr John Olney (of Washington University, St Louis) again pressed the FDA to reconsider their decision. The FDA refused to do so, and in 1984 these objectors filed an appeal in the United States Court of Appeals to force the FDA to conduct formal hearings. In the autumn of 1985, three Appeal Court judges unanimously decided that the FDA had acted properly, and that the objectors had failed to show Aspartame to be unsafe. In spite of these institutional decisions, some scientists remain unconvinced both about the adequacy of these tests, and the interpretation of some of the results; and further lawsuits remain pending in US courts.

Searle's official position is that all their tests have been properly conducted, and that no charges have been preferred. In February 1986, however, US Senator Howard Metzenbaum published a thick dossier of documents which provided *prima facie* evidence that the reason why Searle had never been prosecuted was because their firm of lawyers had exercised undue influence over the Federal Attorney's office until the Statute of Limitations had expired and so ensured that no action could be taken.

Furthermore, in July 1986, the US General Accounting Office confirmed that Dr Arthur Hayes, who had approved Aspartame when FDA Commissioner, had accepted an appointment as a Senior Scientific Consultant to Burson-Marsteller two months after leaving the FDA. This is potentially significant because Burson-Marsteller have been acting as public relations consultants to Searle, but the report indicates that Hayes had not advised Searle before he joined the FDA, or after joining Burson-Marsteller.

This does not show that Aspartame is toxic, or that it was improperly approved, but it is hard to be confident on both counts, because much of the crucial evidence is unavailable. For example, although we do know that the information provided by Searle of both the US and UK governments did include a summary of the results of the three most controversial tests, it is impossible to discover the extent to which the British government, and its expert committees, knew about the doubts and uncertainties.

The consequence of all of these facts is that we cannot be certain that the tests to which Aspartame has been subjected are adequate, even by the relatively poor standards of current best practice, and so we cannot be confident that Aspartame is safe. The problem is made even more severe by the fact that there are some scientists who continue to argue that what we already know about Aspartame is sufficient to show that it is unsafe, at least for some consumers.

Two of the most persistent critics have been Professor John Olney and Professor Richard Wurtman (of the Massachusetts Institute of Technology). Wurtman has published a long series of papers reporting the results of his research on the safety of Aspartame, in which he has argued that serious problems exist. Apparently, Wurtman uses Aspartame himself, and considers it to be safe in low doses, but is worried about effects of consuming large amounts of Aspartame especially in combination with carbohydrates. Wurtman's research has been primarily concerned with the effects of consuming Aspartame on the biochemistry of the brain. He has argued that it may disturb brain functions in a complex variety of ways, which may provoke some severe and acute symptoms. In particular, Wurtman has argued that he has both theoretical and clinical evidence that very high doses of Aspartame can provoke epileptic seizures. Olney's research has concentrated, on the other hand, on the possibility that Aspartame might cause chronic brain damage especially when consumed in combination with Monosodium Glutamate (see 621), and he too remains dissatisfied about its safety.

Regulatory status Aspartame is permitted and used in the UK and USA, and although it is widely approved for use in table top sweeteners, it is not permitted for use in foods and/or beverages in Austria, Belgium, France, Greece, Italy, Holland or Portugal.

Hydrogenated Glucose Syrup

Type This is a complex mixture that is used as a sweetening agent. A range of products is available with this name and they vary from liquid syrups to crystalline solids. They are prepared by hydrolysing starches, that is to say using water and enzymes to get them to decompose. The intermediate product is then reacted with hydrogen to yield a mixture of maltitol and Sorbitol (see E420i) with other related compounds called polysaccharides. Weight for weight, it is not quite as sweet as sucrose, but it is cheaper, and some parts of the food industry are keen to use it as a substitute for glucose and sucrose.

Foods added to No specific uses have been reported.

Toxicological evaluation and possible health hazards Hydrogenated Glucose Syrup was first considered by JECFA in 1980. On that occasion they stated that they did not have sufficient information on its use or safety to permit an evaluation. In particular they noted the lack of adequate information on long-term and reproductive toxicity. In 1982 the FACC reported that the available evidence did not suggest that Hydrogenated Glucose Syrup was unsuitable for use in foods. Since they were satisfied that the Syrup was metabolized into glucose and Sorbitol, they did not insist on long-term tests. Since they had not completed their evaluation of Sorbitol, they listed Hydrogenated Glucose Syrup in Group B as temporarily acceptable pending further consideration. In 1983 JECFA reviewed the available data, mainly on metabolism and reproduction, and established a temporary ADI of 25mg/kg bw, but they still complained at the lack of adequate long-term data. The SCF reported their evaluation in 1985. They did not endorse the JECFA ADI, because they did not consider that the available evidence was sufficient. Although industry had supplied them with a lot of data, they considered much to be inadequate by modern standards. They approved the use of Hydrogenated Glucose Syrup, however, because they were satisfied that rats and humans metabolize it to glucose and Sorbitol. In 1986 JECFA too dropped their requirement for a long-term animal feeding study because they think it is metabolized safely. At moderately high doses it acts as a laxative.

Regulatory status It is permitted and used in the U.K, but it is not approved for inclusion in products intended for babies and young children because they are more vulnerable to its laxative effects.

Isomalt

also known as Isomaltitol or Hydrogenated Isomaltitol

Type This is a compound sweetener which is about half as sweet as sucrose.

Foods added to It can be found in some confectionery, chewing gums, soft drinks and desserts.

Toxicological evaluation and possible health hazards JECFA first considered this compound in 1981, and despite the absence of long-term feeding and reproductive studies, they set a temporary ADI of 25mg/kg bw and asked for further data by 1985. In 1982 the FACC listed it in Group B, meaning that it was considered temporarily acceptable pending their receipt of further data, and they recommended that the extent and pattern of its use should be investigated. No evidence is yet available that this latter recommendation has been followed. The SCF, in 1985, approved its use without setting an ADI, but drew attention to its laxative effects and recommended that it should not be used in products intended for babies or young children. When JECFA reported in 1986 they were then satisfied with the data from metabolic studies and long-term tests, and estab-

lished an ADI 'unspecified', which means that they considered it sufficiently safe to be acceptable without quantitative restrictions.

Regulatory status It is permitted and used in the UK, but it is not approved for inclusion in products intended for babies and young children because they are more vulnerable to its laxative effects.

Saccharin and its Sodium and Calcium Salts

Type Saccharin is a synthetic sweetener which was discovered in 1879. A patent for its commercial manufacture was granted in June 1885, and it was then introduced to the market, initially in Europe, but in the USA too by the turn of the century. In its commercial form it is available as white crystals or a white crystalline powder.

Foods added to Saccharin can be found in a wide range of products that are marketed as 'low calorie', 'diet' or 'diabetic' foods and drinks. These include diet soft drinks, ice creams and fruit preserves, and in grape juice concentrates used in winemaking.

Toxicological evaluation and possible health hazards If it didn't keep happening we should be entitled to be surprised at finding an additive which is still used despite the fact that there has been evidence of its toxicity for many years. The earliest recorded official criticism of the safety of Saccharin was published in 1890 by the Commission of the Health Association of France when they decided to ban the manufacture and importation of Saccharin. In 1898, the German government restricted the use of Saccharin, expressly banning it from food and drink. Similar action was then taken in Spain, Portugal and Hungary. The first formal international gathering to condemn Saccharin as unsafe met in Brussels in 1908 and recommended that the use of Saccharin and similar sweeteners for human consumption should be prohibited.

In 1907 the redoubtable Dr Harvey Wiley, then head of the Division of Chemistry at the US Department of Agriculture (the forerunner of the FDA), recommended that Saccharin should be banned in the USA. President Theodore Roosevelt rejected this recommendation because his doctors prescribed Saccharin for his daily personal use, but Wiley's persistence obliged the President to establish an expert panel to review the issue. Roosevelt appointed as the panel's chairman one of the co-discoverers of Saccharin who stood to benefit financially from the commercial exploitation of his patents. Despite this prejudicial preparation, the panel reported that although in their opinion Saccharin was safe when consumed at low doses they conceded that at high rates of consumption (i.e. over 0.3g per day) it would be toxic. In 1912, while Taft was President, the use of Saccharin was banned in food and soft drinks, but permitted in chewing tobacco, and under prescription.

It was the crises of the two World Wars which created the conditions in which Saccharin gained general acceptance. In Europe and the USA sugar was in short supply at these times, and under those circumstances governments around the world relaxed their restrictions on Saccharin, failing to reimpose them in peacetime. At the end of World War I, C. L. Alsberg (Wiley's successor) tried in vain to prevent Monsanto, the major manufacturer of Saccharin, from expanding its sales, while at the end of World War II Germany permitted the use of Saccharin in ice cream.

The British position has always been more relaxed and permissive than those of other industrialized countries. There have been hardly any restrictions on the use of Saccharin in Britain and to this day it is extensively used. Since the late 1950s and 1960s the market for so-called 'low-calorie' products has been growing rapidly. From 1945 to 1985 the consumption of artificially sweetened products has grown more than 200-fold. One commentator has estimated that by 1978, the advertising budget for diet soft drinks in the USA had reached $40 million. A particularly revealing report has estimated that, in the US at least, 6 per cent of the population consume some 70 per cent of all the Saccharin.

The central issue of the modern debate about toxic hazards from Saccharin dates from the early 1970s and has been focused on the issue of its carcinogenicity. To cut an extremely long story rather short, by the mid-1970s there was clear and consistent evidence from at least four feeding studies in the rat, that Saccharin caused bladder cancer. The results of short-term mutagenicity tests have been equivocal, and it may be that Saccharin causes cancer by a non-genotoxic route. The results of epidemiological studies have also been equivocal. Some studies of groups suffering from bladder cancer have found the victims to have been users of Saccharin-containing products, while other studies have failed to demonstrate any such connection. By 1980, the International Agency for

Research on Cancer stated: 'There is sufficient evidence that Saccharin alone, given at high doses, produces tumours of the urinary tract in male rats and can promote the action of known carcinogens in the bladder of rats of both sexes; and there is limited evidence of its tumorgenicity in mice.'

One of the crucial rat feeding studies, although commissioned by the US National Academy of Sciences, was conducted in Canada, and the reaction of the Canadian authorities was prompt and responsible. On 9 March 1977 the Canadian Health Protection Branch announced its decision to ban Saccharin from food and drink, and this decision has been thoroughly implemented. On 15 April 1977 the FDA announced a similar proposal to ban Saccharin from all processed food, in soft drinks, and as a table top sweetener. Despite the explicit provisions of the so-called Delany Amendment, which obliges the FDA to ban all known carcinogens from the permitted list of food additives, the proposal to ban Saccharin in the US has never been implemented. Primarily at the behest of the American food, drink, and additive industries, a substantial and successful campaign was organized to force the FDA to desist from implementing any restrictions on the use of Saccharin. In the autumn of 1977 the US Congress passed a temporary moratorium which prevented the FDA from banning Saccharin, and this has subsequently been renewed at least three times. Instead of banning it, the US Congress only required that all products containing the chemical must carry a warning label to the effect that: '. . . the use of this product may be hazardous to your health. This product contains Saccharin which has

been determined to cause cancer in laboratory animals'.

JECFA's first review of Saccharin and its Salts occurred almost ninety years after its discovery. For a brief period in the late 1960s and early 1970s JECFA set a full ADI of 5mg/kg bw for these compounds, but in the face of the animal carcinogenicity data, they retreated by making that ADI temporary in 1975, and halved it to 2.5mg/kg bw in 1980, although it remained temporary; and that position was reiterated in 1982. Strictly speaking, the device of the ADI should not be used for known carcinogens, but JECFA justify their bending of the rules because some of the evidence implies that Saccharin is a non-mutagenic carcinogen. If it is a non-mutagenic carcinogen then there might be a threshold, but JECFA are not entitled to take that for granted; they ought rather to be more cautious.

The British response to the fact that Saccharin is an animal carcinogen has been at best dilatory and at worst irresponsible. The official British position is provided by the 1982 Report of the Committee on Toxicity which is included in the FACC Report on Sweeteners in Food. The CoT accepted that Saccharin is known to be an animal carcinogen, but recommended that new restrictions on the use of Saccharin should not be introduced because the epidemiological evidence had not confirmed that Saccharin was a bladder carcinogen for humans as well as for rodents. This is a classic case of giving all the benefit of the doubt to industry, rather than to consumers.

The epidemiological and the animal evidence appear to contradict each other. Despite the fact that there is far greater consistency between the results of the different animal tests than between the various epidemiological studies, the CoT chose to give credence to epidemiology over the animal studies, without adequate scientific grounds. There are many reasons for interpreting the results of the epidemiological studies cautiously. It is possible both that some of Saccharin's victims died before the studies started and so have not been properly counted, and some may not yet have exhibited their symptoms, and so would remain undetected. While Saccharin may cause bladder cancers in rats, it might be causing cancer at different sites in humans, and no epidemiological studies have been conducted which might reveal such possible effects.

The CoT went no further than demoting Saccharin from Group A status to that of Group B, which by definition should mean that further studies are required, although the additive may be used in the interim. In this case, the CoT did not call for any further studies, but proposed merely to keep its eyes on the toxicological literature. The only contribution to the debate from the FACC is to argue that the food industry needs Saccharin, and that it benefits consumers, even in the face of evidence to the contrary. For example, an authoritative report states that '... the use of non-caloric sweeteners and artificially sweetened foods considered as a group do not appear to have any particular value in weight reduction', and a special medical report to the National Academy of Sciences stated that '... there is no essential requirement for the use of saccharin in the medical management of diabetics and obese patients'.

Listing Saccharin in Group B has had no practical effect. No new restrictions on the use of Saccharin have been introduced in the UK, and the use of Saccharin has declined mainly because its newest competitor, Aspartame, has captured much of its market. Although Aspartame is substantially more expensive than Saccharin, it has the advantage of not leaving a bitter after-taste, and for this reason is partly replacing Saccharin, especially from diet soft drinks.

The SCF reviewed Saccharin for the first time in 1977, four years after reliable evidence of its carcinogenicity had first become available. The SCF reported at length and in detail, and suggested that it might not be the Saccharin which caused cancer in rats, but impurities in some of the commercial supplies of the sweetener. They proposed tightening the specifications on identity and purity. They also recommended specific restrictions to reduce Saccharin consumption by children and pregnant women. They emphasized the importance of clear labelling of Saccharin-containing products, and recommended that Saccharin should be prohibited from products prepared and marketed for babies and children up to three years old.

The most remarkable and unprecedented feature of the SCF report is the comment that '... some members of the Committee felt that Saccharin should not be used in food for general consumption'. This implies that those scientists believe that it is sufficiently hazardous for its use to be confined to products intended for people with special dietary needs. The majority view on the SCF, however, was not to give the benefit of those doubts to consumers.

In March 1978, the EEC Commission responded to the SCF's report and made four recommendations concerning the use of Saccharin. In effect, the British government has accepted two of these, but rejected the others. Saccharin may not be used in baby foods, and when it is used at all its presence must always be indicated on the label. The EEC also suggested, however, that labels should include a warning of possible dangers, especially to pregnant women and to young children, and that further quantitative restrictions should be introduced, but these two proposals were not endorsed by the FACC.

Regulatory status The use of Saccharin is permitted in the UK and the USA, but banned entirely in Canada, and banned from food and drinks in France, Greece and Portugal where it is sold only in tablet form, as a table top sweetener. There is no evidence that the UK or the USA are likely to ban this known animal carcinogen from our foods.

Thaumatin

Type This is a sweetening agent and flavour enhancer. It is a naturally occurring substance containing several proteins, and is the most powerful sweetener yet discovered. Its use is limited, however, by the fact that it is relatively unstable. Some industrial laboratories are busy trying to stabilize it. It comes from a fruit which can be found in Central and South West Africa, where traditionally it has been used to sweeten wines, maize bread and sour fruit.

Foods added to No specific uses have yet been reported.

Toxicological evaluation and possible health hazards JECFA first evaluated Thaumatin in 1983. They were then satisfied that it does not cause allergies, mutations or birth defects, but they concluded that they did not have sufficient long-term animal data or human studies to be sure that it is safe; they therefore deferred any decision. In 1985 the SCF reviewed this substance and despite the fact that the toxicological dossier was incomplete by contemporary standards, they recommended that its use be approved without any specific ADI, but pending further data and another review within three years. In 1986 JECFA adopted a similar position, and announced an 'ADI not specified', indicating that they were satisfied that the low levels at which it would probably be used were adequately safe. This was despite that fact that they still did not have the results of the long-term studies which they had requested in 1983. There is no evidence that Thaumatin constitutes a hazard, but we cannot be sure that it is safe either.

Regulatory status The use of Thaumatin is permitted in the UK, but not in foods intended for babies and young children because of its laxative effects.

Xylitol

Type This compound is used as a sweetening agent and as a humectant to keep food products moist. It occurs naturally in a few fruits and vegetables, and in the human body as a metabolite of some carbohydrates. It is about as sweet as sucrose, but is more expensive.

Foods added to It can be found in some chewing gums, fruit preserves, ice cream, confectionery and chewable vitamins.

Toxicological evaluation and possible health hazards JECFA first reviewed it in 1977. They had received some data obtained from mice, rats and dogs but some of the studies were considered to have been incomplete. There was some direct human evidence that it can cause diarrhoea and flatulence. Because of a lack of adequate carcinogenicity test data, and because of conflicting human data, including some evidence that hospital patients fed Xylitol directly into their blood supply had died, JECFA declined to set an ADI or to provide an evaluation. They reconsidered Xylitol next in 1978 by which time they had received further data showing that at high doses Xylitol caused a range of toxic symptoms in laboratory animals, while at low doses no such symptoms were detected, but they still did not set any ADI.

The FACC reviewed Xylitol in 1982, and the CoT listed twenty-seven sources, seventeen of which were unpublished documents submitted by the chemical company Hoffman–La Roche. They shared JECFA's view that although high doses may be hazardous, low doses are probably safe. They recommended approval but asked that, following its introduction, data on its pattern of use should be collected and then reviewed.

In 1983 JECFA set an ADI 'not specified' for Xylitol indicating that they believed it could be safely used without quantitative restrictions, as long as it was used at levels below that at which it could provoke diarrhoea. In 1985 the SCF reported their evaluation of Xylitol. Their comments were extremely brief, but they endorsed the JECFA view that it could safely be used as long as dose levels were low.

Regulatory status It is permitted and used in the UK, and in the USA where its use is restricted to foods required for special dietary needs.

MISCELLANEOUS ADDITIVES

Caffeine

Type Caffeine is a naturally occurring chemical which can be found in several plants including coffee beans, tea leaves, cola nuts and cocoa beans. It has been categorized by the FACC as a natural flavouring agent, but it is used primarily because it is a stimulant which affects the central nervous system, the heart and the kidneys. In its pure form it is an odourless white powder with a bitter taste.

Foods added to It can be found in some baked goods, ice creams, soft confectionery but it is mainly used in cola-type soft drinks. An average cup of tea or coffee may contain from 40 to 90mg of Caffeine, while cola drinks may contain between 40 and 75mg of Caffeine in each can, and a large cup of strong drip-made coffee can contain as much as 150mg. It can also be found in some pharmaceutical preparations. Drugs such as some cold remedies, codeine compounds, diuretics, allergy pills and anti-menstrual pain preparations tend to make people drowsy, and so manufacturers may add Caffeine to counteract that effect. In Britain the average adult probably ingests about 170mg each day, while a coffee addict may easily be consuming more than twice that amount.

Toxicological evaluation and possible health hazards JECFA have never published an evaluation of Caffeine, but the SCF have considered its safety. They reported in 1983 in response to concern about several reports published in the late 1970s suggesting that Caffeine might be a cause of birth defects, cancer and behavioural abnormalities. We have known since the early 1950s that Caffeine causes mutations in bacteria, and more recently we have found that moderately high doses can cause birth defects in laboratory animals, while human epidemiological evidence is, at best, equivocal. The SCF's response, however, was to endorse industry's argument that although it may be hazardous at very high doses, the levels found in the human diet are probably safe. The SCF merely awarded the benefit of the doubt to industry and called for further studies. Unofficial sources warn that Caffeine is addictive and may cause acute symptoms of intolerance. People who drink four or more cups of tea or coffee each day may as a result exhibit nervousness, anxiety, irritability and insomnia. The human foetus is potentially vulnerable to Caffeine, and so in 1980 the Commissioner of the US FDA advised pregnant women to restrict and diminish their Caffeine intake. Similar warnings have not been issued in Britain by MAFF. There is also some evidence that high rates of Caffeine consumption may contribute to the formation of non-malignant breast lumps in women. There is evidence too that, in some cases, a reduction in Caffeine intake can cause the lumps to disperse. Women with breast lumps should, however, immediately seek qualified advice, and not rely simply on dietary modification. The latest evidence, published in

October 1986, from a careful and detailed long-term epidemiological study indicated that people drinking five or more cups of coffee a day were about two and a half times more likely to suffer from heart disease than non-drinkers.

We cannot be sure that Caffeine is safe, but few of us would wish to live without it.

Regulatory status The FACC considered Caffeine in 1976 and approved it for use in small quantities as an additive to foods provided that it was used at levels not exceeding those found naturally occurring in foods; it is also allowed in soft drinks. In the USA, cola drinks must contain at least some, but no more than 0.02 per cent, of Caffeine.

Aluminium Potassium Sulphate
also known as Potassium Aluminium Sulphate and as Potash Alum
Type This can be used as a buffering agent, a firming agent and/or as a neutralizing agent. It is a colourless, odourless, hard, transparent crystalline powder with a sweet antiseptic taste. It can be used as a clarifying agent in sugar, and as a carrier for bleaching agents.

Foods added to It can be found in some bleached flour, sugar products, pickles and cheeses.

Toxicological evaluation and possible health hazards JECFA first considered this compound in 1974, but they were not provided with sufficient information to enable them to make an evaluation and so postponed any decision. They looked at it again, but just restated their ignorance and uncertainty in 1978. There is no evidence that either the SCF or the FACC have considered it. There is one report that large doses may inflame the

mouth, throat and stomach, and one suggesting that it may be hazardous to the kidneys, but current levels of use are very low and plausible doses may be safe, but we do not have sufficient information to be sure.

Regulatory status Permitted and used in the UK and the USA.

Calcium Phytate
Type It can be used as a sequestrant.

Foods added to It can be found in some baked goods, soft drinks and processed vegetables.

Toxicological evaluation and possible health hazards There is no evidence that JECFA, the SCF or the FACC have ever considered this compound, and very little is known about it.

Regulatory status It is permitted in the UK, and in the USA where it is listed as GRAS.

Dioctyl Sodium Sulphosuccinate
also known as DSS and sold by the American Cyanamid Company as Complemix
Type This can be used as an emulsifier or as a wetting agent especially with powders in dry mixtures which need to be mixed with water. It can also serve to modify aromas and flavours and can act to enhance the apparent flavour of citrus fruit products. It is also used as a processing aid in the sugar industry.

Foods added to It can be found in some cheeses, and in many different kinds of product in combination with gums and other thickeners. It may be found in powdered soft drink mixes and canned milk beverages which contain cocoa fat. It is also sometimes used in laxative products to loosen the stools.

Toxicological evaluation and possible health hazards Until 1970 this compound could not legally be used as an emulsifier in foods in the UK. In 1970 the FACC concluded that it could safely be used in a limited range of foods, as long as they were not significant items in the normal diet, and this recommendation was accepted by the government. In 1972 the FACC reported that they had received further data, and they recommended the lifting of the restrictions they had stipulated two years earlier.

JECFA first evaluated this compound in 1974. They reviewed fifteen documents, ten of them published documents, but all referring to work conducted before 1962; all the important recent work remained secret. JECFA reviewed the results of short-term tests on rats, rabbits, monkeys and dogs, and on a (published) long-term rat study. They also had (unpublished) results from a three-generation rat reproduction study. The long-term study was unsatisfactory because the sample size was too small and only one sex had been used, but the reproduction study partly made up for these deficiencies. The reproductive study was interpreted as indicating that DSS is safe just as long as offspring are not exposed to it in their mother's milk. JECFA established a temporary ADI of 2.5mg/kg bw, and commented that it should be used sparingly if its laxative effect was to be avoided. They did not suggest that it should be avoided by pregnant women, but it is not clear why not. They did, moreover, call for further long-term rodent studies, and an investigation of its possible effects on the lungs to be completed within three years. When they looked at it again in 1978 they reported that since the information which they had requested had not been provided, and

given that there was no evidence that such studies were even under way, they withdrew their temporary ADI. In 1980 JECFA reported that they had received a slight amount of new data obtained using horses, guinea-pigs and humans, but they had still not received the data which they had requested six years earlier. They disclosed in 1978 that the compound was in wide use, despite the absence of vital data, and at the time of writing (1986) that remains the case.

The SCF reviewed it in 1978 and without any explanation they set a temporary ADI of 0.1mg/kg bw and requested a long-term rodent feeding study. It is puzzling that while JECFA saw fit to abandon a figure twenty-five times greater, the SCF granted it an ADI at this modest level, and without calling for the lung effect study considered so vital by JECFA. When the SCF considered it in 1983, however, they lined up behind JECFA and listed it as a substance for which an ADI could not be established and which is not toxicologically acceptable for use in foods. None the less despite the fact that we cannot be confident that it is safe, it remains on the list of emulsifiers permitted for use in the UK,

Regulatory status It is permitted and used in the UK and the USA in a wide range of products, but at low levels.

Disodium Edetate
also known as Disodium Ethylene Diamine Tetra-Acetate, and as Disodium EDTA

Type It can be used as a sequestrant, an antioxidant synergist and as a preservative.

Foods added to There is no published information about its use in the

UK, but in the USA it is permitted in processed pulses, pie fillings, mayonnaises and salad dressings, dried and frozen fruits and vegetables, and in gefilte fish balls. There is a suggestion that the use of this compound has declined over the last ten years.

Toxicological evaluation and possible health hazards JECFA have considered this compound alongside its close relative Calcium Disodium EDTA (see 385) in 1965 and 1973. On the first occasion they set an unconditional ADI of 1.25mg/kg bw, and a conditional one up to 2.5mg/kg bw. On the second occasion they reviewed thirty-one documents and, remarkably, all of them were published. They commented that the only long-term study on this compound had been conducted in rats and that the numbers used were small while the mortality rate was high in all groups. One might have expected them to call, therefore, for further studies, but they did not do that, or provide any explanation. In 1977 the SCF endorsed JECFA's ADI of 2.5mg/kg bw for Calcium Disodium EDTA, but without commenting on this relative.

Regulatory status It is used and permitted in the UK and the USA.

Ethoxyquin

Type This is an antioxidant. It is widely used as an additive in animal feeds, but its use on human foods is confined to the surface treatment of apples and pears where it is used to treat a condition known as scald. It can be applied to the fruit by spraying, dipping or wrapping with impregnated materials. When fishmeal intended for animal feed is loaded on to ships, the maritime insurance companies often require it to be treated with Ethoxyquin (and/or BHT (see E321)

to reduce the risk that the cargo will ignite spontaneously.

Foods added to As a result of its use in animal feed, residues of Ethoxyquin can often be found as a contaminant in meat, offal, dairy products and eggs, and therefore in products containing those as ingredients. The SCF estimated in 1975 that fruit consumption may account for only about 15 per cent of our average intake of Ethoxyquin, but they indicated that their figures were incomplete and unreliable. In the USA it is used in chilli and paprika powders.

Toxicological evaluation and possible health hazards JECFA have not discussed Ethoxyquin, but the FSC first evaluated it as long ago as 1963, and the FACC considered it in 1974. During those intervening eleven years no new data became available, but the FACC just endorsed the FSC's previous decision to list Ethoxyquin in Group A, indicating that they thought it sufficiently safe for use.

In 1975 the SCF reviewed the use of Ethoxyquin on fruit. Without identifying any of their sources, they stated that they had received adequate data on the metabolism and short-term toxicity of this compound in several animal species, but that the long-term studies which were conducted in rats, chickens and dogs were all inadequate by modern standards. Their response was to set a temporary ADI of 0.03mg/kg bw, and call for the results of further studies to be provided within three years. There is no evidence that data have been provided, or that the SCF have reconsidered the matter.

The SCF also drew attention to the fact that a close chemical relative of Ethoxyquin called Flectol H, which is used as an antioxidant in rubber products, had produced anomalous and puzzling results in two carcinogenicity studies. Because of the inconclusive nature of those results and the chemical differences between the two compounds, the SCF gave the benefit of the doubt to Ethoxyquin, and assumed it innocent until proved toxic. The SCF approved the use of Ethoxyquin on apples and pears throughout the EEC, but were not prepared to agree to any extension of its use, until the results of more reliable long-term studies became available. Ethoxyquin is not permitted for use in food products intended for babies and young children, which indicates that some British officials have doubts about the safety of this compound.

Regulatory status It is permitted and used in the UK and the EEC on the surface of apples and pears, and in the USA where it can also be used only in chilli and paprika powders. In Britain it cannot legally be used in products intended for babies and young children.

Glycine
also known as Amino Acetic Acid

Type This is an amino acid which is present in all proteins, and is especially abundant in connective tissue, from which it can be extracted.

Foods added to It can be found in soft drinks which have been sweetened with Saccharin, because it is used to mask the bitter after-taste of Saccharin.

Toxicological evaluation and possible health hazards There have been no official toxicological evaluations of this substance, but it is presumed to be safe because it is a natural component of essential nutrients.

Special restrictions Since it is extracted from animals products, it may not be acceptable to vegetarians and vegans, and it may be neither kosher nor halal.

Regulatory status It is permitted and used in the UK and the USA.

Hydrogen
Type This is used in pressurized containers as a packaging gas.

Foods added to It can be found in aerosols and other pressurized containers.

Toxicological evaluation and possible health hazards No toxicological evaluation has been published by JECFA, the SCF or the FACC, but it is presumed to be toxicologically safe when used in small quantities in food products. Since it forms an explosive mixture with air it has to be handled with great care in manufacturing.

Regulatory status It is permitted and used in the UK.

Leucine
Type It is a sweet tasting essential amino acid which cannot be synthesized in the human body. It is extracted commercially from animal proteins, and for this reason may not be acceptable to vegetarians and vegans, and it may be neither kosher nor halal. It is used mainly as a lubricant in table top sweeteners and dietary supplement pills because it helps the pills to drop out of the press mould.

Foods added to It can, therefore, be found in some table top sweetener and dietary supplement pills.

Toxicological evaluation and possible health hazards No evaluation has been published in the official food additive literature, but since it is an essential nutrient it is generally presumed to be safe.

Special restrictions It may not be acceptable to vegetarians and vegans, and it may be neither kosher nor halal.

Regulatory status It is permitted and used in the UK and the USA.

Nitrogen

Type This is a familiar odourless and colourless gas which constitutes about 78 per cent of the volume of our atmosphere. It is used in the food industry as a freezant and a packaging gas. It is used in air-tight packaging to inhibit oxidation.

Foods added to Because it is relatively insoluble it is used as a propellant for products such as ketchup and syrups which are not supposed to foam, and is used in a wide range of products contained in aerosols. It is also used to fill the head space of containers of fruit juice.

Toxicological evaluation and possible health hazards JECFA considered this substance in 1980, and stated that nitrogen was sufficiently inert to be unlikely to react with food components, and so they considered that it could safely be used as long as the commercially available materials were sufficiently pure. They saw no reason to set an ADI.

Regulatory status It is permitted and used in the UK, the EEC, and in the USA where it is listed as GRAS.

Nitrous Oxide

Type This gas has been used in the food industry as a propellant at least since the early 1950s. It has also been used as a surgical anaesthetic especially in dentistry, but in recent years its dental use has declined because of doubts about its safety. Because of its intoxicating properties it has often been known as Laughing Gas.

Priestley first isolated it in 1772, and its anaesthetic and intoxicating properties were first established by Humphrey Davy at the end of the eighteenth century.

Foods added to Because of its relative solubility, it is used as a propellant in products such as aerosols of dairy products and whipped creams and toppings which are intended to foam.

Toxicological evaluation and possible health hazards JECFA first considered Nitrous Oxide in 1978, and on that occasion they concluded that the amounts to which consumers would be exposed from its use in food are so slight as not to constitute any hazard. They approved its use and did not consider it necessary to set an ADI. They looked at it again in 1986 because in the meantime doubts about its safety when used at high doses had been voiced. JECFA's view remained the same, however, because the levels of exposure from its use in food are so low. It remains the case, however, that it could constitute a hazard to food industry workers, and they should handle it very carefully.

Regulatory status It is permitted and used in the UK, the EEC and the USA.

Oxidatively Polymerized Soya Bean Oil

also known as Blown Soya Oil

Type These compounds are thick liquids which are produced by blowing air through heated soya bean oil. They are incorporated into emulsions used to grease baking tins.

Foods added to They can be found as residues on, or near, the surface of a wide range of baked products such as biscuits and pastries.

Toxicological evaluation and possible health hazards JECFA have never evaluated this material, but the SCF and the FACC have looked at it. The FACC report of 1970 lists it in Group B, meaning that they considered it temporarily acceptable pending the receipt of further information. They were not able to be more forthcoming because the available data were very slight, but they were consoled by the thought that residual levels in food are likely to be very low. Most of the data they considered referred to other blown oils and hardly any of it dealt specifically with Blown Soya Oil. The FACC recommended that it should be permitted at levels of up to 50ppm in tin greasing emulsions. They reviewed the matter once again in 1972 in response to requests from the trade for permission to use these compounds at levels of up to 100ppm. The FACC agreed, despite the fact that no new toxicological information had become available. There is no evidence that the FACC has reconsidered this compound, since they have not again reported on emulsifiers, and presumably it remains listed in Group B, while industry has no incentive to test it further. The SCF considered this material in 1978 in the context of a general review of additives in baked products. They approved its use but only up to levels of 40ppm.

Regulatory status It is permitted and used in the UK and the EEC.

Oxygen

Type This familiar colourless and odourless gas constitutes approximately 20 per cent of the volume of our atmosphere. We cannot live without it. It is occasionally used as a packaging gas, and in the modification of some starches.

Foods added to No specific uses have been reported.

Toxicological evaluation and possible health hazards There are no official published reports on Oxygen as a food additive, but common sense indicates that its use as a food additive could pose no hazard to consumers. Bulk liquefied Oxygen does, of course, require very careful handling in industrial processes.

Regulatory status Permitted and used in the UK and the USA.

Oxystearin

Type This is a complex mixture of glycerides of partially oxidized stearic acids and other fatty acids. It is found in, and extracted from animal fats. It is used in the food industry as a sequestrant and a defoamer.

Foods added to It is used both as a sequestrant and defoamer in vegetable oils, and as a defoamer in the processing of beet sugar and yeast. It is also added to some cooking oils to prevent them from clouding or crystallizing at low temperatures.

Toxicological evaluation and possible health hazards JECFA evaluated this material in 1969 and in 1973. On the first occasion they awarded it a full ADI of 25mg/kg bw, and they confirmed this judgement again in 1973. On the latter occasion they reported that they had recently received some additional data, although the 1973 report refers solely to four unpublished reports from Procter & Gamble Ltd, all of which reported work that dated from 1956 or earlier. The SCF have never reported on Oxystearin.

Special restrictions Since it is extracted from animal products, it may not be acceptable to vegetarians and vegans, and it may be neither kosher nor halal.

Regulatory status It is permitted and used in the UK and the USA.

Polydextrose

Type There are two versions of this material, namely the acid form which is known as Polydextrose A, and the neutralized form known as Polydextrose N. This material is chemically similar to cellulose; it is tasteless and has a quarter of the calories of sugar, but it is filling. It is used primarily as a bulking agent, but it also can be used to adjust the texture, thickness and moisture content of food products. It was developed by Pfizer Inc in the USA during the 1970s. On one occasion they advertised it to the food processing industry by saying: 'Polydextrose fattens up your profits without fattening up your customers.' This is because if you just substitute an artificial sweetener for sugar in products such as drinks, cakes or biscuits then the drinks will taste watery, the biscuits will be dry and the cake will fall flat. If, however, you add Polydextrose then this gives them all the bulk, and low-calorie products can be sold (often at premium prices) with a texture and mouthfeel similar to those of, what pass for, normal products.

Foods added to It can be found in diet soft drinks, baked goods, frozen desserts, boiled sweets and instant puddings.

Toxicological evaluation and possible health hazards The FACC evaluated it in 1979, and reported their findings a year later. They recommended temporary approval on the basis of several studies conducted using rats, dogs and humans. Because it can have a laxative effect, they also

recommended that this should not be permitted in products intended for babies and young children, and that recommendation has been incorporated into the regulations. JECFA first evaluated this material in 1980. JECFA were sufficiently satisfied with the toxicological data to set a full ADI of 70mg/kg bw, a judgement which they confirmed in 1981

Regulatory status It is permitted and used in the UK and the USA. In the UK it may not be used in foods intended for babies and young children.

Quillaia
also known as Extract of Quillaia and as Quillaja

Type Quillaia is the name for the dried inner bark of a species of tree with the same name, and Extract of Quillaia is the name for a soapy aqueous solution which is prepared from the dried bark. It contains a complex mixture of several sugar-like compounds. It is used both as a foaming agent and as a flavouring. It has been in commercial use for at least 100 years to give a good head of foam to soft drinks in Britain, Europe and the USA, and has a long history of use as a medicine.

Foods added to It can be found in some soft drinks, ice creams and sweets.

Toxicological evaluation and possible health hazards The 1970 FACC report lists it in Group B. They explained that we know from medical practice that large doses can be severely toxic, and that prolonged consumption even of low doses can cause gastrointestinal irritation. No formal long-term toxicological data were then available, but they had received no reports of acute poisoning from the use of this material in soft drinks. They agreed to the continued use of Quillaia in soft drinks up to a level of 200ppm, but they insisted on a proper long-term study, and data on the problem of intestinal irritation by their next review, if they were then to permit its continued use. They simply restated this position in 1972. By the time the SCF evaluated it in 1978 they had received the results of long-term studies in both mice and rats, and on that basis they set for it an ADI of 5mg/kg bw. JECFA considered it in 1982 and reviewed essentially the same data as that which had been available to the SCF, but they disagreed with the SCF judgement. JECFA were concerned because the chemical identity of the commercial product was poorly specified, and for this reason were not prepared to set an ADI. By 1986, however, JECFA had received a little more data, and they modified their position by agreeing to the ADI of 5mg/kg bw and setting tentative specifications. In short, the SCF and JECFA think that Quillaia is probably safe when used in small amounts as a food additive even though its identity is not properly specified.

Regulatory status Permitted and used in the UK, the EEC and the USA.

Spermaceti
also known as Sperm Oil

Type This is a thin yellow liquid which is obtained from the sperm whale. If it is poorly refined it has a slightly fishy odour. It is used as a release agent or lubricant in baking tins.

Foods added to It can be found in some foods baked in tins.

Toxicological evaluation and possible health hazards JECFA and the SCF have not evaluated it. There are, however, no reports of toxicity.

Special restrictions Since it is extracted from the sperm whale it may not be acceptable to vegetarians and vegans, and it may be neither kosher nor halal.

Regulatory status Permitted and used in the UK.

Tannic Acids
also known as Tannins, or sometimes by the singular Tannic Acid

Type This is a complex and poorly defined, but closely related, group of compounds. The name Tannin derives from the traditional use for this material, in the tanning of leather. Tannins occur frequently in trees and plants, but the commercial product which is used as a food additive is generally extracted from the seed pods, leaves and excrescences that form on the young twigs of the Turkish Aleppo, Chinese Tara or Sicilian Sumac trees. It is used as an astringent flavouring additive. It occurs also in the bark, leaves and fruit of many plants and we consume it mainly because it is found in tea, cocoa and coffee.

Foods added to An average cup of tea, cocoa or coffee may contain between 100 and 500mg of Tannins, and they are found in many red wines. They are used as additives in some caramels, fruit products, ices, sweets, baked goods and alcoholic beverages. Brewers and winemakers sometimes use them to precipitate the proteins from their products.

Toxicological evaluation and possible health hazards Tannins were used by doctors in the 1930s in ointments used to treat burns and scalds. Doctors ceased this practice after concluding that the Tannins were migrating through the bloodstream and damaging the liver. There is evidence that injecting Tannins is very bad for mice and rats, and there is one report of a patient's having died following an enema containing Tannins. At the quite considerable levels at which we consume these chemicals there is no direct evidence of hazard to humans. Many people who suffer food intolerance find it helpful to avoid tea and coffee, but there is no evidence that it is the Tannins which provoke their symptoms.

JECFA evaluated Tannins once, in 1970. They divided them into two groups, separating those derived from the Turkish Aleppo, Chinese Tara and Sicilian Sumac trees from those from the Peruvian Tara, and set an over-all temporary ADI of 0.6mg/kg bw, but called for more studies to determine first the chemical identity of the commercial products, and further studies on the safety of the component materials. One outstanding question is whether or not the problems caused by injecting Tannins arise also when they are incorporated into rodents' diets. Although JECFA called for further data, they have never published any subsequent report on this material. The SCF have not evaluated Tannins, but the FACC commented on them in 1978 in the context of their discussion of additives used in beer production. Since Tannins are often used as processing aids to extract a precipitate from beer, the residue levels are likely to be slight and they should largely be removed with the precipitate. Residue levels are liable to be slight by comparison with those found naturally in common beverages, and so the FACC saw no reason for not listing Tannins in Group A, as safe for use. There are a couple of reports showing that high doses of Tannins may be hazardous, but this has more serious implications for the consumption of tea, coffee and cocoa than for the use of Tannins as additives.

Regulatory status They are permitted and used in the UK, the EEC and the USA.

SOLVENTS

Dichlorodifluoromethane
also known as Freon-12 and as Freezant-12

Type This can be used as an extraction solvent, a propellant and a liquid freezant. Freon is the brand name for a widely used liquid refrigerant and Dichlorodifluoromethane is one ingredient of this mixture.

Foods added to Residues can be found in some frozen foods when it has been used as a freezant, and in cocoa butter, hops, spice extracts, decaffeinated coffee, colours and flavourings when it has been used as an extraction solvent.

Toxicological evaluation and possible health hazards JECFA have evaluated this compound only once, in 1975. The results of tests with this compound on the health and reproduction of rats showed only slight adverse effects, and only at high doses. Tests on dogs, cats and monkeys, however, showed that Dichlorodifluoromethane vapour can damage their lungs if high doses are inhaled, but JECFA judged that these effects were irrelevant to its use as a food additive, and they set an ADI of 1.5mg/kg bw. The FAC evaluated it in 1978, and they were satisfied as to its safety at the residual low levels at which it is likely to be found in foods. The SCF evaluated this compound in 1981. They reported that they fully endorsed JECFA's evaluation, but the remarkable feature of their report is that they stated (wrongly) that JECFA's ADI is 15mg/kg bw when

it is in fact one tenth of that value, but it is the higher figure which they have (perhaps mistakenly) endorsed.

Regulatory status Permitted in the UK and the EEC.

Dichloromethane
also known as Methylene Chloride, and as Methylene Dichloride

Type It is used as an extraction solvent.

Foods added to It is used, for example, to extract Annatto (see E160b), and in some decaffeinated coffees. The decaffeination of coffee used to be accomplished by the use of chloroform and trichlorethylene as solvents, but their use was discontinued when they were shown to be unsafe. They were then replaced with Dichloromethane, and more recently with a steam extraction process. Processers are not required to reveal to consumers which process they have used.

Toxicological evaluation and possible health hazards JECFA have evaluated this compound on three occasions, in 1970, 1979 and 1983. On the first occasion they declined to set an ADI because of the comprehensive lack of toxicological data, but approved its use and recommended merely that it should be used only in accordance with 'good manufacturing practice'. They did not add, but should have done so, that in manufacturing particular care should be taken to restrict the extent to which staff inhale the vapours. On the second occasion they repeated the point that no adequate short- or long-term oral toxicity studies had been conducted with this compound. Despite this they approved its use, and set a temporary ADI at 0.5mg/kg bw because they concluded that much of it was not metabolized, and that part which was became carbon monoxide, and was safely metabolized as long as dose levels were low. For all this, they still called for data from long-term oral toxicity studies in at least two rodent species.

When the FACC evaluated Dichloromethane in 1978 they too complained at the lack of adequate studies, but they reasoned that the residual levels at which this compound was likely to remain in foods was sufficiently slight as to pose no significant hazard to consumers. They did not say it, but their argument does imply that it might be hazardous to industrial workers handling the material in bulk. The FACC recommended approval on the condition that residues should not exceed 5mg/kg. They called, moreover, for the results of an oral carcinogenicity study in the rat within five years, and in the meantime listed it in Group B.

In 1981 the SCF considered it, and stated there were insufficient data to establish an ADI, as well as unresolved indications of possible serious toxicity because it appeared to be mutagenic to bacteria and carcinogenic in animals. Curiously, however, the SCF did not ban it, but recommended that it should be temporarily acceptable (as long as residues did not exceed 10mg/kg of food), pending the results of further tests and a further review by the end of 1983. They have not reported on it since.

By 1983 JECFA had received the results of lifetime feeding studies on mice and rats, but these studies suffered from several shortcomings which prevented JECFA from assessing the possible carcinogenicity of Dichloromethane. In the rat study two different batches of test chemical were used which had different kinds of impurity. The material was not properly administered, and there were high levels of death in all groups. Precancerous lesions were found in rat livers, but in a pattern which could not be linked directly to the dose level of the test substance. Similar problems were encountered with other lesions at other sites in the rats, and with mice and hamsters too. JECFA responded cautiously to this chaos by withdrawing their temporary ADI, and by recommending that the use of Dichloromethane as an extraction solvent should be limited to keep residues as low as practicable.

Given that Dichloromethane is mutagenic to some bacteria, and there is at least some evidence that it might be carcinogenic, we should conclude that there may be no level at which it can safely be consumed. That might be a cautious response, but then consumers are entitled to expect officials to be cautious. In the meantime, however, this compound continues to be permitted and used in the UK, the EEC and the USA.

Regulatory status It is permitted and used in the UK, the EEC and the USA.

Ethyl Acetate

Type It is used as a solvent, a carrier and a flavouring agent. It is one of several solvents used in the decaffeination of coffee.

Foods added to It can be found as a residue in some decaffeinated coffees.

Toxicological evaluation and possible

health hazards JECFA have evaluated this compound only once, in 1967 when an ADI of 25mg/kg bw was allocated. The FACC reviewed it in 1978, and concluded that despite the fact that there are very little data on oral toxicity they were confident that it was effectively safe. They judged it to be temporarily acceptable, listed it in Group B, and called for the results of a 90-day oral toxicity study in rats within two years. The SCF looked at it in 1981, and their view was that while they had evidence that it was metabolized into Acetic Acid (see E260) and Ethyl Alcohol (see below), they did not have sufficient toxicological information to enable them to set an ADI, but in the light of the metabolic information they judged an ADI to be unnecessary. They noted the fact that it was known to be a skin irritant, and to provoke allergic reactions at high doses, but they believed that this was irrelevant for consumers to its use as a solvent. Although they failed to comment on it, this information suggests that it could pose a significant hazard to food industry workers who handle the material in bulk. If there was insufficient information in 1981 for the SCF to set an ADI, we are entitled to ask how JECFA thought they could do it fourteen years earlier. Unfortunately no answer is forthcoming.

Regulatory status It is permitted and used in the UK, the EEC and the USA.

Ethyl Alcohol
also known as Ethanol, or more familiarly as Alcohol

Type It is used as an extraction solvent and carrier. This is the familiar intoxicating constituent of alcoholic beverages.

Foods added to It can be found in varying concentrations in all alcoholic beverages, but it is used as a solvent to deliver other food additives, and (in the USA at any rate) it is used at low concentrations in the manufacture of some sweets, ice creams, sauces and desserts.

Toxicological evaluation and possible health hazards JECFA evaluated this alcohol in 1970 when they concluded that its use as an additive was self-limiting and sufficiently safe that no quantitative restrictions were required, but should be limited by good manufacturing practice. This view was endorsed by the SCF in 1981. Massive doses are notoriously poisonous, but its use as a food additive is presumed to be safe.

Special restrictions Ethyl Alcohol is not acceptable to some religious groups, but they face severe difficulties because the use of this solvent in solutions of other additives is not listed on labels.

Regulatory status Permitted in the UK, the EEC and the USA.

Diethyl Ether
also known as Ether

Type It is used in the food industry as an extraction and a carrier solvent. It has long been used as a surgical anaesthetic. When used as an extraction solvent it also usually contains 20ppm of BHT (see E321) which acts as a stabilizer.

Foods added to It is used as a solvent for the delivery of other food additives, and as an extraction solvent.

Toxicological evaluation and possible health hazards The FAC considered it in 1978, listing it in Group A, believing it to be safe when used as a solvent for natural flavourings.

JECFA considered evaluating this compound in 1980 but concluded that there were too few data on its oral toxicity to enable them to make an evaluation. The SCF considered it in 1981, and reiterated JECFA's comments. The SCF added, however, that its use as an extraction solvent would lead to very low residues in food products, and that there was no need to set an ADI, and this use was acceptable. Since at high concentrations it can irritate sensitive skin such as the lips and mouth, and given that it is highly inflammable, this material should be handled in bulk with great care.

Regulatory status Permitted and used in the UK and the EEC.

Glycerol Monoacetate

Type This compound always occurs in a mixture with Glycerol (see E422) and often with Glycerol Triacetate (see below), and it is used in the food industry as a solvent and carrier for other additives, especially flavours.

Foods added to No specific uses have been reported, but since it is used as a carrier and solvent for flavouring additives it may be found in a very wide range of products, but without being listed on any labels.

Toxicological evaluation and possible health hazards JECFA considered it briefly in 1976, but reported that they were not then aware of its use as a food additive, and so they did not set purity specifications, nor evaluate it toxicologically. The FACC considered it in 1978, and they commented that the standard of the available data was low, and that this compound appears to be more toxic than Glycerol (see E422) itself. They said, moreover, that although residues of these solvents could

be high, the data available to them did not indicate that their use represented a hazard to consumers' health. They listed it in Group B, and recommended continued use, on a temporary basis, pending the results of a 90-day oral toxicity study in the rat within two years. JECFA returned to it in 1980, and then decided that since they expected it to be safely metabolized they would include it under the ADI which the committee had already established for Glycerol (see E422) and Glycerol Triacetate (see below). In 1981 the SCF endorsed JECFA's position on this compound, and approved it for use on the basis of its likely metabolic pathway, but in the absence of data from toxicological studies.

Special restrictions Since it is produced from animal sources, it may not be acceptable to vegetarians and vegans, and it may be neither kosher nor halal.

Regulatory status It is permitted and used in the UK and the EEC.

Glycerol Triacetate
also known as Triacetin

Type This is used mainly as a carrier solvent, but can also be used as a humectant. Unlike Glycerol Monoacetate (see above), this compound can be prepared to a high degree of purity.

Foods added to No specific uses have been reported, but since it is used as a carrier and solvent for flavouring additives it may be found in a very wide range of products, but without being listed on any labels.

Toxicological evaluation and possible health hazards JECFA considered it in 1975 when they concluded that it was safely metabolized and could therefore be permitted for use as a food additive without either formal detailed toxicological studies and any need for an ADI. This assessment was endorsed by the SCF in 1981. The FACC considered it in 1978, and they stated the data available to them did not indicate that its use represented a hazard to consumer health. They listed it in Group B, and recommended continued use, on a temporary basis, pending the results of further studies.

Special restrictions Since it is produced from animal sources, it may not be acceptable to vegetarians and vegans, and it may be neither kosher nor halal.

Regulatory status It is permitted and used in the UK, the EEC and the USA.

Isopropyl Alcohol
also known as Isopropanol

Type It is used in the food industry as an extraction solvent and carrier mostly to dissolve other additives and primarily flavours.

Foods added to No specific uses have been reported, but since it is used as a carrier and solvent for flavouring additives it may be found in a very wide range of products, without being listed on any labels.

Toxicological evaluation and possible health hazards JECFA considered this substance briefly in 1970. They explained that this was a naturally occurring minor constituent of some alcoholic beverages, and that some short-term human studies and long-term animal studies were then in progress. As and when the results of those tests became available, they might be able to set an ADI. In the meantime they temporarily approved its use because they considered that if its use was restricted by good manufacturing practice then residual levels would be negligible. In 1981 they commented again, and said that they had been informed that toxicological studies had by then been conducted, and JECFA asked for the resultant data to be made available to them. They did not, however, explain why they had not already received them. They revised their specifications of purity, and designated them merely as temporary, pending the results of further studies on levels of impurities. They again set no ADI.

The FACC has commented twice on this compound, in 1974 and in 1978. On the first occasion they reported that they had received the results of a long-term feeding study on rats which had shown slight adverse effects at high doses. They conjectured a possible NEL, but this had not been established. They took the view that because of the long-standing use of Isopropyl Alcohol as a food solvent they regarded it as temporarily acceptable not exceeding a level of 1 per cent in foods. On the second occasion they reaffirmed the view that it could safely be used, and listed it in Group A.

The SCF evaluated it in 1981 and they reported that they had received the results of several studies on its oral toxicity in rats. A reproduction study which they characterized as having an 'unusual design' indicated adverse effects at low doses, but the SCF disregarded these results because they had not received sufficient information about the identity and purity of the test substance. They set a temporary ADI at 1.5mg/kg bw, and asked for the results of a proper reproduction study by 1983. At the time of writing, 1986, they had not returned to the subject.

Regulatory status It is permitted

and used in the UK, the EEC and the USA.

Propylene Glycol

Type   It is used in the food industry mainly as a solvent and carrier for other food additives, but it can also be used as a wetting agent and a humectant. It is a slightly bitter tasting viscous fluid.

Foods added to   It can be found in some wines where it has been used to dissolve the parabens which in turn are used to preserve the wine. It can also be found in some confectionery, ice creams and baked goods.

Toxicological evaluation and possible health hazards   JECFA have considered it twice, in 1963 and 1973. On the first occasion they reviewed nineteen published reports including short-term studies on rats, rabbits and dogs, but only one long-term study on rats, but using very small test groups. The short-term studies indicated that at high doses it was severely toxic, while at low doses the animals metabolized it safely. On these grounds JECFA set an unconditional ADI of 20mg/kg bw, and a conditional one at twice that figure. By 1973 JECFA had received the published results of a two-year feeding study on rats which used five dose levels, and thirty animals per sex and dose level, and a dog study using three dose levels and five animals per group. On the basis of these latter two studies they set a full ADI at 25mg/kg bw. In 1974 the FACC reviewed essentially similar data, and approved the use of this compound.

Regulatory status   It is permitted in the UK and the USA where it is listed as GRAS.

INDEX OF CHEMICAL AND BRAND NAMES

FOR THE BEST IN PAPERBACKS, LOOK FOR THE

In every corner of the world, on every subject under the sun, Penguin represents quality and variety – the very best in publishing today.

For complete information about books available from Penguin – including Pelicans, Puffins, Peregrines and Penguin Classics – and how to order them, write to us at the appropriate address below. Please note that for copyright reasons the selection of books varies from country to country.

In the United Kingdom: For a complete list of books available from Penguin in the U.K., please write to *Dept E.P., Penguin Books Ltd, Harmondsworth, Middlesex, UB7 0DA*

In the United States: For a complete list of books available from Penguin in the U.S., please write to *Dept BA, Penguin, 299 Murray Hill Parkway, East Rutherford, New Jersey 07073*

In Canada: For a complete list of books available from Penguin in Canada, please write to *Penguin Books Canada Ltd, 2801 John Street, Markham, Ontario L3R 1B4*

In Australia: For a complete list of books available from Penguin in Australia, please write to the *Marketing Department, Penguin Books Australia Ltd, P.O. Box 257, Ringwood, Victoria 3134*

In New Zealand: For a complete list of books available from Penguin in New Zealand, please write to the *Marketing Department, Penguin Books (NZ) Ltd, Private Bag, Takapuna, Auckland 9*

In India: For a complete list of books available from Penguin, please write to *Penguin Overseas Ltd, 706 Eros Apartments, 56 Nehru Place, New Delhi, 110019*

In Holland: For a complete list of books available from Penguin in Holland, please write to *Penguin Books Nederland B.V., Postbus 195, NL–1380AD Weesp, Netherlands*

In Germany: For a complete list of books available from Penguin, please write to *Penguin Books Ltd, Friedrichstrasse 10 – 12, D–6000 Frankfurt Main 1, Federal Republic of Germany*

In Spain: For a complete list of books available from Penguin in Spain, please write to *Longman Penguin España, Calle San Nicolas 15, E–28013 Madrid, Spain*